Germ Plasm

Resources

A SYMPOSIUM PRESENTED AT THE CHICAGO MEETING OF

THE AMERICAN ASSOCIATION FOR THE ADVANCEMENT OF SCIENCE,

28-31 DECEMBER, 1959

Edited by

RALPH E. HODGSON

Publication No. 66 of the
AMERICAN ASSOCIATION FOR THE ADVANCEMENT OF SCIENCE
Washington, D. C., 1961

Preface

The 1959 program of the Section on Agriculture of the American Association for the Advancement of Science was planned to review the plant and animal germ plasm resources useful to the agricultural industries of this country, to measure the progress made in the genetic improvement of these resources, and, if possible, to chart a course for the future development and protection of the plant and animal organisms that provide the food and fiber needs of the people. Not since 1934–35, when the *Yearbooks of Agriculture* were published by the United States Department of Agriculture, giving the results of a nationwide survey of plant and animal germ plasm, had there been an attempt to review the status of these resources on which this nation's great agricultural industries are based.

The program plans culminated in a series of five half-day sessions from December 28 to 31, 1959. Each session included four or five papers by outstanding authorities, devoted to a particular phase of the general subject. A summary and discussion of the subject of each session were made by an outstanding authority. Basic and applied research in all phases of genetics, biometry, and plant and animal breeding and the extension of findings into practical use were reviewed. The broad coverage of the subject, including the origin of presently used species, the need for additional sources, the development, utilization, evaluation, perpetuation, and preservation of plant and animal resources dealt with expertly by authors, provides an excellent reference material for students and workers engaged in this field of endeavor. This volume includes the papers and the discussions presented at the five-session symposium.

It seemed particularly appropriate that a symposium of this kind should be held at the end of 1959, the year that the world was celebrating the centennial of Charles Darwin. Darwin has had a profound effect upon the development of plant and animal germ plasm. The Darwin theory provided an important bench mark in the development and guidance of genetic thought and activity in this country and elsewhere in the world. As applied to this symposium, the following paragraphs taken from his book, *The Variation of Animals and Plants Under Domestication,* published in 1900, seem appropriate:

The subject of inheritance is wonderful. When a new character arises, whatever its nature may be, it generally tends to be inherited, at least in a temporary and sometimes in a most persistent manner. What can be more wonderful than that some trifling peculiarity, not primordially attached to the species, should be transmitted through the male or female sexual cells, which are so minute as not to be visible to the naked eye, and afterwards through the incessant changes of a long course of development, undergone either in the womb or in the egg, and ultimately appear in the offspring when mature, or even when quite old, as in the case of certain diseases. Or again, what can be more wonderful than the well-ascertained fact that the minute ovule of a good milking cow will produce a male, from whom a cell, in union with an ovule, will produce a female, and she, when mature, will have large mammary glands, yielding an abundant supply of milk, and even milk of a particular quality? . . .

. . . In fact, the whole art of breeding, from which such great results have been attained during the present century, depends on the inheritance of each small detail of structure. But inheritance is not certain; for if it were, the breeder's art would be reduced to a certainty, and there would be little scope left for that wonderful skill and perseverance shown by the men who have left an enduring monument of their success in the present state of our domesticated animals.

It is evident that many of the domesticated animals and plants presently used in the agricultural production of this country came from material introduced from other parts of the world. Many of the basic stocks were developed even before Darwin's lifetime. Much of this material came with the peoples who migrated to our shores. Nearly all domestic livestock is exotic in origin. Most of it arrived before the turn of the present century. A large percentage of the many species of field, horticultural, and vegetable crops is exotic in origin. Expert plant explorers have continued the search throughout the world for new, useful germ plasm. The flow of such material will continue to the benefit of the entire society. For reasons of disease, it is much more difficult to introduce animal species, and this practice is almost non-existent. Yet there are, no doubt, important sources of animal germ plasm that could benefit the American animal industry. An important need exists to find a way to introduce animal species to the United States safely.

Plant and animal geneticists and breeders have made important strides in the last half century to bring about genetic improvement in crops and livestock. The marked increases in per-acre yields of crops and per-animal yield of meat, milk, eggs, and wool may be attributed to a significant extent to genetic improvement. Present-day crops are more resistant to disease than their ancestors. New, more disease-resistant, drought-resistant, higher-yielding, higher-quality varieties of crops are continually being introduced. Many of the current varieties grown now were not known even twenty years ago. Constant and steady improvement in existing breeds of livestock is taking place. In addition, new breeds, well adapted to specific regions and conditions, are finding their places in the livestock economy. Performance testing, selection, inbreeding, line crossing, and crossbreeding are tools geneticists and breeders have used and are using to bring about these important improvements. The development and universal adoption of hybrid corn is an excellent example to illustrate the progress that is being made in developing germ plasm to the benefit of those engaged in farming.

The need for preservation and perpetuation of germ plasm in seed stocks is of great importance. The National Seed Storage Laboratory and its program of testing, preserving, and utilizing plant material will greatly advance the work of improving plant material. A similar program is needed for vegetative stocks. On the animal side, a similar program is needed. Much progress has been made in the use of artificial insemination, especially the use of frozen semen with some classes of livestock. This has made it possible to extend greatly the use of superior germ plasm over larger populations. A national semen storage laboratory, especially for research purposes, is needed to advance animal breeding research.

Geneticists and animal breeders are constantly in search of new techniques, principles, and methods to study inheritance. Population genetics, statistical techniques, blood antigen techniques, radiology, chemical genetic techniques, etc., offer approaches to new breakthroughs in the knowledge of inheritance. The degree of progress that will be made in the years ahead will depend in no small measure on the attention given by scientists to these basic research concepts. It is believed that this collection of symposium papers will serve a useful purpose in advancing this progress.

The assistance of Dr. D. N. D. Bayley, Leader, Dairy Cattle Breeding Investigations, Animal Husbandry Research Division, Agricultural Research Service of the United States Department of Agriculture, is gratefully acknowledged. Credit is due him not only for invaluable help in organizing the symposium but also for coordinating and reviewing papers and in preparing the Index.

RALPH E. HODGSON, Chairman
Section on Agriculture

Contributors

N. D. Bayley, Animal Husbandry Research Division, Agricultural Research Service, United States Department of Agriculture, Beltsville, Maryland

Glenn W. Burton, Coastal Plains Experiment Station, University of Georgia, and Crops Research Division, Agricultural Research Service, United States Department of Agriculture, Tifton, Georgia

T. C. Byerly, Agricultural Research Service, United States Department of Agriculture, Washington, D. C.

Richard S. Caldecott, Department of Agronomy and Plant Genetics, University of Minnesota, St. Paul, Minnesota

A. B. Chapman, Department of Genetics, University of Wisconsin, Madison, Wisconsin

W. A. Craft, Animal Husbandry Research Division, Agricultural Research Service, United States Department of Agriculture, Beltsville, Maryland

F. P. Cullinan, Crops Research Division, Agricultural Research Service, United States Department of Agriculture, Beltsville, Maryland

Gordon E. Dickerson, Kimber Farms, Inc., Fremont, California

C. D. Gordon, Animal Husbandry Research Division, Agricultural Research Service, United States Department of Agriculture, Beltsville, Maryland

H. J. Gorz, Department of Agronomy, University of Nebraska, Lincoln, Nebraska, and Crops Research Division, Agricultural Research Service, United States Department of Agriculture, Lincoln, Nebraska

Jack R. Harlan, Department of Agronomy, Oklahoma State University, and Crops Research Division, Agricultural Research Service, United States Department of Agriculture, Stillwater, Oklahoma

L. N. HAZEL, Department of Animal Husbandry, Iowa State University, Ames, Iowa

F. B. HUTT, Department of Poultry Husbandry, New York State College of Agriculture, Cornell University, Ithaca, New York

M. R. IRWIN, Department of Genetics, University of Wisconsin, Madison, Wisconsin

EDWIN JAMES, National Seed Storage Laboratory, Crops Research Division, Agricultural Research Service, United States Department of Agriculture, Fort Collins, Colorado

QUENTIN JONES, Crops Research Division, Agricultural Research Service, United States Department of Agriculture, Beltsville, Maryland

W. V. LAMBERT, College of Agriculture, University of Nebraska, Lincoln, Nebraska

R. E. LARSON, Department of Horticulture, Pennsylvania State University, University Park, Pennsylvania

J. L. LUSH, Department of Animal Husbandry, Iowa State University, Ames, Iowa

A. W. NORDSKOG, Department of Poultry Husbandry, Iowa State University, Ames, Iowa

RALPH W. PHILLIPS, International Organization Affairs, Foreign Agricultural Service, United States Department of Agriculture, Washington, D. C.

H. A. RODENHISER, Agricultural Research Service, United States Department of Agriculture, Washington, D. C.

REECE I. SAILER, Entomology Research Division, Agricultural Research Service, United States Department of Agriculture, Beltsville, Maryland

G. M. Sidwell, Animal Husbandry Research Division, Agricultural Research Service, United States Department of Agriculture, Beltsville, Maryland

W. K. SMITH, Departments of Agronomy and Genetics, University of Wisconsin, and Agricultural Research Service, United States Department of Agriculture, Madison, Wisconsin

G. F. SPRAGUE, Crops Research Division, Agricultural Research Service, United States Department of Agriculture, Beltsville, Maryland

H. H. STONAKER, Department of Animal Husbandry, Colorado State University, Fort Collins, Colorado

W. H. STONE, Department of Genetics, University of Wisconsin, Madison, Wisconsin

N. L. VanDEMARK, Department of Dairy Science, College of Agriculture, University of Illinois, Urbana, Illinois

HENRY A. WALLACE, Farvue Farm, South Salem, New York

E. J. WARWICK, Animal Husbandry Research Division, Agricultural Research Service, United States Department of Agriculture, Beltsville, Maryland

MARTIN G. WEISS, Crops Research Division, Agricultural Research Service, United States Department of Agriculture, Beltsville, Maryland

IVAN A. WOLFF, Northern Utilization Research and Development Division, Agricultural Research Service, United States Department of Agriculture, Peoria, Illinois

CHAIRMEN OF SYMPOSIUM SESSIONS

A. E. BELL, Poultry Science Department, Purdue University, West Lafayette, Indiana, Session IV

C. O. ERLANSON, Crops Research Division, Agricultural Research Service, United States Department of Agriculture, Beltsville, Maryland, Session I

ROY MAGRUDER, Agricultural Research Service, United States Department of Agriculture, Washington, D. C., Session V

H. J. SLOAN, Minnesota Agricultural Experiment Station, University of Minnesota, St. Paul, Minnesota, Session II

E. J. WARWICK, Animal Husbandry Research Division, Agricultural Research Service, United States Department of Agriculture, Beltsville, Maryland, Session III

Contents

I. Origin of Germ Plasm

Geographic Origin of Plants
Useful to Agriculture

Jack R. Harlan

United States Department of Agriculture and Oklahoma State University, Stillwater, Oklahoma

A great deal has been said about the geographic origin of crop plants and it is unlikely that I can add anything that is really new. The purpose of a symposium such as this one is to attempt to weave together the various and diverse threads of thought on a subject into a comprehensive or at least comprehensible body of information. Consideration of how diffuse and nebulous some of these threads of thought are and how some of them are tucked away in dusty alcoves of literature or mind leads me to believe that I may be of some service in this respect.

Since 1959 marks the centennial of Darwin's publication *On the Origin of Species*, it seems fitting to begin with the Great Naturalist. Darwin was interested in cultivated plants and domestic animals because he felt they had something to teach us about evolution. He was impressed at once by their great variability and by the magnitude of their differences from their wild progenitors. If plants and animals could be so greatly modified by their culture under domestication and by the practice of artificial selection, why would not wild species be equally subject to modification by natural selection and the struggle for survival? Darwin was ahead of his time. Not until recent years have geneticists and evolutionists once again turned their attention to cultivated crops as evolutionary subjects. The reasons for this may become apparent as we develop the subject further.

The first really serious modern treatment of the origin of cultivated plants was in some ways the best. The 1886 (second) edition of *The Origin of Cultivated Plants* by Alphonse de Candolle was reprinted in 1959 in New York (12). It is surprisingly modern and up to date. After over 70 years there is really very little to add and very few corrections to make. If you want to know about the geographic origin of crop plants, de Candolle is still an excellent reference and, with but few exceptions, a reliable source of information.

The next serious treatment of the subject was made by the great Russian agronomist Vavilov (51). His work was on a much vaster scale and much more experimental. "The tremendous mass of material assembled by the institute which he directed for many years made possible a geographic survey of crop plants on a scale which has never been duplicated. In no other country and at no other time has an agronomist had such facilities at his disposal. The work is so monumental that it stands today neither substantiated nor disproved by independent research. Some of his claims have been questioned, but the principal theses of Vavilov are known and appreciated the world over, with the possible exception of his native land where his genius inspired jealousy and his integrity invited liquidation (18).

The most useful and important generalization of the Vavilovian work was the concept of geographic centers of variability or gene centers. The fact that these are not necessarily centers of origin does not make the concept less useful. Geographic concentration of variability is a real phenomenon and bears certain definite genetic and agronomic connotations. There has not been a comprehensive treatment of the origin of cultivated plants since Vavilov, and following the custom of twentieth century science, the vast problem has been attacked by a multitude of specialists, each working on small, often independent, segments of the subject. Here the threads of ideas become quite diffuse, and I shall do my best to pull some of them together.

In the late 1920's, H. V. Harlan and M. L. Martini began a series of experiments with barley that have become classics of their kind. The work has been adequately published (16, 19, 32, 49), and I called attention to its significance at the Brookhaven Symposium of 1956. It is not necessary, therefore, to discuss the work in detail. The essential features of the composite cross studies were: (*a*) to select carefully a number of varieties of quite diverse origin, (*b*) to cross them in all possible combinations, and (*c*) to sit back and see what settled out.

One of the most striking things to settle out was a remarkable array of aberrants, odd-balls and/or "mutants." As far back as 1923, Kajanus (22) had reported a very high incidence of speltoid mutants in certain wheat crosses, but this in no way prepared us for the startling display of types hitherto unknown to agronomists. A check among some of the populations in which crosses were kept separately revealed that two varieties from India were especially effective in producing mutants in hybrid populations. This was an early and dramatic demonstration of what has now come to be a well-known fact, i.e., the mixing of strange germ plasm is mutagenic. Mangelsdorf (29) has been even more specific and has shown that the fourth chromosome of teosinte has rather specific mutagenic effects when substituted into maize inbreds.

Other things have settled out of well-stirred composite cross populations including something over thirty improved varieties now grown in this and other countries. The method is a proven and tested procedure for plant improvement and even composite cross populations themselves, after a sufficient number of generations, may show sufficiently superior adaptation and performance to warrant their release as varieties (49).

Meanwhile, other people working with other plants began to come independently to at least a partial understanding of the role of hybridity in evolution. Griggs in 1937 (15) traced the history of cannas and pansies and showed that little progress was made until the introduction of exotic germ plasm brought about an almost explosive increase in variability. Students of maize became impressed by the role played by teosinte in maintaining or increasing variability. Workers with rice noted the continuous crossing of tame varieties with *fatua* types and speculated as to its significance. Cytogenetical evidence began to suggest that the north Indian sugarcanes were products of the hybridization of noble canes with *Saccharum spontaneum*.

Many other studies were conducted tending to lead in the same direction. Finally, in 1949, Anderson (1) formalized his ideas concerning introgressive hybridization. This was a major generalization of great utility. Knowing a little better what to look for and how to look for it, biologists the world over have been able to detect the results of introgression in many species, both wild and tame.

As a result we now know considerably more than we did about the nature of variability in species. For example, Snyder (45) and Stebbins (46) have shown that microspecies in the *Elymus glaucus* complex may be ascribed, in part at least, to introgression by *Sitanion*. Clausen (10, 11) and his co-workers have demonstrated that much of the variability in *Poa pratensis* can be accounted for by the introduction of germ plasm from a number of species of *Poa*. Harlan (20) and Harlan and Celarier (21) have shown that the single species *Bothriochloa intermedia* has received germ plasm from at least five species donors. Many other examples could be cited.

Turning to crop plants, Anderson and Brown (3) were able to show that corn belt maize as such is very new and that the whole germ plasm system, which now constitutes corn belt maize, originated in the last century by introgressive hybridization between northern flints and southern dents. A more thorough analysis of Mexican and Central American maize (31, 54, 55) indicates a prolonged introgression of *Tripsacum* germ plasm by way of teosinte into maize while there is considerable evidence of direct introgression of South American *Tripsacum* into Colombian maize (31, 42). The presence of teosinte germ plasm in Mexican maize has been genetically demonstrated by Mangelsdorf (29) and the experimental substitution of teosinte chromosomes has been shown to be mutagenic. There is now little or no reason to doubt that both teosinte and *Tripsacum* have played important roles in the origin and evolution of maize as a crop.

The situation alluded to in sugarcane has been studied more intensively in recent years. *Saccharum barberi* and *S. sinense* appear definitely to be the result of complex hybrids between *S. officinarum* and *S. spontaneum* (36). The hybrids are complex in that both reduced and unreduced eggs of *S. officinarum* can be fertilized, and chromosomes can be eliminated in blocks. The wild *S. robustum* of New Guinea may have originated in a similar way. Cytogenetic studies have shown that *Sclerostachya fusca* and the "genera" *Narenga* and *Erianthus* are probably also involved (36, 38). As the ancient culture of sugarcane expanded geographically, the noble canes were brought into contact with other species with which they introgressed and added substantially to the store of variability. This process can be seen today in New Guinea (53) and is being utilized extensively in sugarcane breeding.

The case of rice seems to follow the same basic pattern. According to Sampath and Narasinga Rao (43), both the African and Asiatic cultivated rices were selected from *Oryza perennis*. The former is called *O. glaberrima* and the latter *O. sativa* by most taxonomists, but crossing studies suggest they are no more different than the *indica* and *japonica* varieties of *O. sativa*. Interestingly enough, both the African and the Asian rices have their own weed forms, *O. breviligulata* and *O. sativa* var. *fatua*, respectively. Introgression is evident between the weed form and the cultivated form in each case (43).

The case of wheat has been studied more intensively than perhaps any other. Kihara began a long, painstaking, and dedicated investigation of genome homologies of wheat and wheat relatives in 1918. He is still at it, but has lots of company today. According to Kihara's classification, the diploid wheats, both wild and tame, have the genomic constitution AA. Most of the tetraploid wheats, wild and tame, have the constitution AABB, while the common cultivated hexaploid has the constitution AABBDD. McFadden and Sears (33) and Kihara (25) demonstrated independently that the D genome came from *Aegilops squarrosa*. The source of the B genome defied analysis for a number of years, but *Ae. speltoides* was incriminated in 1956 by Sakar and Stebbins (44) and substantiated by Riley, Unrau, and Chapman (41) in 1958.

The fact that wheat can be crossed rather easily with other species has, perhaps, been misleading. Crosses between wheat and *Agropyron intermedium* and *A. elongatum* are rather easy to make, many crosses have been made with species of *Aegilops* (37) and *Haynaldia*, and large scale spontaneous hybridizations with *Secale* have been recorded (28, 52). In such cases the small amount of chromosome pairing can usually be attributed to autosyndesis (26, 47). Under normal conditions very little homology is demonstrable between the various genomes of wheat and those of the species mentioned. In the absence of chromosome V, however, homeologous chromosomes may pair and much wider homologies are demonstrable. Modifications of the mechanism on chromosome V might well permit the injection of germ plasm from a wide variety of sources into wheat. This mechanism has caused difficulties in the interpretation of the evolution of wheat somewhat analogous to the difficulties posed by the behavior of the tunicate factor in maize (31, 41).

At any rate, wheat also falls into the same pattern as the other crops discussed. Wheat is, perhaps, more widely grown than any other crop and has enormous diversity. This diversity can be largely accounted for by the contributions of germ plasm from other species and, presumably, by continued introgression with the weed forms. In the case of wheat the weed forms are species of *Secale, Haynaldia, Aegilops,* and possibly *Agropyron* which, under appropriate conditions, cross readily with one form of wheat or another. The fact that chromosome pairing is very poor does not preclude some gene flow and the tendency toward sterility in backcross hybrid derivatives is an invitation to cross pollination and further crossing.

In barley, the weed form is *Hordeum spontaneum,* and introgression has been clearly demonstrated in Israel by Kamm (23). It has also been suggested that *H. agrocrithon* from Central Asia is an introgression product (13, 50, 58). Nor is the oat crop without its weed forms with which introgression of various types can take place, Table I. The cultivated sorghums of Africa and Asia cross readily with a variety of spontaneous forms and "chicken corn"

TABLE I.   The major cereal crops of the world
and their weed forms

Crop	Weed Forms
Maize, *Zea mays*	Teosinte, *Z. mexicana*
Rice, Oriental, *Oryza sativa*	Red rice or wild rice, *O. sativa* var. *fatua*
Rice, African, *O. glaberrima*	Wild rice, *O. breviligulata*
Wheat, *Triticum* spp.	*Secale cereale, Haynaldia villosa, Aegilops* spp., *Agropyron* spp.
Barley, *Hordeum vulgare*	*H. spontaneum, H. agrocrithon*
Oats, *Avena sativa*	*A. sativa* var. *fatua* and *Avena* spp.
Sorghum, *Sorghum vulgare*	A wide variety of spontaneous forms of the species

is a weed form now rather extensively naturalized in the Mississippi River system.

What are these weed forms, and what do they mean? Investigators are not yet in agreement on this point. Formerly, the weed forms were generally considered to be the ancestors of the crops. Later and more penetrating investigations have shown rather convincingly that this is not the case. Weed forms are specialized and derived. In the case of teosinte, archeological evidence indicates maize to be much older than teosinte (5, 14, 30). According to de Candolle (12), rye was unknown to the ancients. Sampath and Narasinga Rao (43) state, "Such a complex and artificial group as spontanea paddies are not likely to be a species ancestral to *Oryza sativa*." Most recent workers are fairly well agreed as to what the weed forms are *not*, but few have advanced theories as to what they *are*.

From the very beginnings of agriculture to the present time, farming people have developed a certain ritual with respect to the growing of crops. They stir the soil with tools of stone, bone, wood, or steel. They sow the seed by hand or stick or drill and pray to their gods of fertility or take out crop insurance. They weed, spray, fertilize, and otherwise tend their fields. They harvest with stone sickle, digging stick, or self-propelled combine and return thanks to their gods or pay their income taxes. The ritual, however varied it may be, always provides a special ecological niche designed for the culture of the crop in question. The niche provided is always a little wider than that which fits the crop alone. There is room in the niche for other species called weeds.

The cereal crops have been especially adept at providing weed forms to fill these niches. The weed forms developed naturally without special selection by man and were improved in adaptation by selection practiced on the crop. As man developed better varieties, these genes infiltrated the weed forms by introgressive hybridization and the weed forms were improved also. The weed forms always retained their capacity to shatter their seeds as well as the various seed and seedling adaptations that permit them to volunteer readily when the ecological niche is provided by man's farming activities. Should man cease providing these niches, both the crop and weed forms would disappear together.

The weed forms are able to maintain their identity through distinct barriers to crossing with the parental or companion crop. In the case of wheat and sugarcane the sterility and incompatibility barriers are formidable. Barley is naturally self-pollinated and in oats, crosses are difficult under the best of circumstances. Barriers to crossing in rice and maize are less strong, but still very substantial. It is one of the features of the theory of introgressive hybridization that the less intense the introgression, the more important it is (1).

With the knowledge we now have of introgressive hybridization and the mutagenic effect of strange germ plasm when introduced into crop plants, there can be little doubt that the weed forms of our crops have played immensely important roles in the evolution of the diversity which is so characteristic of them. It has been shown experimentally that teosinte can be used to improve maize (39). *Saccharum spontaneum* is used regularly in sugarcane improvement. Even primitive agriculturalists had some vague feeling that benefit might be derived from growing teosinte and maize together (31), or wheat and rye together (51). The weed forms, then, serve as reserve gene pools and as sources of strange germ plasm which can induce not only the production of swarms of aberrants but also the production of forms better fitted to the niches provided.

Returning to the Vavilovian centers of diversity, we find the weed forms always present in abundance (18, 51, 52) in primary centers. In secondary centers, this is not necessarily true. I speculated one time (17), for instance, on the reasons for the enormous varietal diversity of certain New World crops in Asia Minor. Anatolian maize is remarkably diverse, but teosinte is not present. A second and closer look at Turkish popcorn was taken by Anderson and Brown (4). It was evident from their studies that at least two very different races had been introduced into Turkey from different sources and by different routes. This is likely to be true of the field corns as well, although they have not been studied so thoroughly. The explanation of maize diversity in Anatolia does not appear to be so much due to primitive agriculture as to local introgression between widely different races of maize.

I have gone into a discussion of these problems in some detail in order to show that our thinking with respect to the geographic origin of crop plants is somewhat more sophisticated than it was some twenty years ago. The problems involved are immensely complex, but our tools of investigation are much more refined and sophisticated now than they were. With present or improved techniques for introgression analysis, with a better understanding of genetic systems and the effects of genetic background on gene expression, with more trained workers and more extensive research programs, many of the perplexing problems concerned with the origin and evolution of cultivated plants should, in time, yield satisfactory solutions. Darwin was right in that crop plants are excellent evolutionary subjects, but they are much too complicated to be understood by the methods of investigation available in his time. A century later we are beginning to make some progress.

At the present time, students of crop evolution are tending to think in terms of diffuse origins—origins diffuse in both time and space. In the beginning, a given plant was wild, but adapted to disturbed sites. It may have had a wide distribution so that more than one nuclear area of incipient domestication could have developed. As the plant was used more and more and as man learned better how to provide a special ecological niche for it, the culture of the incipient crop spread into new areas. Introgressive hybridization between the incipient crop and wild forms of the new area induced an increase in variability. Selections permitted still wider use of the crop and more infiltration of strange germ plasm and still more cycles of induced variability. When varieties from different nuclear areas came together, still more variability and still wider adaptation became possible.

With the coming of extensive culture, the weed forms developed with their inherent capacities for increasing variability and speeding up evolution of the crop. As the crop expanded in usage, it also changed radically in morphology. Altogether new types may have developed in new areas. To speak of the origin of wheat has little meaning. We must investigate the origin of einkorn or emmer or spelt or shot wheats or other specific kinds of wheat, for it is quite likely that the different kinds had different origins. Ethiopia may be the home of irregular and *deficiens* barleys, but it is not the home of barley. Colombian maize originated in Colombia and corn belt maize in the United States, but neither area is likely to be the original nuclear area of *Zea* culture. It is hardly fair to say, "Maize originated in Mexico." It may well be that the primitive *Zea* from which maize developed was first used as a food in Mexico, but Burmese maize did not originate in Mexico, nor Colombian maize, nor Anatolian maize. The changes that take place in time and space force upon us the concept of diffuse origin which is basic to our problem.

For this reason, Burmese maize or Anatolian maize may be quite different from any maize in the Americas. Kuleshov (27) was quite impressed by the distinctness of Asiatic maize, as were Stonor and Anderson (48). Some Turkish varieties are earlier in maturity than anything in the American collections. In our search for germ plasm for breeding purposes, it would be short-sighted, indeed, to confine our interest and our collections to primary centers of diversity. Furthermore, the idea of diffuse origins means that we can never quite solve the question of the geographic origin of an ancient cultivated plant. Crop plants did not originate in any one geographic area. They are still in the process of origination wherever they are being grown, and centers of diversity are centers of the most active origination (18).

My remarks so far have been confined to the cereal grains and sugarcane. Most other crops assume the same basic pattern, although a few of them do not have weed forms. *Citrus* has weed forms in southeast Asia and some of these have escaped extensively in tropical America. Most of the edible bananas are sterile, parthenocarpic triploids and consequently do not introgress with other species. All of them were derived, however, from the introgressive hybridization of the species *Musa acuminata* and *M. balbisiana* or from these species directly (8, 9). In addition, bananas have special mechanisms for chromosomal variation in somatic cells (8). Introgression and semi-weed forms have been recorded for coffee in Ethiopia (2), and potatoes have weedy forms in South America and Mexico. Weed melons, lentils, hemp, radishes, and carrots are described by Vavilov to introgress with the cultivated sorts (51).

It is admittedly dangerous to generalize too much concerning so diverse and anomalous a group as cultivated plants, but many crops at least appear to have evolved along the same lines as the cereals just described. I shall, however, generalize on the concept of diffuse origins which tend to make the question of the geographic origin of cultivated plants somewhat academic. The nuclear areas of incipient domestication may be quite widely removed from areas of maximum diversification. The mango, *Mangifera indica*, appears to have originated in the Malay Peninsula, but the area of greatest varietal diversity is said to be India (35). Sesame is thought to be African in origin but has centers of evolutionary activity in India and central Asia. The pumpkin, *Curcurbita pepo*, is North American in origin (57), but Vavilov placed the center of diversity in Asia Minor (52). The regions of ancient origination are of less agronomic interest than the areas of current evolutionary activity.

I would now like to discuss briefly some geographical problems which are not quite so knotty but which are extremely interesting and over which there is little unanimity of opinion. I refer to such plants as the coconut, sweet potato, yam, bottle gourd, cotton, and even maize which for various reasons are held by some to indicate pre-Columbian contacts between the New and Old Worlds.

The genus *Cocos* is basically American as is indeed the whole tribe *Cocoineae* of over 20 genera and perhaps 200 species. Yet *Cocos nucifera* had a pre-Columbian distribution across the Pacific and around the shores of the Indian Ocean. Ancient Sanskrit names and other evidences suggest extensive culture in the Orient from early times (24).

The sweet potato, *Ipomoea batatas*, is also American, but was known at the time of discovery in Polynesia, Melanesia, and Hawaii. The names applied were claimed to be similar to the Quechua names in South America. The yam, *Dioscorea alata*, is thought to be East Indian, possibly Javanese, but according to Carter was reported from the Caribbean by Columbus and Spanish chroniclers in the early sixteenth century (7).

The bottle gourd, *Lagenaria*, has ancient traditions in both Africa and Asia including Sanskrit names, and is well documented archeologically as pre-Columbian in the New World (56). In cotton, the 26 chromosomed American species contain a genome of Asiatic cotton, while the distinctness of Asiatic maize has led Kuleshov (27), Stonor and Anderson (48), and others to speculate concerning early contacts (7).

I do not wish to force myself into a controversy which has sometimes been rather bitter. I only wish to point out that pre-Columbian transport by man is not necessary to account for these distributions nor will it solve the problem of similar distributions of wild species. I am rather inclined to believe myself, that the evidence for early contact before A.D. 1000 is fairly good and that man *may* have transported a crop like the sweet potato at that time. That man could have transported maize from South America to Asia without leaving a trace in the whole of the Pacific area, however, strains credulity to the breaking point. This is especially true considering how rapidly maize is *known* to have spread after Columbus.

The point is that there are other similar distributions to be accounted for among wild species. That a Polynesian or an American Indian might transport sweet potatoes or coconuts across vast stretches of the Pacific is plausible. But what native in his right mind would also transport a *Bothriochloa* or a *Sorghastrum* or an inedible *Oryza?* In the case of the Gramineae we have been forced to the conclusion that such bicentric distributions are of geological origin, probably dating back to the Cretaceous.

For palms, the fossil record strongly favors such an ancient distribution. *Cocos* has been reported from the early Tertiary of India and this supports the idea that *Cocos nucifera* is probably an Old World plant despite its New World relatives (24). *Phoenix*, an Old World genus, is similarly reported from the Texas Tertiary. A Cretaceous distribution of *Gossypium* and *Lagenaria* is just as likely. In defense of genetic stability, I can report that we have crossed American and Australian species of *Bothriochloa* for which no one has yet claimed human transport.

The case for pre-Columbian transport of maize appears hopeless. The case for *Dioscorea* disappears upon reexamination of the evidence by Burkill (6). The only evidence remaining is the *possibility* of the introduction of the coconut to the New World and the importation of the sweet potato into the Pacific islands from the New World (34). These two cases of human transport are indeed possible, but rushing ships and men across the South Pacific does not solve the problems of plant geography.

Finally, I would like to point out a few reasons why investigations of the geographic origin of cultivated plants are useful to agriculture. In the first place a better understanding of how our crop plants evolved can help direct our efforts toward improvement. Anderson and Brown (3) have pointed out that if corn belt maize originated in the United States by the introgression of northern flints and southern dents, then we might expect to obtain near maximum heterosis by developing inbreds with many of the characteristics of these diverse groups. Riley *et al.* (41) pointed out that if common wheat is, in fact, two-thirds *Aegilops*, we might well have a better chance of improving wheat by devoting more attention to *Aegilops*. If our cultivated plants represent species put together by introgression from other species or from the weed forms, we might well plan our improvement programs with this in mind. If specific genes or blocks of genes bearing desired characteristics cannot be introduced by conventional breeding methods, then the use of substituted chromosomes, induced translocations, or similar methods might be employed. The more we know about a crop and how and where and when it originated, the better are our chances of bringing about the desired improvement.

Secondly, knowledge of where and how and by what means a plant is introduced into cultivation could be of great use in the development of new crops. It has often been stated that there has not been a single staple crop added to the human diet since the Stone Age. It is true that our most important crops are ancient ones and their origin recedes into the mists of prehistory. Our recent domesticates are likely to be ornamentals or technical crops like *Hevea, Cinchona, Derris,* or similar plants grown for industrial, medicinal or insecticidal purposes. An important branch of current agricultural research is devoted primarily to the finding of new uses for old crops or new crops which have industrial potential. It is difficult indeed to bring a wild plant into cultivation and expect it to compete with old, established crops. The more we can learn about crop domestication the better are our chances of succeeding. Such information can be of especial use to the breeders of forage crops who are often dealing with wild or near wild species.

Finally, knowledge of crop geography tells us where to look for variability which we might use in our breeding programs. Centers of diversity are the best sources of such variability and we have for many years attempted to sample such centers and transport the variability to our experiment stations for use.

Unfortunately, the geographic centers of diversity upon which we have depended so much in the past for our sources of germ plasm are in great danger of extinction. Modern agriculture and modern technology are spreading rapidly around the world. New, uniform varieties from the experiment stations are replacing the old mixed populations that have grown, in some cases, since the Neolithic— The old centers of diversity are disappearing, and time is running out faster than most of us realize. Adequate and thorough exploration must be made *now* before it is too late. World collections in the future must be preserved with great care lest material be lost that can never be replaced.

A predicament now exists in which the technologically backward countries cannot afford to keep their great varietal resources and the more progressive countries cannot afford to let them be discarded. The only answer is an extensive exploration and collection program devoted to assembling as much of the germ plasm of the world as possible and the diligent maintenance of the material once it is obtained (19).

References

1. Anderson, E. *Introgressive Hybridization.* John Wiley and Sons, New York, 1949.

2. Anderson, E. Personal communication.

3. Anderson, E., and W. L. Brown. Origin of corn belt maize and its genetic significance. *Heterosis*, J. W. Gowen, Editor, pp. 124-148. Iowa State Press, Ames, Iowa, 1952.

4. Anderson, E., and W. L. Brown. The popcorns of Turkey. *Ann. Missouri Botan. Garden, 40,* 33-48 (1953).

5. Barghoorn, E. S., M. K. Wolfe, and K. H. Clisby. Fossil maize from the Valley of Mexico. *Botan. Museum Leaflet Harvard Univ., 16,* 229-240 (1954).

6. Burkill, I. H. Aji and batata as group-names within the species *Ipomoea batatas. Ceiba, 4* (4), 227-240 (1954).

7. Carter, George F. Plant evidence for early contacts with America. *Southwestern J. Anthropol., 6,* 161-182 (1950).

8. Chakravorti, A. K. Origin of cultivated bananas of South East Asia. *Indian J. Genet. and Plant Breeding, 11* (1), 34-46 (1951).

9. Chandraratna, M. F. The origin of cultivated races of banana. *Indian J. Genet. and Plant Breeding, 11* (1), 29-33 (1951).

10. Clausen, Jens, David D. Keck, and W. M. Hiesey. Experimental taxonomy. *Carnegie Inst. Wash. Yearbook, 46,* 95-103 (1946-47).

11. Clausen, Jens, W. M. Hiesey, and M. A. Nobs. *Poa* investigations. *Carnegie Inst. of Wash. Yearbook, 57,* 272-278 (1957-58).

12. de Candolle, Alphonse. Origin of Cultivated Plants (2nd edition, 1886). Noble Offset Printers, Inc., New York, 1959.

13. Freisleben, R. Ein neuer Fund von *Hordeum agrocrithon* Åberg. *Züchter*, *16*, 49-63 (1943).

14. Galinat, Walton C., P. C. Mangelsdorf, and L. Pierson. Estimates of teosinte introgression in archaeological maize. *Botan. Museum Leaflet Harvard Univ.*, *17*, 101-124 (1956).

15. Griggs, R. F. The role of hybridity in evolution. *J. Wash. Acad. Sci.*, *27*, 329-331 (1937).

16. Harlan, H. V., M. L. Martini, and Harlan Stevens. A study of methods in barley breeding. *U. S. Dept. Agr. Tech. Bull. No. 720*, 1940.

17. Harlan, Jack R. New World crop plants in Asia Minor. *Sci. Monthly*, *72*, 87-89 (1951).

18. Harlan, Jack R. Anatomy of gene centers. *Am. Naturalist*, *85*, 97-103 (1951).

19. Harlan, Jack R. Distribution and utilization of natural variability in cultivated plants. *Genetics in Plant Breeding. Brookhaven Symposia in Biol. No. 9*, pp. 191-206, 1956.

20. Harlan, Jack R. *Bothriochloa intermedia* A. Camus. A study in speciation. *Proc. 10th Intern. Congr. Genet.* (1958).

21. Harlan, Jack R., and Robert P. Celarier. Apomixis and species formation in the Bothriochloeae Keng. *Proc. 9th Intern. Botan. Congr.* (1959).

22. Kajanus, Birger. Über Ährchenabst und Ährchenzal bei einigen Weizenkreuzungen. *Hereditas*, *4*, 290-350 (1923).

23. Kamm, A. The discovery of wild six-rowed barley and wild *Hordeum intermedium* in Israel. *Ann. Roy. Agr. Coll. Sweden*, *21*, 287-320 (1954).

24. Kaul, K. N. Some interesting features of the distribution of palms in relation to their origin. *Indian J. Genet. and Plant Breeding*, *11* (1), 108-110 (1951).

25. Kihara, H. Die Entdeckung des DD-Analysators beim Weizen. *Agr. Hort. Japan*, *19*, 889-890 (1944).

26. Kihara, H. Considerations on the evolution and distribution of *Aegilops* species based on the analyser-method. *Cytologia*, *19*, 336-357 (1954).

27. Kuleshov, N. N. Some peculiarities of maize in Asia. (Trans. by H. J. Kidd and H. C. Reynolds.) *Ann. Missouri Botan. Garden*, *41*, 271-299 (1954).

28. Leighty, C. E., and J. W. Taylor. "Hairy neck" wheat segregates from wheat-rye hybrids. *J. Agr. Research*, *28*, 567-576 (1924).

29. Mangelsdorf, P. C. The mutagenic effects of hybridizing maize and teosinte. *Cold Spring Harbor Symposia Quant. Biol.*, *23*, 409-421 (1958).

30. Mangelsdorf, P. C., and R. H. Lister. Archaeological evidence on

the evolution of maize in northern Mexico. *Botan. Museum Leaflet Harvard Univ., 17,* 151-178 (1956).

31. Mangelsdorf, P. C., and Robert G. Reeves. The origin of corn: Five papers commemorating the Darwin Centennial. *Botan. Museum Leaflet Harvard Univ., 18,* 329-440 (1959).

32. Martini, M. L., and H. V. Harlan. Barley freaks. *J. Heredity, 33,* 339-343 (1942).

33. McFadden, E. S., and E. R. Sears. The origin of *Triticum spelta* and its free-threshing hexaploid relatives. *J. Heredity, 37,* 81-89 (1946).

34. Merrill, Elmer D. The botany of Cook's voyages and its unexpected significance in relation to anthropology, biogeography and history. *Chronica Botanica, Vol. 14* (5/6), pp. i-iv, 161-384, Waltham, Mass., 1954.

35. Mukherjee, S. K. The origin of Mango. *Indian J. Genet. and Plant Breeding, 11* (1), 49-56 (1951).

36. Parthasarathy, N. Some cytogenetical aspects of the origin of sugarcane. *Indian J. Genet. and Plant Breeding, 11* (1), 34-46 (1951).

37. Popova, G. Species of *Aegilops* and their mass hybridization with wheat in Turkestan. *Trudi Priklad., Gen. i Selek., 13* (1), 461-482 (1923).

38. Price, S. Cytological studies in *Saccharum* and allied genera. II. Geographical distribution and chromosome numbers in *S. robustum. Cytologia, 22* (1), 40-52 (1957).

39. Reeves, Robert G. The use of teosinte in the improvement of corn inbreds. *Agron. J., 42,* 248-251 (1950).

40. Riley, R. Chromosome pairing and haploids in wheat. *Proc. X Intern. Congr. Genet., 2,* 234-235 (1958).

41. Riley, Ralph, John Unrau, and Victor Chapman. Evidence on the origin of the B genome of wheat. *J. Heredity, 49,* 91-98 (1958).

42. Roberts, L. M., U. J. Grant, R. Ramirez E., W. H. Hatheway, and D. L. Smith, in collaboration with P. C. Mangelsdorf. Races of maize in Colombia. *Natl. Acad. Sci.–Natl. Research Council Publ. No. 510,* 1957.

43. Sampath, S., and M. B. B. Narasinga Rao. Interrelationships between species in the genus *Oryza. Indian J. Genet. and Plant Breeding, 11* (1), 14-17 (1951).

44. Sarkar, P., and G. L. Stebbins. Morphological evidence concerning the origin of the B genome in wheat. *Am. J. Botany, 43,* 297-304 (1956).

45. Snyder, L. A. Cytology of inter-strain hybrids and the probable origin of variability in *Elymus glaucus. Am. J. Botany, 38,* 195-202 (1951).

46. Stebbins, G. L. The hybrid origin of microspecies in the *Elymus glaucus* complex. *Proc. Intern. Genet. Symp.* suppl. vol. *Cytologia,* pp. 336-340, 1956.

47. Stebbins, G. L., and F. T. Pun. Artificial and natural hybrids in the Gramineae, tribe Hordeae. VI. Chromosome pairing in *Secale cereale* × *Agropyron intermedium* and the problem of genome homologies in the Triticinae. *Genetics, 38,* 600-608 (1953).

48. Stonor, C. R., and E. Anderson. Maize among the hill peoples of Assam. *Ann. Missouri Botan. Garden, 36,* 355-404 (1949).

49. Suneson, C. A. An evolutionary plant breeding method. *Agron. J., 48,* 188-191 (1956).

50. Takahashi, R. The origin and evolution of cultivated barley. *Advances in Genet., 7,* 227-266 (1955).

51. Vavilov, N. I. Studies on the origin of cultivated plants. Leningrad, 1926.

52. Vavilov, N. I., 1949/50. The origin, variation, immunity and breeding of cultivated plants. (Trans. by K. Starr Chester.) *Chronica Botanica,* Vol. 13, Waltham, Mass., 1949/50.

53. Warner, John N., and Carl O. Grassl. The 1957 sugar cane expedition to Melanesia. *Hawaiian Planters' Record, 55,* 209-236 (1958).

54. Wellhausen, E. J., A. Fuentes O., and A. Hernandez C. in collaboration with P. C. Mangelsdorf. Races of maize in Central America. *Natl. Acad. Sci.–Natl. Research Council Publ. No. 511,* 1957.

55. Wellhausen, E. J., L. M. Roberts, and E. Hernandez X. in collaboration with P. C. Mangelsdorf. Races of maize in Mexico. Bussey Inst. Harvard Univ., Cambridge, Mass., 1952.

56. Whitaker, T. W. *Lagenaria:* a pre-Columbian cultivated plant in the Americas. *Southwestern J. Anthropol., 4,* 49-68 (1948).

57. Whitaker, T. W., and G. F. Carter. Critical notes on the origin and domestication of the cultivated species of *Cucurbita. Am. J. Botan., 33* (1), 10-15 (1946).

58. Zohary, Daniel. Is *Hordeum agrocrithon* the ancestor of six-rowed cultivated barley? *Evolution, 13,* 279-280 (1959).

Origin of Animal Germ Plasm Presently Used in North America

H. H. STONAKER

*Department of Animal Husbandry, Colorado State University,
Fort Collins, Colorado*

Qualitatively there is a considerable variation in the farm animal germ plasm available in the United States. In 1958, 78 breeds of farm animals were represented by breed organizations in the United States (3). Mason (16), in his comprehensive coverage of breeds throughout the world lists the following numbers of "recognized breeds": asses, 12; buffaloes, 7; cattle, 231; goats, 62; sheep, 224; and swine, 54. Breeds of dogs, cats, poultry, rabbits, and other domesticated species were not compiled.

The importance of a breed of livestock in the United States is reflected directly in its population size, which in turn reflects its serviceability in terms of food or other demands and the economy of its production. Per capita consumption of animal source foods in the United States has expanded despite the rapid rise in human population (Fig. 1). This phenomenon has taken place with relatively little dependence upon importation. It is in contrast to reasoning based along Malthusian lines that, as population increased, competition with meat animals for cereals and other plant source foods would drive down meat animal production. The structure of the livestock population, however, is not stable, for costs and demands indicate recent marked shifts to increased per capita consumption of poultry and beef with somewhat reduced per capita consumption of pork, lamb, and veal. Consumption has remained stable for fish and for the most commonly used vegetable substitute for animal food products, dried beans. To increase consumption of meats in spite of increasing population numbers has necessitated an almost explosive increase in efficiency of livestock production. These population trends are shown in Fig. 2 for humans, beef cattle, sheep, swine, dairy cattle, and horses.

21

These shifts in demand, availability, and use of different animal products thus have a direct bearing on the quantitative importance of different breeds. Examples are not unusual of breeds which formerly were important and now are near extinction. The most

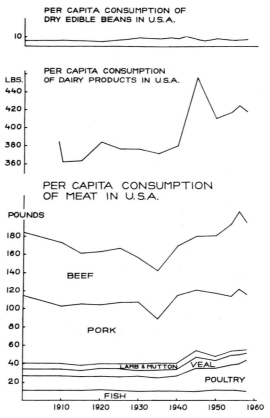

Fig. 1. Per capita consumption of beans, dairy products, and meats in the United States.

dramatic example is in the horse population. In 1910, 12,000 pure-bred Percheron and Belgian draft horses were registered in the United States. In 1958, only 483 of these horses were registered. In contrast, the American Quarter Horse, which was not even known in 1910, registered more entries than any other breed in

1958 (Figs. 3, 4). There are more total entries in the purebred horse registries than ever before, although the total horse population is at a low ebb.

Among the early purebred beef breeds, the Shorthorns predominated, reaching maximum total registrations in the 1920's. The

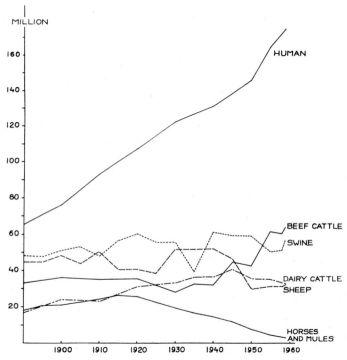

Fig. 2.   Livestock and human population trends in the United States.

Hereford breed, formerly in a much less prominent position than the Shorthorn, now leads all other beef breeds and all breeds of livestock in annual registrations (Figs. 5, 6).

Numerous minor breeds contribute to the total purebred population. These are competitively striving, through the efforts of breeders and promoters, to replace or augment predominantly popular breeds. They serve as a stimulus and source for greater genetic diversity of material than otherwise would be accessible.

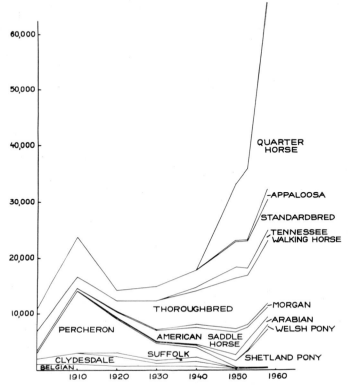

Fig. 3.   Total annual horse registrations in the United States.

In dairy cattle, as well as beef cattle, total registrations have increased greatly within the last fifteen years (Figs. 7, 8). Domestic breeds thus follow patterns of wild populations, having periods of expansion and contraction, leading occasionally to near extinction.

To ignore the work of early breeders, the geographic origin, and the background history which has led to the development of present breeds is to deny a source of wealth that becomes available in ever increasing abundance. It is difficult to chart precisely the magnitude of man's accomplishment in shifting the germ plasm of animals as bred under the native or wild state into channels of production that more nearly suited his needs at a given place and time. Undoubtedly, he found some species easier to domesticate

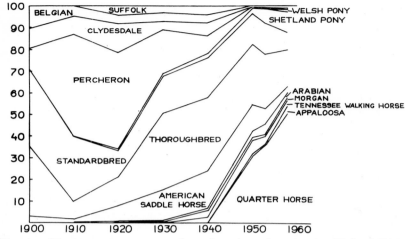

Fig. 4. Horses as a per cent of total registrations in the United States.

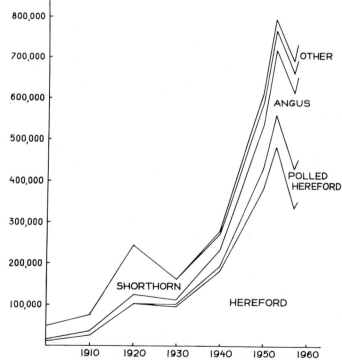

Fig. 5. Total beef cattle registrations in the United States.

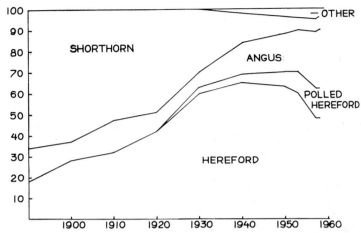

Fig. 6.   Beef cattle as a per cent of total registrations in the United States.

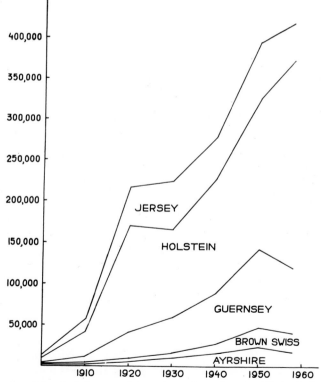

Fig. 7.   Total dairy cattle registrations in the United States.

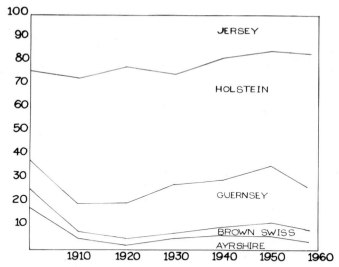

Fig. 8.   Dairy cattle as a per cent of total registrations in the United States.

than others, but in his Swiss Family Robinson or Robinson Crusoe method, his first steps had to be toward domestication—selecting those animals best adapted for living with him. Although this process must have preceded his ability or interest in recording it, the impact he had upon the genotypes of his animals through selection, isolation, and outcrossing is evidenced today in the animals themselves.

Among the classic experiments which provide more precise evidence of the probable difference in man's original material and the product of generations of breeding under domestication is the one at the Iowa Station. Culbertson and Evvard (7) sought material for a dramatic demonstration of the impact of genetically improved stocks on swine production. Their experiment was designed to compare the productivity of the European wild hog, *Sus scrofa*, with a stock of purebred Poland China sows. In their unusual "grading down" experiment they found, as relationship to wild stocks increased, litter size was decreased, feed requirements were doubled, but the wild pigs were more vigorous at birth (Table I). Reversing to a degree the pressures of natural selection and supplanting them with others of their own choosing, breeders found it possible to supply themselves with more cheaply produced and better quality meats and animal products. They continue along these lines today at what must be much accelerated rates.

TABLE I.   Costly influence of an inferior sire (7)

	High-Grade Poland China	Fifty Per Cent Wild	Seventy-five Per Cent Wild
Pigs farrowed	10	5	3
Birth weight, pounds	2.1	2.2	3.6
Weight at 60 days	39.	27.	22.
Vigor at birth	Medium	Very strong	Very strong
Average daily gain	.65	0.64	0.48
Feed per 100 lb gain	390	477	757
Cost of feed per 100 lb gain	$6.56	$7.94	$12.71

In contrast to Europe and Asia, the New World, upon its discovery, was found to be almost devoid of useful domestic animals. Bourne (1), stated, "Gloriously rich in some aspects of nature, the New World was notably poor in food plants and domestic animals, those two indispensable aids to advancing culture." The Spanish explorers from Columbus on stressed the need for the importation of domestic animals from Europe. The American Indian primarily was a hunter, not a domesticator. The turkey has been the exclusive contribution to the domesticated species on the North American continent. Wild sheep existed on the North American continent, and bison, too, might have seemed a promising animal for domestication. Thus, there was a need for importation of farm animals into north America.

On his second voyage Columbus brought farm animals that helped establish an agriculture along European patterns. These introductions were successful, and the West Indies by 1512 had a thriving cattle population of Spanish origin (2). There are written accounts of the slaughter of these cattle for hides and tongues, the rest of the carcass being discarded. The similarity in use to that of the abundant bison herds in the West is striking. Introductions of cattle to the Florida coast were made by 1567. Their slaughter by

Indians together with unfavorable environment apparently kept them from increasing. From later Spanish introductions into Mexico, the Southwest, and California, stocks of cattle, horses, sheep, and swine were developed. The Spanish types were progenitors of the early Longhorn herds so prevalent in the Southwest. The wild horses of the plains undoubtedly were of the Arab-Barb type introduced by the Spanish armies. The spread of swine, sheep, and poultry is less well charted. Spanish cattle were introduced in the Northeast, as well, in the 1500's, for the French and English settlers later found them running wild on Sable Island off the Newfoundland coast (22). Some of these cattle later were taken to New England.

In the seventeenth century livestock of all kinds was brought in numbers from England and Continental Europe. Advertisements in London papers were directed toward ships' captains concerning availability of goats and cows in milk (19). The animals were used to supply milk during the voyage and to help the settlers establish an agriculture upon arrival. These introductions preceded the widespread interest in breed development that was to come later in England and which was destined to become an important factor in the further development of animal agriculture in the United States.

Robert Bakewell was considered the father of modern animal breeding (18), and his work and animals were early appreciated in the United States. His development of Longhorn cattle and Leicester sheep and the breeding principles of which he was the proponent provided an early written record of procedures in breed formation and animal improvement.

Agriculture in England during the middle eighteenth century was receptive to contributions such as Bakewell could make. Interest in his work and philosophy was widespread, as accounted for by the steady stream of visitors to Dishley Farm. Bakewell, in correspondence, wrote concerning his methods. His thinking and its impact on other breeders were spread mostly through the writings of his disciples. Bakewell stimulated a new era in livestock breeding that established Britain as the world center in the breeding of improved meat animals. His Longhorn breed of cattle reportedly was imported into the United States in small numbers (12). His Leicester sheep were more widely used.

Bakewell's principles of breeding were early appreciated in the United States. In 1825 there was a debate between agricultural editors concerning the merit of native stocks versus the stocks forming so many new breeds in Britain and Europe. Thomas Pickering of Massachusetts urged New Englanders to follow the pattern of Bakewell and to develop new breeds from native stocks. Others urged importation of the breeds being formed in Britain (12). The process of breed formation was being carried on in the United States as well as in Britain in the late eighteenth and early nineteenth centuries. The colonists had made some steps toward establishment of cattle breeds and there was well-recorded progress in horse breeding, with the development of strains later to be recognized as breeds. The Morgan and Standardbred breeds were in early developmental stages by the early 1800's. Hambletonian 10, the principal early sire of the American trotter or Standardbred, was foaled in 1849 (23). He traced to the thoroughbred stallion Messenger imported to Philadelphia in 1788. Messenger's get showed a natural inclination to trot, and this characteristic was exploited by early horse breeders. Justin Morgan, the foundation sire of the Morgan breed, was foaled in 1793. There were early attempts to establish one or two cattle breeds. The Creampot breed (12) originated from a cross of a Shorthorn bull, Coeleb, and a superior native cow. In developing this breed, Samuel Jacques, of Charlestown, Massachusetts had the objective of building a breed of cattle that would give more and richer milk than the Shorthorns and have lighter, less square frames. By 1839 Jacques had bred three generations of these cattle.

In swine, the Poland China was being established from 1800-1840 and had breed status by 1845. Chester Whites were established by 1848 and Duroc Jerseys by 1860 (23).

The period 1760-1860 in Britain is important to the livestock industry in the United States because it marked the origin and development of the principal meat breeds of cattle and sheep as well as some of the swine. In Europe, the draft breeds of horses, later to be important in the United States, were bred, as were the dairy breeds presently most important. If recommendations and principles were written as precisely concerning the development of the European breeds as for the development of British breeds, they apparently are not known or appreciated. Nevertheless, insofar as excellence of the product of the breeders' skills is concerned, the dairy cattle of Holland, Switzerland, and the Channel Islands have contributed generously to the agricultural wealth in this country. The same may be said of the heavy draft horse breeds of Europe, particularly the Belgian and Percheron breeds.

Systematic analyses of breeding structure were not possible until the invention of inbreeding and relationship coefficients by Wright (25). The degree of inbreeding found varied considerably between breeds (Table II). Its evaluation was difficult because of the lack of pedigree information in the formation periods. Since individual animal pedigrees are required, it was impossible to make computations for breeds where only flock or herd records were kept. Other breeds varied as to the date of establishment of herd

TABLE II. Summary of studies on degrees of inbreeding and relationships

Breed[a]	Base: Year Dates of Sample	Per Cent Inbreeding	Per Cent Inbreeding per Generation	Per Cent Inter se Relationship
Cattle				
Aberdeen Angus (21)	1850-1939	11.3	.30	13.3
Brown Swiss (26)	1883-1929	3.8	.50	4.3
Hereford cattle (24)	1860-1930	8.1	.68	8.8
Holstein (15)	1889-1931	4.0	.4	3.4
Shorthorn (17)	1790-1920	26	.87	40
Horses				
American Standardbred (20)	1935-1940	4.0 ±	0.6	8.2 ± 3.9
American Saddle Horse (20)	1935-1940	3.2 ±	1.1	6.0 ± 0.8
American Quarter Horse (9)	Before 1930	0.86, 1.64,		2.46, 1.34,
	1935 & 1940-1	1.75		0.98
Arabian Horse (11)	1907-1916	1.0		1.0
	1917-1926	2.0		4.0
	1927-1936	1.8		2.0
	1937-1946	4.8		4.0
	1947-1950	2.2		3.3
Clydesdale (13)	1925 (Calder)	6.2		0.9
Tennessee Walking Horse (10)	Foundation	1.24		2.95
	1924-25	1.4		3.12
	1930	2.5		6.30
	1935	3.1		6.45
	1940	3.6		5.80
Thoroughbred (20)	1935-1940	8.3	0.6	15.2 ± 1.9
Sheep				
Hampshire (6)	1911-1935	2.9	0.9	0.5
Rambouillet (8)	1892-1926	5.5	.69	2.6
Swine				
Poland China (14)	1886-1929	9.8	.61	14.2
Minnesota 1 (5)	1937-1949	32.0	about 3.0	

[a] Numbers in parentheses are references.

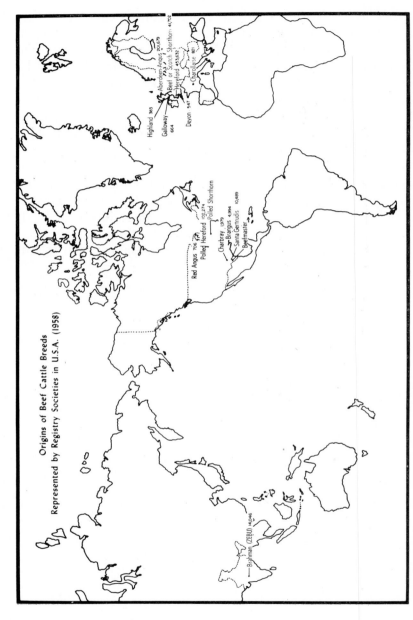

Fig. 9. Origins of beef cattle breeds, represented by registry societies in the United States in 1958.

books and pedigree information relative to the actual development or establishment of the breed. Nevertheless, the pedigree studies do give objective evaluations of the degree of inbreeding and indicate those animals important as the sources of the gene stream. In all breed studies, the number of effective sires has been found to be much less than the number in use, effective sires being the restricted number that would be required for inbreeding to rise at the calculated rate. Similarly, the ancestry of breeds evolves through herds coming from only a few of the total number of breeders. Individual sires become prominent and important as the gene source for the next generations, in contrast to the structure in human populations where there traditionally has been little genetic impact of a few individuals on the entire race.

It has been demonstrated in some of these studies that degree of inbreeding is cyclic (21). This was interpreted as reflecting the effects of economic pressures. In boom times more outcrossing takes place; in depression years there is less movement of breeding animals and inbreeding rises. Cyclic patterns are due, as well, to the waves of alternating popularity and disinterest in strains of breeding that exist. In shifting from one to another, rapid outcrossing occurs with an accompanying lowering in inbreeding for the population as a whole. Inbreeding is forced up as one or a few animals become more popular.

Geographic origins of breeds (4, 16, 23) presently represented by breed organizations in the United States and 1958 registrations are shown on the four maps (Figs. 9-12). The geographic origin for most of our beef cattle germ plasm quantitatively is shown to come from England and Scotland (Fig. 9). At present breeds with this source make up almost all beef cattle registrations (3). These British beef breeds are found throughout the entire United States. Indian or Brahma cattle have had an impact in the southern and Gulf Coast regions of the United States. Commercially, they are usually crossbred with other cattle, although some purebred herds are found. The full range of their adaptability and productivity in the United States is not yet known. The number of purebred Brahmas registered is not an accurate indication of Brahma influence because of the number of crossbred bulls used. The use of crossbred bulls otherwise is not a common practice.

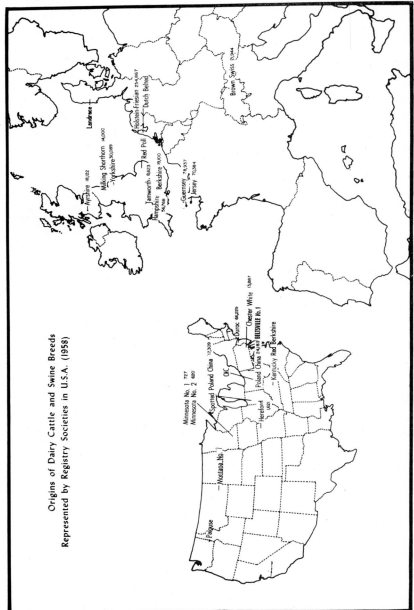

Origins of Dairy Cattle and Swine Breeds
Represented by Registry Societies in U.S.A. (1958)

Fig. 10. Origins of dairy cattle and swine breeds, represented by registry societies in the United States in 1958.

Offshoots of parent breeds such as a red strain of Aberdeen Angus and polled strains of Shorthorn and Hereford are listed as separate breeds. Other breeds are known in the United States at this time but have only a minute influence on the genetic constitution of the beef cattle population.

There has been practically no development of dairy cattle breeds in the United States; also there are fewer minor breeds (Fig. 10). Holland, Switzerland, and the Channel Islands are the homes of our major dairy breeds, although the Ayrshire originated in Scotland. Just recently Indian milking breeds have been used experimentally for crossing purposes in the South. The value of their contribution is uncertain at this time.

On the same map (Fig. 10) the birthplaces of swine breeds are shown. With swine, the American farmer has largely evolved his own breeds. Major breeds such as Poland China and Duroc Jersey are American in origin. The Hampshire apparently does not exist as an English breed although its origin is indicated there. (The imported stock apparently did not undergo appreciable crossing in this country.) Landrace, Yorkshire (Large White), and other bacon type breeds are presently increasing rapidly in the United States (3), perhaps at the expense of some of the American-derived breeds. These also have entered into the development of new breeds at several of the state agricultural experiment stations and the United States Department of Agriculture.

The important mutton breeds originated almost altogether in England and Scotland (Fig. 11). A great variety of English and Scotch mutton breeds offers a wide genetic base in this country for sheep producers. Rambouillet, Delaine Merino, and American Merino stem from the Spanish Merino. The Rambouillet was developed from Merino crosses in France and has been a widely used western range sheep. In the West new American breeds have been developed involving primarily crosses between long wools and Rambouillet, with selections out of these crosses.

The origins of horse breeds (4, 16, 23) are indicated on Fig. 12. The lineage of the Arab horse is perhaps as well charted as that of any breed of livestock. Not only is it one of the longest established of all breeds, but it also thrives throughout the world and has influenced most, if not all, other prominent breeds. With

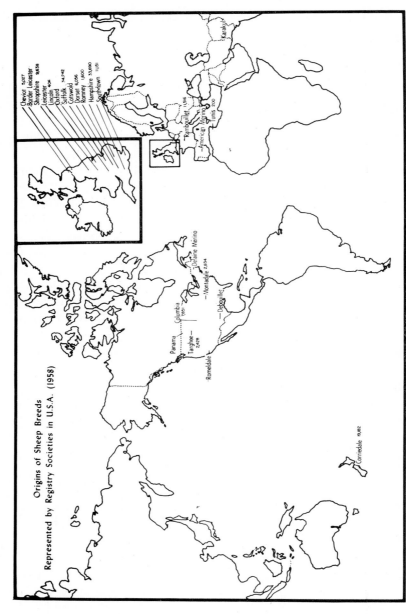

Fig. 11. Origins of sheep breeds, represented by registry societies in the United States in 1958.

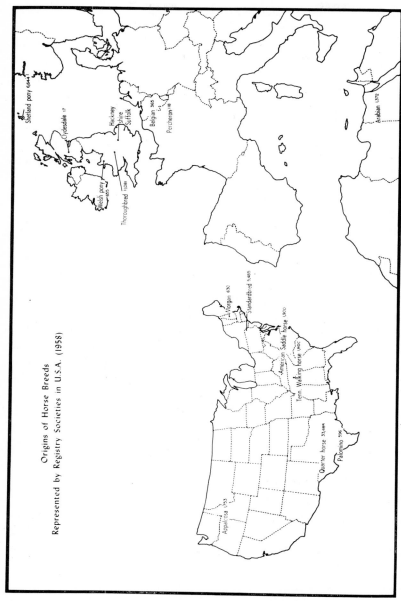

Origins of Horse Breeds

Represented by Registry Societies in U.S.A. (1958)

Shetland pony 6,644
Clydesdale 17
Welsh pony 665
Thoroughbred 11,081
Hackney
Shire
Suffolk
Belgian 365
Percheron 118
Arabian 1,372
Morgan 650
Standardbred 5,485
American Saddle horse 1,900
Tenn. Walking horse 9,800
Quarter horse 33,484
Palomino 596
Appaloosa 1,753

Fig. 12. Origins of horse breeds, represented by registry societies in the United States in 1958.

horses, as indicated earlier, the most drastic shift in structure of the population has taken place with draft breeds.

Steps in breed formation, regardless of origin, are so uniform in their pattern that they assume a stereotype that could be described as a law of breed formation. Crosses between existing strains or breeds are made. These progenies are subjected to tests or observations on their comparative usefulness. If successful in the first cross, they may be interbred. If these results are still promising, a period of selection in the more or less isolated population continues as a phase of breed development. The stage at which recognition of the group as a breed will take place is almost completely a subjective matter. With some it may be in the F_2 generation; in others, there may be intensely inbred groups originating from crosses of breeds that still are not considered breeds.

Our indebtedness to the rest of the world, particularly the British, for many of our improved domestic animals repeatedly has been indicated in this paper. In our own country, following the British tradition, non-profit associations made up of many small breeders and guided by directors elected by these breeders have served the economy in their interests of breed promotion and improvement.

Contributions from extensive genetic research with farm animals well underway indicate further changes in the structure of our seedstock supply. In poultry, for example, a completely different organization of breeders exists now than formerly. This is due primarily to extensive use of hybridizing programs for supplying both layers and broilers. Trade terms for strain crosses are largely replacing the use of breed names. Thus, in the United States nationally advertised strains are used, such as Hy-Line, H and N, Kimber, DeKalb, Vantress, Arbor Acres, and Nicols. These terms take the place of the breed sources contributing to the companies' own special but apparently shifting genetic formulations. The impact of this new industrialized breeding process is indicated by data in Table III, which shows the increase since 1941 in hybrid birds sold by hatcheries approved by the National Poultry Improvement Plan. These hatcheries have two-thirds of the nation's hatching capacity (USDA, ARS 53-3, 1955).

Thus, in poultry at the present time, the breed concept as traditionally developed by many small breeders has been largely

TABLE III.   Standard breeds and hybrids hatched by NPIP approved hatcheries in the United States[a]

Year	States	Total Birds	Standard Breed, %	Cross Mated and Incross Mated, %
1941-42	33	10,712,027	89.6	10.4
1951-52	47	37,559,597	78.5	21.5
1957-58	47	35,588,558	32.7	67.3

[a] USDA, ARS 44-2. September 1958. Chickens in NPIP hatchery supply flocks and their distribution by states and varieties.

replaced by strains exclusively held or developed in large competing industry breeders. It is well understood that the breeding programs of these large industrial type breeders are based upon competitive advances in the application of genetic research—far greater, it seems, than has been possible under associations made up of many breeders. However, information on breeding in terms of providing a general knowledge of pedigrees and mating systems is subject to a restraint not previously experienced in livestock breeding.

There has been some attempt to adapt the same industrial system to swine breeding in the United States but thus far with less success at replacing the traditional procedures. The system would seem even less adaptable to livestock with slower reproduction rates and longer generation intervals unless it is perhaps exercised eventually through artificial insemination programs. To date, widespread use of artificial insemination in dairy cattle has focused greater attention on animals thought to be outstanding. It does not appear to have led to an appreciable change in the basic organization or policies of individual dairy breeders.

In view of the ever increasing knowledge developing from experimental populations, the perpetuation and improvement of farm animal populations may well be in an important transitional stage. This could mean increased private as well as public development of methods and stocks which lead to further advances in the efficiency of our farm animals. It is hoped the available knowledge of these processes will keep pace at a favorably concurrent rate.

Acknowledgment

The author is indebted to Laura Ann Harris and Charlene R. Lickley for most of the preparation of the bibliography and maps. Helpful data and historical references were kindly furnished by officers of breed associations representing the following breeds: Aberdeen Angus, Brahma, Charollais, Charbray, Devon, Hereford, Red Poll, Santa Gertrudis, Scotch Highland, Shorthorn, Milking Shorthorn; Albino, Appaloosa, Arabian, Standardbred, Tennessee Walker, Thoroughbred; Cheviot, Corriedale, Hampshire, Karakul, Rambouillet, Romney, Southdown, Suffolk, Targhee; Beltsville 1, Maryland 1, Montana 2, Minnesota 1 and 2, Hampshire, Palouse, Poland China.

REFERENCES

1. Bourne, E. G. *Spain in America*. Harper & Brothers, New York, 1904.
2. Bowling, G. A. The introduction of cattle into Colonial North America. *J. Dairy Sci.*, *25*, 129-154 (1942).
3. *Breeders' Gazette* (Registrations of purebreds), *124*, 36-38 (March 1959).
4. Briggs, H. M. *Modern breeds of livestock*. The Macmillan Company, New York, 1949.
5. Brugman, H. H., and L. M. Winters. A genealogy study of the Minnesota No. 1 hog. *Minn. Univ. Agr. Expt. Station Tech. Bull. No. 184*, 1-28 (1949).
6. Carter, R. C. A genetic history of Hampshire Sheep. *J. Heredity*, *31* (2), 89-93 (1948).
7. Culbertson, C. C., and John M. Evvard. The costly influence of an inferior sire. *Iowa Leaflet 1*. Iowa Agr. Expt. Sta., Ames, Iowa, 1923.
8. Dickinson, W. F., and J. L. Lush. Inbreeding and the genetic history of the Rambouillet sheep in America. *J. Heredity*, *24*, 19-33 (1934).
9. Fletcher, J. L. A genetic analysis of the American Quarter Horse. *J. Heredity*, *36*, 346-352 (1945).
10. Fletcher, J. L. A study of the first fifty years of Tennessee Walking Horse breeding. *J. Heredity*, *37*, 369-373 (1946).
11. Gazder, P. J. The genetic history of the Arabian Horse. *J. Heredity*, *45*, 95-98 (1954).
12. Lemmer, G. F. The spread of improved cattle through the eastern United States to 1850. *Agr. Hist.*, *21*, 79-93 (1947).
13. Lush, J. L. The amount and kind of inbreeding which has occurred in the development of breeds of livestock. *Proc. 6th Intern. Congr. Genet. 2*, 123-126 (1932).

14. Lush, J. L., and A. L. Anderson. A genetic history of Poland-China swine. *J. Heredity, 30* (4), 149-156 (1939).

15. Lush, J. L., J. C. Holbert, and O. S. Willham. Genetic history of the Holstein Friesian cattle in the United States. *J. Heredity, 27,* 61-72 (1936).

16. Mason, I. L. World dictionary of breeds, types, and varieties of livestock. *Tech. Commun. 8.* Commonwealth Bureau of Animal Breeding, Edinburgh, Scotland, 1951.

17. McPhee, H. C., and Sewall Wright. Mendelian analysis of the pure breeds of livestock. *J. Heredity, 16,* 205-215 (1925).

18. Pawson, H. Cecil. *Robert Bakewell: Pioneer Livestock Breeder.* Crosby Lockwood & Son, Ltd., London, 1957.

19. Prentice, E. P. *American Dairy Cattle: Their Past and Future.* Harper & Brothers, New York, 1942.

20. Steele, D. G. A genetic analysis of recent thoroughbreds, Standardbreds, and American Saddle horses. *Kentucky Agr. Expt. Station Bull. 462,* 1-25 (1944).

21. Stonaker, H. H. The breeding structure of the Aberdeen Angus breed. *J. Heredity, 34* (11), 323-328 (1943).

22. Towne, C. W., and E. N. Wentworth. *Cattle and Men.* University of Oklahoma Press, Norman, Okla., 1955.

23. Vaughan, H. W. *Breeds of Livestock in America.* R. G. Adams & Co., Columbus, Ohio, 1931.

24. William, O. S. A genetic history of Hereford Cattle in the United States. *J. Heredity, 28* (8), 283-291 (1937).

25. Wright, S. Coefficients of inbreeding and relationship. *Am. Naturalist, 56,* 330-338 (1922).

26. Yoder, D. M., and J. L. Lush. A genetic history of the Brown Swiss Cattle in the United States. *J. Heredity, 28,* 154-160 (1937).

Untapped Sources of Animal Germ Plasm

RALPH W. PHILLIPS

Foreign Agricultural Service, United States Department of Agriculture, Washington, D. C.

Many types of livestock and poultry exist in the world, but relatively few have found a place in the livestock and poultry industries of the United States. This applies also to Canada, for the types and breeds in use are the same to a considerable degree, and there has been rather free interchange of breeding stock between the two countries.

The types and breeds of livestock now in use are largely of British and northwestern European origin. The initial selection of types was closely related to the points of origin of the people who settled the new continent. We have brought some new types into the United States since colonial days, and we have looked somewhat farther afield in the selection of types of poultry than we have with livestock. But, in relation to the numbers and variations in the reservoirs of germ plasm that are available in the world, we must consider ourselves a conservative nation, content to work mostly within the limits of the breeding materials our forefathers made available to us, and, when we do make importations, to return to essentially the same sources for new breeding animals. In this respect, our approach to animal improvement stands in rather marked contrast to our approach in the plant field, where we have constantly sought new breeding materials.

It is clear that our animal breeders have made substantial progress in the development of more productive breeds and strains, making use of the stock that has been available to them. It is also clear that a very large segment of the animal germ plasm available in the world has not been used in the development of our livestock and poultry industries. It is not clear, however, just how much we might profit from the use of germ plasm from these untapped reservoirs. Here is a largely unexplored field of scientific endeavor. Exploration of it would no doubt yield a lot of negative results, but there are possibilities of positive results that could be of considerable benefit to our livestock industry and to the well-being of our people. We are inclined to think that we have the best, not only in livestock but also in many other things. However, it is hardly reasonable to assume that, somehow, all the best germ plasm was concentrated in those areas from which our foundation stock came.

Nature of Untapped Sources and the Problem of Exploring Them

The untapped sources of animal germ plasm that we might explore are of two general kinds: (*a*) improved types that have been developed and used in other countries, but which for various reasons have not been introduced into or have not become established in the United States (and Canada); and (*b*) types that are generally regarded as unimproved, and which have been used primarily only in the localities where they originated, or in nearby areas, and which have not been the object of organized programs for improvement through breeding. In this second point, the phrase, "organized programs for improvement through breeding," is used in the sense that considerable numbers of well-informed breeders have undertaken to improve a type or breed and have made substantial progress toward commonly understood objectives.

In many types of livestock in the world substantial degrees of uniformity and reasonable levels of productivity have been achieved, without the benefit of organized breeding programs, commonly agreed objectives, and breed associations to promote the interests of the accepted types. Many of the recognized breeds of today had their origins in just such circumstances; recognition as breeds and establishment of organizations to promote them have generally been by-products of the emergence of distinctive, productive types.

This is a point we should remember when we refer to the "unimproved" types that are little known in the United States and Canada, and which are used primarily in underdeveloped areas.

Many of these types or breeds have reached levels of uniformity and levels of productivity under the environmental conditions in which they have been developed that compare favorably with the levels achieved by the breeds we think of as "improved," at the times they emerged as recognized breeds, and when herd books and breed societies were established, and promotional activities were undertaken.

Uniformity and moderate levels of productivity in these "unimproved" types have resulted from varying circumstances. Even the illiterate farmer, or the nomadic tribesman, who has no knowledge of the formal principles of genetics and animal breeding, is usually aware of the relative merits of his animals and of the long-recognized idea that "like begets like." So, over the centuries, selection pressure has no doubt been exerted in favor of the cattle and horses that had superior pulling power; cows, goats, and sheep that had better than average milk production; chickens that were superior in the fighting arena or in producing meat for the table, and so on. Or, selection pressure may have been exerted for some color or color pattern that pleased the owners. On the other hand, uniformity may have been achieved because of the geographic isolation of a particular group of people and their animals. In other cases, one breeder, who may have been a wealthy landowner or a religious leader, became interested in a local breed and, by example as well as by providing bulls to his neighbor, did a great deal to develop uniformity in breeding objectives. In some cases, government-owned farms have performed a similar function.

Quite apart from man's effort to direct breeding in any particular direction, it seems reasonably certain that natural selection has played a part in the establishment of types that could withstand the rigors of the environment and could therefore be most useful to man. Extreme examples are the yaks of the Tibetan highlands, the llamas and alpacas of the Andean highlands, and the water buffaloes of the tropical countries. Other examples (14) of such adaption to the environment, applied to broad groups of animals, are: the Bactrian camels of central Asia that are adapted to cold climates, compared with the dromedaries of the Near East and southwestern Asia that can withstand extreme heat; the Zebu cattle of India, Pakistan, and parts of Africa that are better able to withstand tropical conditions than are cattle of European origin; the fat-tailed and fat-rumped sheep of Asia that are much better adapted to extensive, sparse grazing areas than the highly specialized mutton breeds of the United Kingdom; and the native chickens of many tropical and subtropical countries that, while producing only 60 to 100 eggs a year, manage to survive under the difficult conditions imposed by the environment and the lack of good poultry management on the part of their owners.

The spreading of a type or breed beyond the confines of the area where it originated has been, to a considerable degree, a matter of chance related to factors other than the merits of the animals as compared with those available in other areas, countries, or continents. Factors such as custom, ability of a people as seafarers, and large migrations over land routes have, in many cases, determined which types were taken to other lands.

It is only natural, as I have already mentioned, that when people move to a new land they take with them the kinds of livestock they have available and to which they are accustomed. Thus, it was because the Spanish were a seafaring people that the Longhorn cattle became a part of the tradition of the southwestern United States. Also, because the British were a seagoing race, and because population pressures and other factors led them to settle new lands, the British breeds of cattle, sheep, and horses have tended to dominate the livestock scene in the United States, Canada, Australia, and New Zealand. A few continental European breeds, such as Holstein cattle and Percheron and Belgian horses, also followed the migrants to the new lands. Other types and breeds, developed in countries that did not participate so actively in the initial settlement have found relatively little place in the new lands. However, in more recent times, certain of the Zebu breeds of cattle have been used in southern United States, Brazil, and other tropical and subtropical countries, for beef production; the Danish Landrace swine have found a place in breeding programs in the United States; and other types, such as Charollais and Red Sindhi cattle, have been recognized as possible contributors respectively to beef and dairy improvement programs in the United States.

Among the many types or breeds of livestock and poultry that have not been used in the United States, there are no doubt some that possess qualities that might be of value to us. They may be grouped into two broad categories: (a) types or breeds that are sufficiently productive that they might be considered for use instead of a type or types now in use; and (b) types or breeds that could not compete directly with our existing breeds, but which might be used successfully for crossbreeding or for blending with existing breeds in order to combine certain desirable traits with the productive characteristics of our domestic breeds.

There are, of course, good reasons why either of these two approaches should be used only after careful consideration. First, any risk of introducing diseases and parasites not now present in the United States should be carefully avoided. Second, careful evaluation of types for prospective use would be necessary in most cases, owing to the paucity of information now available. This is true with regard to some of the types that might be considered for use instead of existing breeds. It is applicable to a very high degree to many types that might possibly contribute characteristics in crossing programs or in programs designed to blend their characteristics with those of breeds now in use. I shall return to this point later. Third, we should avoid trying to use more types and breeds than are necessary to meet the demands of various kinds of production operations. Fourth, we should keep in mind the economic problems of those who now have vested interests in the production of breeding stock for sale to commercial producers. This is also a point to which I shall return later.

Although there are good reasons for caution, there are also reasons for objective exploration of possible new sources of animal germ plasm. In the plant field, the United States Department of Agriculture has maintained an active search for new germ plasm and has carried out a plant introduction program ever since the time when David Fairchild regarded the world as his garden (7). You are all aware of the many benefits that have come to United States agriculture as a result of that work. Although the problems of seeking out superior animal germ plasm are more complex and more costly than is the case for plant germ plasm, the reasons for doing so may be just as compelling. They are apt to be more compelling as time goes on.

Population pressures are increasing. Although we are now

plagued with surpluses of our chief food grain, wheat, if the population spiral continues here and around the world, that picture could change markedly in a few decades or a half century. Our grandchildren conceivably could be faced with a need to reduce animal production and to depend to a greater degree on plant sources for their food. Competition between foods of plant and animal sources seems almost certain to increase. Already, oils and fats of plant origin have gone a long way toward pushing animal fats off the American table. It will be more difficult to find plant protein sources to replace animal protein, both in quality and taste. Large segments of the world's population are already faced with this problem, and, unless the population curve tapers off and plateaus at a reasonable level, we too shall have to face it. If animals are to meet man's needs effectively in the years ahead, the effort to find the most productive and efficient animals from within our present stock should continue, and the possibilities of improvement by introduction of yet untapped sources of animal germ plasm should be explored. This, too, is a point to which I shall return later. But now I should like to mention some of the types we have not used and that might be among the types to be studied, if the idea of animal exploration were to be taken up seriously. These are only examples from among many that might be cited, not a catalog of types proposed for study and possible importation.

Some Examples of Untapped Sources

Cattle

I shall mention only eleven types or breeds, three from Europe, three from Africa, and five from India and Pakistan.

Charollais. This breed has been receiving some attention in the United States during the last few years (6), and has shown sufficient promise to illustrate the point that we have, in the past, tended to overlook some important sources of animal germ plasm.

The Charollais (Figs. 1, 2) which originated in central France, in a temperate climate where the animals have access to fertile pastureland, is a large, heavy breed. It is well muscled, and mature animals reach average weights of 2300 to 2400 pounds for bulls

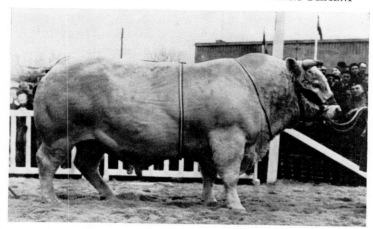

Fig. 1.   A Charollais bull, age 6 years, weighing 1230 kg or about 2700 lb (France).

and 1700 to 1800 pounds for cows. In their home country they are used for both work and beef. They are raised and fattened largely on grass, and in winter they are stall-fed hay, straw, and roots. Few concentrates are fed.

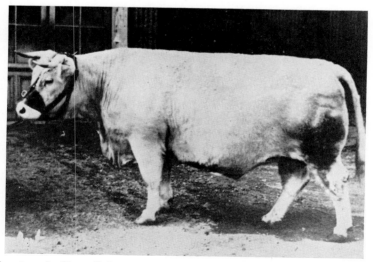

Fig. 2.   A Charollais cow, age 5 years, weighing 1100 kg or about 2420 lb (France).

The growth potential, heavy muscling, and ability to grow and fatten on a minimum of concentrates would seem to justify further exploration into the possible usefulness of this breed.

Simmental. The Simmental (Figs. 3, 4) of western and north-western Switzerland is another European breed that has received

Fig. 3.   A Simmental bull (Switzerland).

Fig. 4. A Simmental cow (Switzerland).

very little attention in the United States, but it has found rather wide acceptance in countries near its home and in the U.S.S.R. It is maintained on high mountain pastures in summer, and in villages in winter where the animals are fed silage, hay, root crops, and (for milk cows and fattening cattle) concentrates. These are triple purpose animals, i.e., milk, work, and meat. Adult bulls weigh in the vicinity of 2100 to 2500 pounds while cows average about 1600 pounds. The average production of 75,000 cows tested from 1935 to 1945 was 4045 kg (about 8900 pounds) of 4.04% milk in 300 days. In one test in Italy, males gained 2.2 pounds per day from birth to eighteen months while females gained about 1.75 pounds.

In the areas where dual purpose animals are desired, these animals seem to offer enough in milk production, beefiness, and growth rate to justify careful study.

Fig. 5. A Chiana bull (Italy).

Chiana. The Chiana, *Chianina* in Italian (Figs. 5, 6), is native to the Chiana Valley in Tuscany, Italy. Both males and females are used for work. Surplus males are stall fattened, and killed for meat at twelve to eighteen months. Mature bulls weigh about 2750 pounds. These are noble beasts, whose backs bear much of the burden of farming in Tuscany and nearby areas.

Fig. 6.   A Chiana cow (Italy).

Few data are available on meat qualities, but this breed is regarded as one of the best sources of beef in Italy. Liveweight increases of 1.3 kg (2.86 pounds) per day from birth to 500 days of age have been reported in Italy. Dressing percentage of animals at eighteen months is reported to be about 60%.

The animal explorer might find in these animals a growth potential and meat qualities that would be very useful in the United States, even though the first reaction of the livestock judge probably would be to discount them as being too "leggy."

Another Italian breed that I shall mention only in passing is the Romagnola. These cattle, found in northern Italy, are massive, well-muscled, docile beasts and should be of considerable interest to the animal explorer.

Boran.   With the exception of the Africander of South Africa, which has been tried in a limited way in the Gulf Coast area, African types of cattle have received practically no attention in the United States. However, this vast continent has a wide variety of cattle types (9). Most of them are maintained under quite primitive conditions so it is difficult to evaluate their production

Fig. 7. A Boran cow (Kenya and adjacent parts of East Africa).

potentials under conditions of good feeding and management. The Africander is one of the local types which was taken over and improved by the European settlers. Another such type is the Boran.

The Boran (Fig. 7) is native to southern Ethiopia and adjoining parts of Somalia and northern Kenya. During the present century, settlers in the drier parts of Kenya have used these animals, have selected for beef qualities, and have developed what is called the "improved Boran," in which there may be some traces of European blood. Mature cows weigh 760 to 920 pounds, while mature oxen weigh from about 1180 to 1440 pounds. Cows produce moderate amounts of milk. A few tested cows averaged 1918 pounds in 295 days and 2661 pounds in 362 days while suckling calves. Allowing for an estimated daily consumption by calves of 6 pounds would increase these figures to 3688 and 4833 pounds of actual milk production. The animals are used primarily for beef.

The Zebu blood, moderate level of milk production, and good beef conformation suggest that this breed might contribute something to the beef industry of the Gulf Coast and other portions of our southern tier of states.

Jiddu. This breed, also known as Galla and Tuni in various parts of East Africa (Fig. 8) is similar in conformation to the Boran, but is somewhat smaller. Bulls weigh around 900 and cows around 700 pounds. As with many other African types, little has

Fig. 8. A Jiddu bull (Somalia and adjacent parts of East Africa).

been done to improve them. However, animals of this breed have heavy muscling, good beef conformation, and are adapted to rugged conditions in a hot environment. So, in hot areas of rather sparse grazing, this breed might prove useful. In Kenya, the cows are used primarily for crossing with bulls of European breeds.

Nguni. Among the many other African types that might be considered, I shall mention only one, the Nguni (Fig. 9), which has also been called Zulu and Swazi after the tribes that produce these cattle. Generally, the climate in the native area of the breed is warm, with high humidities. The indigenous people maintain cattle primarily for milk, but animals are slaughtered for festive occasions, and cattle that die from natural causes may also be eaten. Also, they constitute "bride wealth," so play an important part in

Fig. 9. A Nguni cow (Swaziland, Zululand, and southern Mozambique).

the social system. Although used for milk production, the yields are low. Steers, at 4½ years, weigh about 1000 pounds. This is a breed which might be useful in areas such as the Gulf Coast and the Southwest.

Red Sindhi. Among the Zebu milking breeds of India and Pakistan, the Red Sindhi (Fig. 10) is the only one that has had even a limited trial in the United States (12). Although small in size (mature bulls weigh 950 to 1000 and cows 650 to 700 pounds), these animals are compact, rather well muscled, and for their size have quite a good milk potential. Average milk production on a governmental farm in Pakistan is around 4000 pounds and individual records of as high as 12,000 pounds in 300 days have been obtained (10). The sample of Red Sindhis available for this work carried out in the United States was too small to be considered representative of the germ plasm the breed may have to offer, and for dairy production in the subtropical areas it appears worthy of further study, either for crossbreeding or for use in developing new types, where a small to medium-sized animal is desired.

Sahiwal. The Sahiwal (Fig. 11) is another of the Zebu milking breeds. These animals are also low set and well muscled, and are somewhat larger than the Red Sindhi. Mature bulls weigh about 1200 pounds and cows 900 pounds. In milk production, they are also about 1000 pounds per lactation higher than the Sindhi, the

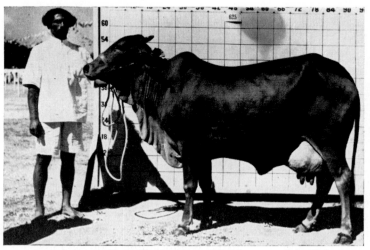

Fig. 10.   A Red Sindhi cow (Pakistan and India).

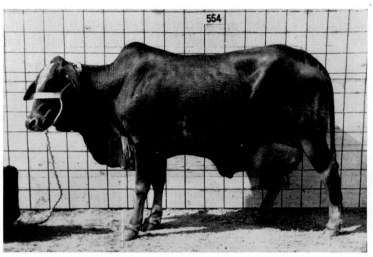

Fig. 11.   A Sahiwal cow (Pakistan and India).

average on the better farms being about 5000 pounds of milk, testing 4.3 to 6%, in 300 days. Selected groups of individuals have averaged about 9000 pounds. Some cows have records above 10,000 pounds.

The Sahiwal was crossed with the Jersey to provide the basis for the Jamaica Hope breed in Jamaica. However, it has not been used in the United States. In view of its beefiness and relatively high milk potential, it may have more to offer than any other Zebu breed for use in developing dairy and dual purpose animals for the tropics and subtropics.

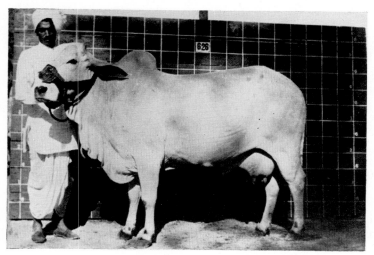

Fig. 12.   A Tharparkar cow (Pakistan and India).

Tharparkar. The Tharparkar (Fig. 12) is one of five lyre-horned gray breeds of Zebu cattle of India and Pakistan. This breed, like the Red Sindhi and Sahiwal, is native to west Pakistan, an area characterized by semi-arid grazing. These animals are used primarily for work and milk. They are medium in size, and have fairly deep, thick bodies. Under good farm conditions in Pakistan milk production averages around 3500 pounds.

The so-called Brahman cattle of the southern United States were developed primarily from the Kankrej, which in its native environment is a large, more upstanding animal than the Tharparkar or the Malvi. All three breeds belong to the same general group, and it is possible that a breed such as the Tharparkar, which has moderately good beef conformation and probably a somewhat higher milk potential than the Kankrej, could make a contribution to beef improvement in the Gulf Coast area.

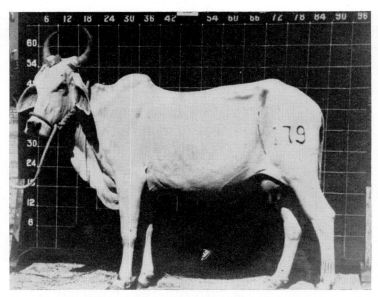

Fig. 13. A Krishna Valley cow (India). Although this animal is extremely thin, the depth and blockiness of the body are evident.

Krishna Valley. The Krishna Valley breed (Fig. 13) is one of nine shorthorned white or gray Zebu breeds found in India and Pakistan. It is used primarily for heavy draft purposes. Cows produce only about 2200 to 2700 pounds of milk in a lactation. Mature bulls weigh about 1200 and mature cows about 700 pounds in their native conditions. This breed may have made a limited contribution to the Brahman type in the southern United States. Like some other breeds in the group to which it belongs, it might have something to contribute that would be useful to us.

Dhanni. As a final example of Zebu breeds that might be examined, I shall cite the Dhanni (Fig. 14). These striking animals, with their Dalmatian-like spotting, are native to the northern portions of west Pakistan. They are prized as draft animals in the plains of India and Pakistan. Dhanni animals are medium sized (mature males weigh 1050 to 1300 and cows 750 to 900 pounds), compact and well muscled. Milk production, averaging between

Fig. 14.   A Dhanni bull (Pakistan).

1500 and 2000 pounds, with some animals exceeding 3000 pounds, is too low to offer any dairy potential, but this breed may be worth exploring for possible use, either in the southwest or in the Gulf Coast areas, for beef production.

Longhorns.   Before moving on to some examples of sheep, I should like to mention (perhaps facetiously) one last idea regarding cattle. If we should ever need to renew our supply of Longhorn cattle for use in celebrating frontier days and in honoring that noble creature's contribution to early development of the Southwest, we might turn to the Ankole (Fig. 15) of Uganda and nearby parts of East Africa for some germ plasm that would "outlonghorn" our Longhorns.

Fig. 15. An Ankole cow (Uganda and adjacent areas of East Africa). The horns of this animal measured 52 in. between the tips. (Photo from Department of Information, Uganda Protectorate.)

Sheep

A few examples of types of sheep that might make contributions in the United States are mentioned below. In this connection, it should be recalled that, with the exception of the Karakul, our sheep have come almost entirely from the British Isles or from Spain, or in the case of the Rambouillet, from Spain via France. We have concentrated on mutton and/or wool qualities, and have given relatively little attention to milking capacity, or to the special traits that may be required in the more rugged environments. In the work which has been done under rugged environments, for example at Fort Wingate, New Mexico, the germ plasm available was from the same two sources, including the Navajo sheep, which presumably had descended from early introductions from Spain. Thus, except for the Karakul, we have not looked to the East (of Great Britain and Spain) for germ plasm. There are many interesting types in Europe and Asia, and a few in Africa. Many of the types that do exist have been described briefly, with illustrations, in the *Sheep and Goat Raiser* (1-4). I shall mention only three.

Texel. The Texel (Figs. 16, 17) is a Dutch breed that is generally comparable in conformation to the medium-wooled breeds of Great Britain. It is a heavy, blocky sheep which yields high-grade lamb and mutton, and is adapted to farm conditions where pastures are good and feed is abundant. Fleeces of ewes are re-

Fig. 16.   A Texel ram (The Netherlands).

ported to weigh 8 to 10 pounds, to be of 48's to 56's in fineness, of combing length, and with clean yields of about 60%. Milk production is higher than in most mutton breeds, and is reported to be above 660 pounds per lactation. Thus, most ewes can raise twins and triplets, which occurs rather frequently. Mature animals may attain weights of 220 to 250 pounds. The milk production, twinning, and growth potentials, combined with good mutton conformation, seem to indicate that this breed is worth exploring.

East Friesian. The East Friesian (Fig. 18), like the Texel, is a mutton breed with a high level of milk production. It is well adapted to the good pastures of its native home, East Friesland, Germany, and has been used to a considerable extent for crossing to improve mutton production in southern and southeastern

Fig. 17.   Texel ewes and lambs (The Netherlands).

Fig. 18.   An East Friesian ewe, aged 3 years (Germany). This breed is noted for high milk production.

European countries. Milk yields are reported to be as high as 1100 pounds in five months. Information published by one breeder indicates that some controlled or tested ewes yielded about 1365 pounds of 6.6% milk in 249 days. Fleeces weigh about 8 to 9 pounds; wool is of medium quality (50's to 56's) and clean yields are 55 to 65%. Mature rams weigh 130 to 170 pounds and ewes 90 to 155 pounds. The ewes are prolific, twinning tending to be the rule and triplets being frequent, and growth rate appears to be rapid. This breed might be explored for crossing for introduction of higher milk production, and perhaps for mutton production on the breed's own merits.

Fig. 19.   An Awassi ewe (Near East) from Finci (1957).

Awassi.   The Awassi (Fig. 19) belongs to the large group of fat-tailed carpet-wool sheep that is distributed through much of Asia and parts of Africa. The Awassi is found in Iraq, Israel, Jordan, Lebanon, Syria (U.A.R.), and in small numbers in southern Turkey. Typical animals are white-wooled with brown heads and legs, and large drooping ears. Males are mostly horned, females mostly hornless. Well known as a milk producer, its potential has become most evident in Israel where serious efforts are being made to improve it. According to Finci (8), 22,519 ewes in 109 flocks averaged about 615 pounds of milk during the 1955-56 milking season. In the same season, 276 ewes in the best flock averaged nearly 995 pounds. In the eleven best flocks 1292 ewes exceeded 880 pounds, and the highest yield for one ewe was about 1950 pounds. Butter fat content averages about 7.0%.

Finci reports average body weights of about 110 pounds for ewes, 163 pounds for rams, and weaning weights of 45 and 56.6 pounds respectively for ewe and ram lambs. In a flock where some attention has been given to improvement for wool production, average fleece yields of 6.6 pounds are reported, with a maximum yield of about 14.3 pounds. Twinning is rather infrequent, 9.28% in 4549 births. The Awassi is a good grazing animal, able to use the driest pastures and to withstand intense summer heat and heavy winter rainfalls. The tail is quite large, particularly in animals in good condition, and starts with a broad fat cushion, which narrows and turns upward, ending in a thin part hanging down. The mutton and lamb yielded by this breed are reported to be of fine flavor.

In areas of the Southwest, where grazing conditions are difficult and where the fat tail would provide a reserve for periods of poor feed supply, and where there is a demand for carpet wool for rug making, a breed such as the Awassi may have something to contribute.

Swine

It may seem presumptuous to suggest that the United States, with its corn belt and with its intensive swine breeding and production programs, has not already taken advantage of the best that the world has to offer in swine germ plasm, and by processes of recombination and selection produced the best that can be had. But it must be recalled that, within our lifetimes, the United States has witnessed one of the really big shifts in livestock types which has been achieved in so short a time and has affected such a large number of livestock. I refer, of course, to the shift from the heavy lard type of hog that was in vogue during the first quarter of this century to the leaner type that prevails today.

It must also be recalled that, in making this shift, we not only selected within the existing types here in the United States but also turned to Europe for germ plasm, for experimental purposes, in the form of breeds such as the Landrace from Denmark and the Large Black from England. One of the most useful types to emerge from interbreeding of these imported and domestic breeds is the Beltsville No. 1 (Fig. 20). I cite this example only to illustrate the

Fig. 20.   A Beltsville No. 1 meat type sow, weighing approximately 220 lb. This line originated from Danish Landrace—Poland China crosses.

point that, in relatively recent years, there has been good reason to seek swine germ plasm overseas. It is entirely possible that other germ plasm exists outside our borders that is worthy of exploration. This may be true in relation to meat type characteristics, to such important factors as litter size and mothering ability, and possibly other characteristics. The nature and extent of some of the other changes in livestock type and productivity that have occurred in the last fifty to eighty years have been summarized by Lush (11) and are brought up to date in Lush's chapter in the present volume.

One possible source of useful germ plasm, in relation to level of fertility, is the Chinese pig (15, 16). At present, obtaining such animals for experimental breeding purposes is hardly a practical possibility, but this is a source of germ plasm that does exist and might eventually be explored. Chinese swine, at least of some types, appear to mature sexually much earlier than American breeds. Although gilts are normally bred when about five months old, it is not unusual for gilts to farrow at about six months of age. Litter size and mothering ability also appear to be exceptional in some strains. A survey of farms in four areas in Szechwan revealed an average litter size of 8.8. However, in some controlled experimental work, Neichang and Yungchang sows farrowed 12.7 and 12.0 pigs, and weaned 10.5 and 8.5, respectively, on the average. In the Canton area, a sow is supposed to be able to nurse at least 10 pigs, and as many as 15 are reported to be seen frequently. In the Chiangpei area of Kansu, 31 native (North China) sows were observed that farrowed an average of 13.9 pigs. One North China sow, at Minghsien College, is reported to have had 32 teats and to have farrowed 25 live pigs in one litter. In some experimental trials with North China sows, an average of 13.9 pigs were born and 10.7 weaned.

The data are few and may not be based on representative samples of the swine in the areas mentioned. However, they support the view that germ plasm worth exploring does exist. For comparison, it might be recalled that the United States Department of Agriculture statistics for 1945 to 1957 inclusive indicate annual average litter sizes weaned in the United States, including both spring and fall litters, varying from 6.06 to 7.09. Craft (5) cites figures on litter size in the herds of 300 Master Swine Producers in Iowa during the previous twelve-year period. During that period the average number farrowed increased from 9.1 to 10.8 and number marketed from 8.1 to 9.5.

Poultry

In our highly developed poultry industry, much attention has been given to breeding. Testing, particularly for egg production, is relatively easy, and generations can be turned over rapidly, so breeding materials have been quite flexible in the breeders' hands compared with the large domestic animals. So it would be difficult to find new germ plasm that could make immediate contributions to productivity.

However, there is a great deal of largely untested and untapped germ plasm in various parts of the world. There are native types of chickens in many countries, varying from bantams to large meat type birds, that have been the object of few if any organized attempts at improvement. Egg production is often only 60 to 100 eggs per year, but in certain breeds is somewhat higher. But these birds usually manage to survive and grow under conditions of poor feeding and management and may have traits such as resistance to disease and adaptability to unfavorable environments that could be utilized. Other traits might also be found such as early sexual maturity or meat qualities that would repay the poultry explorer for his efforts.

Apart from the unimproved types and granting that we have ranged farther afield in our search for poultry than for large animal germ plasm, there may also be some profit in exploring further some of the improved types or breeds that have received little attention in the United States. For example, the Sussex chicken, which has been used extensively in some other countries, may have something to contribute. The same may be true of the Favorelle, a French table fowl which is reported to be an excellent meat producer. Among types of poultry other than chickens, the Khaki Campbell duck, which has a very high egg-producing potential, is worthy of note; also the Muscovy duck which might offer something of value for meat production.

Returning to the unimproved types or breeds of chickens, I shall mention only three.

Fayoumi. This breed (Fig. 21) is native of Fayoum Province in the western portion of Egypt, U.A.R. The feathers are barred, but barring is not uniform. Silver-like feathers cover the neck and saddle, particularly in the male. Hens weigh 4 to 5 pounds, and males are about one pound heavier. Egg yield for 245 birds under experiment station conditions at Giza averaged 156.4 eggs per year (17).

The breed has been used experimentally in the United States (Iowa), and Nordskog (13) reports some differences in laying

Fig. 21. Fayoumi chickens (Egypt, U.A.R.).

house mortality between the Fayoumi (and its crosses) and the other types tested. Mortality was lowest in the Fayoumi × heavy crosses and next lowest in the Fayoumi.

Baladi. These birds (Fig. 22) are somewhat smaller than the Fayoumi. Hens weigh about 3 to 3.5 pounds. The color is variable. A strain that is white and another that is similar to the Brown Leg-

Fig. 22.   A white strain of Baladi chickens (Near East).

horn in color have been selected. A flock of 286 hens tested at Giza (17) averaged 154.6 eggs in a year. Ragab and Assem indicate that this breed is not known outside Egypt. However, there are reports that it exists in other Near Eastern countries including at least Lebanon, the Sudan, and Iraq. It is not clear whether these are chickens that had been taken in fairly recent times from Egypt, or whether they are similar local types that have existed for a long time in these countries. They probably fall in the later category, since the term "Baladi" is used to designate the local types of chickens in most Near Eastern countries.

Like the Fayoumi, the Baladi does not offer high egg or meat-producing potentials, but it might contribute something in breeding programs where disease resistance or adaptability to unfavorable environments is a major objective.

Muzungu. These chickens are found in Kenya, and perhaps in adjacent areas. They are very tall birds, the body is almost perpendicular, and their gait is similar to that of Indian game birds. The neck is free of feathers down to the crop and is usually crimson red in color. According to the Director of Veterinary Services in Kenya, it apparently derives its name from this red-necked characteristic; "Muzungu" means a white man or European. Colors are usually brown or black or a mixture of the two. The birds are slow to mature but well-grown cockerels weigh up to 8 pounds. The hens are said to lay large white eggs. They live chiefly by scavenging, and have an exceptional burst of speed when pursuing insects. They are found in the hottest parts of Kenya, i.e., the coastal and lake areas, so appear to have a high adaptability to hot climates. The males are vicious fighters, and when two become involved they usually continue until one is dead. This breed has not only been evolved under conditions where survival of the fittest is the rule, but also has some capacity for meat production, so may be worth exploring.

Before leaving the question of possible sources of poultry germ plasm, I should mention that we have done little in the United States to exploit commercially the game birds and fowls. For example, the Coturnix quail is reported to be sexually mature at six weeks and to have considerable capacity as an efficient producer of meat. The guinea fowl, which is difficult to find in most American markets, may also merit more attention than it has had.

A POSSIBLE APPROACH TO ANIMAL EXPLORATION

I have already pointed out that much might be gained, in the long run, by a systematic investigation of the types of livestock and poultry that are available in various countries, and which seem to offer some promise for use in improvement programs. Now, speaking in a personal capacity and painting with a very broad brush, I should like to venture a few suggestions as to the manner in which animal exploration investigations might be undertaken. Such investigations might proceed in several stages, as follows.

1. Examining of such data as may be found on size, conformation, productivity, etc., including visual examination of typical animals under the conditions in which they are normally kept, and under other conditions if they are being used outside their native areas.

2. Cooperating with appropriate institutions in other countries in the carrying out of tests to secure additional information on the characteristics and performance of the more promising types, under local conditions, and under experimental conditions comparable to those in which they might be used in the United States or as nearly comparable as may be feasible.

3. Undertaking further work with the most promising types, by actually carrying out comparative production trials, using as controls animals of the types now used in the United States, and with feeding and other conditions as comparable as possible to those in which animals might later be used in the United States. By this device, data could be obtained on the productivity of the local types, and also on crossbreds to determine their possible use for crossing or for development of new types based on crossbred foundations.

4. Undertaking further tests in the United States with small groups of imported animals of the types that showed sufficient promise to justify such action.

5. Finally, if any types were proved to be of value for use in improvement programs, steps could be taken to bring them to the United States in substantial numbers for the establishment of foundation herds, with assurance that such efforts would be worth the cost.

The second and third procedures would provide not only basic data at moderate expense, compared with trying to do such work in the United States, but also would reduce to a relatively small number the types that might be brought to the United States, and thus would keep to a minimum the risk of introducing diseases and parasites. Any animals or semen imported would, of course, have to be handled in full conformity with quarantine regulations.

It may be claimed that breeders of the existing breeds would oppose the introduction of other types on the assumption that they would create competition. Actually, a testing and introduction process of the type outlined would have to be carried out over a considerable number of years, perhaps over two or three decades at the least. If valuable types were found, the process of introduction and building up numbers adequate to make substantial contributions in commercial production would also require a considerable period; much longer, for example, for cattle or sheep, than for swine or chickens. For all the large animals a considerable number of years would be involved. This is an activity which, if undertaken, would proceed in stages over decades, perhaps a half century or even a century. In cases where the use of new types might appear justified, surely the persons best equipped to multiply such stock and to make it available to commercial producers are the present producers of sires for sale to commercial producers of cattle, sheep, and swine, and of hatching eggs and chicks for sale to commercial producers of poultry. Thus, the end result should be a more useful and therefore more salable product in the hands of those already in the business.

In the first and second procedures above, I have referred to the examination of such data as may be found and to the need for collecting additional data. Anyone who probes at all into the problem of evaluating types and breeds of livestock and poultry around the world is immediately struck by the paucity of information. During the last sixteen years I have had the opportunity of observing many types and breeds of livestock in many countries, and of participating in the preparation of a number of publications in which some of these observations are recorded. Of these publications, I shall refer, by way of examples, to only three of the larger volumes that have shed some light on the subject (9, 10, 16). Yet these volumes, which bring together a great deal of information, have probably done more to show how little we know rather than how much we know. The lack of information is no doubt a factor that has contributed to our conservative attitude regarding animal exploration.

Here in the United States, where we pride ourselves on progress, we do have a substantial amount of information on the performance of our poultry and dairy cattle, but when one seeks performance data on the meat animals, outside the experiment stations, it is to be found in only limited quantities. I am reminded that, twenty-two years ago when trying to make a start on some work to develop techniques of measuring performance, I found that at least one outstanding Land Grant Institution in the corn belt had no scale in its sheep barn. In order to obtain even such simple data as weights, we had to drive the animals a considerable distance to the swine barn. So we cannot be too critical of the lack of precise data on the productivity of animals in other countries, particularly those in the less developed areas.

Conclusion

In a symposium such as this, one can present only limited information and put forth some ideas. The information presented has been sketchy, for the field is too wide to permit detailed coverage. My object has been to give, by citing examples, a rather broad impression of the field which awaits the animal explorer. At the same time I have tried to suggest a "safe and sane" approach to animal exploration through which the best of the yet untapped animal germ plasm might be sought out and utilized. Here, too, it has been necessary to deal in general terms and to present an idea rather than a program. If the idea finds acceptance, then it would fall to those who administer federal, state, and private projects for animal improvement to determine how far, and with which types of livestock and in what areas of the world, they should pursue it. A group of men may yet emerge who can say, with Fairchild, "The world is our barnyard."

If one uses a text, it is usually quoted at the beginning, but I should like to close with one from Craft (5): "Introduction of stock from other countries has been of tremendous importance in the past. It still may offer much in respect to further improvements. We should not be allergic to effort in that direction."

Acknowledgment

In the course of assembling the information upon which this paper is based, the author has, over a period of fifteen years, been assisted by many persons in many countries. Specifically, in the preparation of the manuscript, he obtained information, photographs and/or ideas from Eugene Bertone, Dr. Hans Engler, N. R. Joshi, and E. A. McLaughlin of the Food and Agriculture Organization staff in Rome, Italy; Hassan

Abdallah of the Ministry of Agriculture of the United Arab Republic; Dr. T. C. Byerly, Dr. H. O. Hetzer, Dr. Robert E. McDowell, and Dr. C. E. Terrill of the Agricultural Research Service of the United States Department of Agriculture; and Grover C. Chappell, Dr. Phil S. Eckert, Frank W. Ehman, and Robert H. Reed of the Foreign Agricultural Service of the United States Department of Agriculture.

REFERENCES

1. Anonymous. The story of the sheep breeds—International sheep breeds. *Sheep and Goat Raiser*, 22, 32-92 (December 1941).
2. Anonymous. International sheep breeds. *Sheep and Goat Raiser*, 23, 76-86 (December 1942).
3. Anonymous. International sheep breeds (including Bunadarfelag Islands—Iceland, by H. Plasson; and The Chinese breeds, their characteristics and distribution, by T. Y. Hau). *Sheep and Goat Raiser*, 24, 78-85 (December 1943).
4. Anonymous. International sheep breeds (including the sheep of Iran). *Sheep and Goat Raiser*, 26, 6-11, 85 (December 1945).
5. Craft, W. A. Advancing the livestock industry through research in genetics and animal breeding. *J. Anim. Sci.*, 14, 295-299 (1955).
6. Damon, R. A., Jr., S. E. McCraine, R. M. Crown, and C. B. Singletary. Performance of crossbred beef in the Gulf Coast region. *J. Anim. Sci.*, 18, 437-447 (1959).
7. Fairchild, David. *The World Was My Garden*. Charles Scribner's Sons, New York, N. Y., 1938.
8. Finci, M. The improvement of the Awassi breed of sheep in Israel. *Bull. Research Council Israel*, 6B (1-2), 1-106 (1957).
9. Joshi, N. R., E. A. McLaughlin, and Ralph W. Phillips. *Types and Breeds of African Cattle*. Agricultural Studies No. 37. Food and Agriculture Organization of the United Nations, Rome, Italy. Published also in French under the title *Les Bovins d'Afrique Types et Races*, and in Spanish under the title *Tipos e Razas de Bovinos Africanos*, 1957.
10. Joshi, N. R., and Ralph W. Phillips. *Zebu Cattle of India and Pakistan*. FAO Agricultural Study No. 19. Food and Agriculture Organization of the United Nations, Rome, Italy. Published also in Spanish under the title *El Ganado Cebu de la India y del Pakistan*, and in French under the title *Les Zebus de l'Inde et du Pakistan*, 1953.
11. Lush, J. L. Genetics in animal breeding. In *Genetics in the 20th Century*, L. C. Dunn, Editor, Chap. 22, pp. 493-525. The Macmillan Company, New York, 1951.
12. McDowell, Robert E. Adaptability and performance of cattle under the climatic conditions existing in the southern United States.

Proceedings of the XV International Dairy Congress, Vol. I, Sec. 1, pp. 333-340. Richard Clay and Co., Ltd., Suffolk, England, 1959.

13. Nordskog, A. W. Reciprocal cross comparisons involving Leghorns, Heavies and Fayoumi. *Poultry Sci., 35,* 1163 (1956).

14. Phillips, Ralph W. *Breeding Livestock Adapted to Unfavorable Environments.* Food and Agriculture Organization of the United Nations, Agricultural Study No. 1. Published also in French under the title *L'élévage en Milieux Defavorables* and in Spanish under the title *La Cria de Ganado en Ambientes Desfavorables,* 1948.

15. Phillips, Ralph W., and T. Y. Hsu. Chinese swine and their performance compared with modern and crosses between Chinese and modern breeds. *J. Heredity, 35,* 365-379 (1944).

16. Phillips, Ralph W., Ray G. Johnson, and Raymond T. Moyer. The Livestock of China. *U. S. Dept. State Publ. No. 2249.* Far Eastern Series 9. Chinese edition translated by Y. Z. Tang. Chung Hwa Publishing Co., Shanghai, 1945.

17. Ragab, M. T., and M. A. Assem. Effect of atmospheric temperature and daylight on egg weight and yield of Fayoumi and Baladi fowls. *Poultry Sci.,* 1021-1027 (1953).

Origin and Utilization of Germ Plasm in the United States

Henry A. Wallace

Farvue Farm, South Salem, New York

Understanding the origin, nature, and potentialities of germ plasm is the most important activity of man on this earth, infinitely more important than the probing of space with rockets. When man uses this knowledge to control the evolution of germ plasm, he becomes almost godlike in his creativity. To you who understand, protect, preserve, and productively use germ plasm to make it continually exceed its previous best—my most respectful salutation.

I have associated with hundreds of Doctors of Science and have invariably profited thereby. However, the scientific mind occasionally finds it a little hard to recognize facts if they have not been written up in scientific papers. For example, I was personally responsible for the United States Department of Agriculture importing Danish Landrace swine, the Large Black hog from England, and many other activities which have had a profound influence on the quality of germ plasm used by the American farmer. In 1921 I urged my father, as Secretary of Agriculture, to call in leading geneticists to revamp some of the outworn techniques of the Department of Agriculture. In 1935, I myself as Secretary of Agriculture appointed O. E. Reed to head a committee to prepare the *Genetics Yearbooks* of 1936 and 1937. Here in these yearbooks is spread out a description of the genetic wealth of the farms of the United States. If the Department of Agriculture were to bring the *Genetics Yearbooks* of 1936 and 1937 up to date, it would find a vast amount of information in the 1959 papers of Section O of the AAAS. The recent discoveries concerning ribonucleic acid (RNA) and deoxyribonucleic acid (DNA) suggest that we are on the verge of entering a brave new world of knowledge concerning germ plasm. It is time for the Department of Agriculture to compile a new set of *Genetics Yearbooks*.

I can enlarge on the preceding three excellent papers but I find it difficult to criticize. Dr. Stonaker's four maps showing the registration by points of origin of various pure breeds of animals are interesting, but discussion of rapid shifts of germ plasm during the past fifty years is very much to the point. Probable shifts during the next ten years are worthy of even more discussion. Registration associations for purebred livestock serve a useful function even though Parmallee Prentice was highly indignant about purebred scrubs. But registration associations tell only part of the story. Figure 10 of Dr. Stonaker's paper does not tell, for example, the story of the Landrace swine influence. Sixty years ago it was a hard fight to get away from the "watch charm" or "hot blood" type of hog favored in the shows of that day. Peter Mouw of northwest Iowa led the revolt in the Poland Chinas. Then came an increased interest in Durocs and Hampshires because of their larger litters. After that came an increased use of meat type hogs as exemplified by the Landrace, Yorkshire, and the large litter, meat types evolved by the Department of Agriculture and the Minnesota Experiment Station.

Before 1950 no Landrace hogs were formally registered. In 1957 there were 23,571, and the Landrace had passed the Yorkshire, Poland, Chester White, and Berkshire in number of registrations. Only the Hampshire and Duroc were ahead. About 94% of the hogs going on the market today in the Midwest are produced by using purebred boars of one breed on purebred sows of another breed or on sows which themselves are crosses. There are many modifications of this program, some of which involve hybrid boars as well as hybrid sows. The crossbred or hybrid sows average at least one pig more per litter. The pigs may be slightly smaller at birth but they gain slightly faster and more efficiently. Undoubtedly the Hampshire and Duroc rank very high in all crossbreeding programs, but the synthetic breeds originated by the USDA and by the Minnesota Station, together with the Landrace and Yorkshire, will steadily become more important as the emphasis is more and more on a meatier type of hog. The Poland China, in spite of having somewhat smaller litters than most breeds, will probably continue to be used up to one-fourth of the cross because of its growthiness and its ability to combine well with other breeds. Today the Duroc, Hampshire, and Poland China between them represent considerably more than half the genes of the crossbred hogs coming on the market. Most of the rest of the genes come from the Yorkshire, Landrace and the synthetics from the Minnesota Station and the USDA. In an informal and not as yet regularized manner, swine breeding for the corn belt market has followed the direction pointed out by corn and chickens.

Egg laying chickens since 1940 have been changing their germ plasm with exceeding speed. At the moment, strain crosses and crosses of inbred lines of White Leghorn are busily trying to chase the heavy bodied brown egg breeds out of existence. In the fall of 1959, there were roughly 100 million strain and inbred crossed White Leghorn pullets coming into production. During the next ten months they will lay roughly 20 billion eggs. These eggs will cost 4 or 5 cents a dozen less to produce because the body weight of these Leghorn crosses is one or two pounds less and therefore the feed cost is less. Nevertheless, the Leghorn of 1959 weighs fully a pound more than the Leghorn of 1900. Somebody put heavy blood into the Leghorn in a way which increased the egg size and strengthened the vitality. The White Leghorn came from Italy (the town of Livorno or Leghorn was merely the shipping port) about 100 years ago. Ninety years ago the White Leghorn went to England where its body size was increased. There is some dispute as to how much the British Leghorn, bounding back again to the United States, has influenced the high-production, modern White Leghorn. So-called pure breeds of chickens have not been alone in quietly permitting infiltration by other breeds.

At the moment, I am gravely concerned about the rapid elimination of brown egg breeders. Certain egg laying strains of Rhode Island Red and New Hampshire are on the point of passing out forever. Who knows what irreplaceable germ plasm will go with them? Some of these strains may have certain types of disease and cold resistance not found in any of the Leghorn strains. Certainly they have a calmer disposition.

Turning to beef cattle, I am concerned that the Angus and Hereford should so rapidly replace the Shorthorn. I think of Burt Neal of Mt. Vernon, Iowa, who died a year or two ago and left to his son a herd of Shorthorns into which no outside bull had been introduced in fifty years. The coefficient of inbreeding must be high. Some method must be found to maintain this herd until tests have demonstrated its capacity or lack of capacity to produce hybrid vigor when crossed with other beef strains or breeds.

It seemed to me that neither Dr. Stonaker nor Dr. Phillips sufficiently appreciated the potentiality of the Charollais breed of beef cattle. The company which I founded in 1926 has been using Charollais bulls on Shorthorn and Hereford cows with excellent success. The crossbreds have gained 15% faster than the Shorthorn or Hereford. They dress out 1 to 2% higher, and there is much less tallow waste and more red meat. If the packers discriminate against these crossbreeds on the foot because of hair color, they will be disregarding consumer preference over the meat counter or in the restaurant.

Dr. Phillips' discussion of Italian, Swiss, Indian, and African cattle breeds interested me greatly. One dual purpose breed I would add to his list from the standpoint of the tropics and subtropics. This is the Criollo as found in Cuba, Colombia, and Venezuela. For centuries it has had to survive tough conditions in the tropics. The Hope breed of Jamaica, referred to by Dr. Phillips, is undoubtedly good but an ambitious breeder for the tropics might well consider incorporating some Criollo blood and perhaps a little Brown Swiss and Red Sindhi. Why the Brown Swiss should do so well in the tropics I cannot understand, except on the basis that originally there must have been some Brahman blood introduced, perhaps a thousand years ago. Brahman blood, whether by way of the Sahiwal Brahman or the Red Sindhi, is likely to incorporate a certain amount of nervousness. In the ideal breed for the tropics I would try to hold the Brahman blood down to perhaps one-fourth. The Jersey should not be more than a fourth because it tends to make too high a fat content. The Brown Swiss should not be more than a fourth because it tends to make too large a body size. Good milking strains of Criollo might well be a fourth because of their toughness. The all-important thing at the present time is that steps be taken to preserve the Criollo.

From the standpoint of dairy blood for the northern United States, some mention should be made of the Red Dane imported by the USDA in 1934 and now found in small numbers in Michigan. I note from the November 1959 issue of a farm paper that semen from four Red Dane bulls recently imported from Sweden is now available at East Lansing, Michigan. In *Technical Bulletin 1074* of the USDA an account is given of crosses involving the Red Dane. Because of its 4% milk the most practical cross, in my opinion, was with the Holstein. Seven Red Dane-Holstein heifers gave slightly less milk than their Holstein dams at the same age but 10% more total fat, and their body weight was somewhat less than that of their Holstein mothers. It is unfortunate that this cross was not repeated on a much larger scale to discover just which family of Holsteins crossed with which family of Red Danes to give the greatest yield of 4% milk with a body smaller than the Holstein. The animals I saw of this cross at Beltsville seemed to me to have less pendulous udders than the Holstein and somewhat smaller teats than the Red Dane. If the seven comparisons listed on page 39 of *Technical Bulletin 1074* are borne out by later experimental work it would seem that one of the best ways to turn a minimum of feed into the maximum of 4% milk in northern states is to cross the right Red Dane bulls on Holstein cows.

The Simmental and Chianina breeds, as described by Dr. Phillips, may possibly have some beef value in the United States for the purpose of producing rapid rates of gain, but with foot and mouth disease regulations as they are, I see no prospect of importing them. Moreover, their contribution would seem to be somewhat similar to that of the Charollais which we already have in the United States.

Dr. Phillips' description of the early maturing, high fecundity characteristics of certain strains of Chinese swine sounds most interesting. Sooner or later I would hope that some of these might be brought to Guam and finally to the United States by the USDA. Perhaps an early maturing Beltsville No. 3 breed could be evolved. It is my guess, however, that it would take repeated backcrossing to make the China hog meaty enough to meet modern United States requirements.

Ever since Dr. Nordskog has been working with the Fayoumi at Iowa State University, I have been intrigued with its possible contribution. Its egg size is too small and its egg production is too low, but that does not mean that the disease resistance factors could not be incorporated into a hybrid. I think of many examples of this procedure in the world of plants.

I think, for example, of the South Dakota farm boy, Edgar McFadden, working at the South Dakota Experiment Station to incorporate stem rust resistance from Yaroslav Emmer with its 14 chromosomes into Marquis wheat with its 21 chromosomes. For several generations after the cross there was great sterility and many shriveled kernels but McFadden kept going even after he was farming for himself. Finally he found the wheat called Hope, the genes of which have conferred stem rust resistance on so many of our modern wheats. How many livestock breeders would have had the time, money, and courageous vision to make a transfer of this sort?

I think of the recent transfer of a whole block of genes from a wild grass called *Aegilops umbellulata* into wheat to give greater leaf rust resistance.

I think of the speed with which oat varieties have changed in Iowa to meet the challenge of new races of rust and blight. From 1943 to 1947 a variety of oats from Uruguay crossed with special selections of the Russian oat called Kherson dominated the picture. When Helminthosporium or blight knocked out the various varieties derived from this cross, an Australian sort was brought into the picture which involved oats from North Africa crossed with a famous Swedish sort known as Golden Rain. Now oat breeders are turning to a minor species known as *Avena strigosa* and special African selections of the Russian Kherson variety. Can you imagine livestock breeders going so far afield? Except in the case of chickens, it might cost too much money. But surely a few short steps might be taken in this direction if it were not for ancient prejudices.

I think of the Food and Agriculture Organization's efforts to cross the Indica species of rice with the Japonica, only to run into sterility based apparently on cytoplasmic incompatibility. This has finally been overcome and there are indications that the introduction of Japonica genes will help the rice yields of Southern Asia.

Again I think of T. W. Whittaker of the USDA and his associates salvaging one particular dominant gene from a wild Russian lettuce and incorporating that gene which confers mildew resistance on modern varieties of lettuce.

Above all, I think of the story told by Jack Harlan in his 1956 Brookhaven paper concerning twice gathering together of the wild melon varieties of the world in order to discover types of disease resistance which did not exist in cultivated melons. How much longer will these all-important primitive sorts continue to exist? Civilized man is on the march, and civilized man is careless about the primitive forms of life. How many forms of life will we wipe out before we wake up?

One reason I accepted the kind invitation to come to this meeting was to meet Jack Harlan whose father I first met about thirty-five years ago. Jack Harlan in his Brookhaven paper, described his father's work with mixing up twenty-eight varieties of barley from all parts of the world. Incidentally, I may say that I look on this paper of Harlan's as one of the two or three most stimulating plant breeding papers which I have ever read. H. V. Harlan, the father, in his long-time barley experiment grasped the significance of the phrase "all shook up" long before the teenagers. After the shaking-up process was completed, there was a shaking-down process both in terms of internal harmony and external adaptability. Many different climates and soils enforced different types of external adaptability. Neither shaking up nor shaking down will do the job of picking out the best germ plasm combinations unless good plant breeders are ultimately present working against the background of specific environments. The composite mixture after the style of the Harlan long-time barley experiment substitutes nature and time for a lot of expensive labor. This composite mixture method may be one way of maintaining a large number of off-beat genes. However, we must recognize that different techniques may have to be followed with different organisms as the composite mixture method is applied. Moreover, I am not at all sure that the composite mixture grown each year is the best form in which to maintain exotic germ plasms. It should be supplemented by such techniques as those used in storing ancient strains of corn. Here the National Academy of Sciences—National Research Council co-operates in a truly remarkable way all over the New World.

More than 12,000 strains of corn have been stored in tight containers at less than 30° F. At such temperatures and moistures most strains can retain germination for at least fifteen years. Strains which give signs of not germinating can be grown and a fresh stock started. For preserving exotic or primitive germ plasm the corn germ plasm banks, as set up in many different countries by a cooperative committee, are an example to all those who deal with other organisms. Prompt action is all-important before many germ plasms are lost forever.

We should have periodic surveys to assure ourselves. In this connection I know of no better summary than that made by Jack Harlan in 1956 at Brookhaven:

> Adequate and thorough exploration must be made *now* before it is too late. World collections in the future must be preserved with great care lest material be lost which can never be replaced. . . . Items in a world collection should be examined for the genes they contain rather than as varieties competing with the best adapted checks. . . . Desirable characteristics may often be uncovered in the material at hand when suitable procedures are used.

The true geneticist who cooperates with plant and animal breeders must always look for unique blocks of genes. Almost never will he find a new variety or breed fit to compete with that which civilized man has already found. These unique genes, many of which are on the point of disappearing forever, deserve more consideration than even Harlan has suggested. Finding the unique genes is one thing. Transferring them in usable form to our high-powered modern varieties and breeds is a longer and more expensive job. Often we do not know precisely what new genes we are looking for. So we cross in the spirit of H. V. Harlan to produce a great variety of mutants. The resulting mess takes a long time to shake down. Who has the wisdom to know just when and how to step in with modern selection techniques? How many segments of our mixture should be tested against our standard civilized sorts? In corn we often use a civilized composite as a male against a number of promising segregates which have emerged from our exotic mixture.

Undoubtedly in many food plants, especially vegetables, increasing efforts will be made to furnish hybrid vigor. Some of these hybrid vegetables will depend on cytoplasmic male sterility as, for example, in the onion where an ever higher percentage of the onion acreage is being planted to hybrids. The modern vegetable varieties lay very great emphasis on disease and even insect resistance. But since the diseases are continually changing, the task of the plant breeder is continually changing, and the need for the preservation of primitive stock is continually emphasized. We shudder as we think of genocide being practiced by the Chinese against the Tibetans. Wild plants and animals are not as important as human beings, but their potentials are such that we should have the deepest concern about any form of life disappearing completely.

The plant breeders seem to be more aware of the situation than the animal breeders. The beef cattle breeders, for example, assume for the most part that all that is necessary is to rely on the three British breeds and modify them slightly to fit the show ring demand for short leggedness and blockiness. Of course, all plantsmen are aware that the British climate is so different from ours that most British varieties of plants are at their best only in rather limited areas along the coasts of the Northwest and Northeast. While I am a strong believer in the maintenance of pure breeds, I am also aware that increasingly the function of the pure breeds will be to furnish stock of known functional ancestry for the purposes of crossbreeding. Crossing to get hybrid vigor for the purpose of making money demands that in order to get top performance we must have "Yield Tests" to guide us rather than "Show Rings." The poultrymen know this. The dairy cattle breeders know it to a somewhat lesser extent. Both have made rapid progress as a result of yield testing. From a plant breeder's point of view, even the poultrymen and dairymen have a long way to go before they utilize fully the poultry and dairy germ plasm available to them in the New World. The excuse is the enormous expense of carrying out repeated livestock yield testing on a large scale. Nevertheless, more and more, the principle of hybrid vigor will be utilized in the animal world. This means that many primitive breeds will be preserved, like the Criollo in Cuba or the Fayoumi chicken in Egypt. New diseases in the animal world may have to be combated by genetic methods.

Let me close with an illustration taken from corn breeding.

Fig. 1. Cytoplasmic male sterility in corn. The ears were obtained from reciprocal crosses. The ear lower continually produced defective ears, generation after generation, no matter how many times it was top-crossed with normal corn.

Figure 1 shows an ear from one of the lesser known and lower yielding strains of the primitive Mexican corn. The exceedingly small ears and very low yields of the corn shown in Fig. 2 were overlooked because it tolerated the long days of the Iowa summer

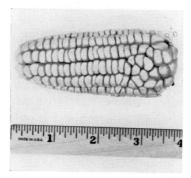

Fig. 2. Ear of primitive tropical Mexican corn.

without growing too tall and maturing too late and because it came from a lowland part of southern Mexico where tropical corn diseases abound. Karl Jarvis of Iowa crossed it twice to Iowa dent corn and by selection evolved corn of the type shown in Fig. 3. Outward appearance would indicate no trace of the small-eared Mexican corn. Yet this corn, which was three-fourths Iowa and

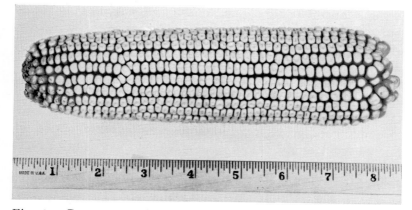

Fig. 3. Corn ear resulting from two crosses of Mexican corn with Iowa corn, three-fourths American and one-fourth Mexican.

only one-fourth Mexican, survived and looked promising at the Palmira Experiment Station in Colombia when the ordinary dent hybrids were miserable. Edgar Anderson had a good idea when he picked out this particular Mexican corn for Karl Jarvis to work with.

Lettuce breeders have shown even more imagination when they went back to the wild. Potato breeders again and again have gone back to the wild.

The question I would pose is why we do not have men like Edgar Anderson and T. W. Whittaker at work in the field of domestic animals. Is it enough to have Nordskog working at Iowa State with Fayoumi chickens? Of course there is no merit in introducing wild blood if you have no purpose in mind. With regard to the cross of the wild boar on the Poland China, cited by Dr. Stonaker, I wonder if an Edgar Anderson and a Karl Jarvis with livestock insight might not have made a three-fourths Poland and one-fourth wild boar cross, and then gradually by selection have put some additional vigor into the Poland. Undoubtedly, the first generation of the three-fourths cross would have been very unpromising but so was three-fourths Iowa one-fourth Mexican corn at first. Frankly, this is not a cross I would have made in the first place to search for greater hardiness. Just the same, from the standpoint of pure science and to wake up the livestock breeders, I would like to see what might evolve in four or five generations from a cross which was three-fourths Landrace and one-fourth wild boar in the first instance. Of course, it might be rather expensive if there were as many individuals to select from as Karl Jarvis had in corn.

The only point I am really making is that we do not have all the good genes in the animals of the United States. To discover and infuse good genes into our present domestic animals is one of the great challenges of the last forty years of this century. We must incorporate good genes at minimum expense into the best of what we now have. Until we have the knowledge to work out a program of this sort, let us at least do what we can to preserve in the different parts of the world the various unused varieties, breeds, and indigenous strains.

II. Need for and Utilization of Additional Sources of Germ Plasm

Horticultural Crops

F. P. Cullinan

Agricultural Research Service, United States Department of Agriculture, Beltsville, Maryland

Search for new and better kinds of plants has gone on ever since man began growing horticultural crops to serve his needs. Naturally as populations increased and people moved to new locations or migrated to other countries, they took along their best and most useful plants. Thus fruits and vegetables were moved from their native habitat and selected and improved to meet the ecological conditions of new environments in various geographical regions of the world. We have come to appreciate the progress made through the centuries in the use of germ plasm that resulted in improved varieties. Agriculture in the United States developed from introduced plants.

Centers of origin of plants are places or geographical regions where indigenous plants exhibit the greatest natural diversity of subspecies and varieties. N. I. Vavilov pointed out that the primary regions of progenitors of our present-day cultivated plants occupy as little as one-fortieth of the land area of the earth. About 640 of some 250,000 known species are important cultivated plants today. Of these more than 500 were found in the Old World. The greatest number of cultivated plants (over 400 species representing almost two-thirds of all crop plants in cultivation) had their origin in southern Asia.

The fruit and vegetable varieties of today came from the following Old World centers: China, central and southern Asia, Near East, Indo-Malaya, the Mediterranean, and Abyssinia (a few). In the western hemisphere centers were in South and Central America.

Old World Germ Plasm from Europe and the Western Hemisphere

Few of the crops grown in the United States were indigenous. Among the fruits are the cane berries, strawberries, blueberries, and cranberries. Native species of apples, some plums, and nuts, including pecans, represented the native fruits and nuts. About the only vegetable is the so-called Jerusalem artichoke. This is not a very impressive list of germ plasm for our contribution to Old World horticulture.

Most of our present horticultural species came to us by way of Europe, Central America, Mexico, or South America. In the past we depended upon the northern countries of Europe for our principal varieties of cabbage and spinach. The Netherlands, Germany, and Denmark, for instance, contributed much of the germ plasm of these plants. England developed superior varieties of peas. Improvement of this crop has been underway since Thomas Andrew White began his hybridization of peas in 1787. This is the same vegetable on which Gregor Mendel performed his classic experiments in Austria some seventy-five years later, the results of which were to have such a marked effect on plant breeding and variety improvement.

The situation with our tree fruits is much the same. We exploited the kinds that had been improved in Europe and selected those best adapted to our needs. We refer to some of our varieties of plums (*Prunus domestica*) as European, German, Hungarian, and Italian prunes and of *P. salicina* as Japanese plums. We have varieties of pears from France and Belgium and cherries from Germany. Many varieties of these species introduced in the eighteenth century are still commercially important. Our apple of commerce of this country, however, was developed largely from chance discovery by orchardists or nurserymen of seedlings of varieties brought in by the explorers or colonists. With fruits the preservation of germ plasm has been through vegetative propagation rather than by seeds. Promising seedlings discovered in this country and abroad have been propagated as clones. We have continued to grow and maintain the varieties that have done best here. The variety picture, however, changed rapidly in the past fifty years with the increase in commercial production. Old varieties no longer commercially profitable were discarded, and in some instances the germ plasm was lost. Many of these varieties possessed genetic characters of aroma, flavor, and quality not found in present-day varieties. They also lacked characters essential for profitable commercial production in modern times.

Other horticultural plants that received attention in this country are the group called ornamentals, made up of flowering herbaceous plants, flowering trees, and shrubs. Most of our ornamentals resulted from introductions. With the initiation of planned collecting expeditions by the United States Department of Agriculture in 1898, ornamental species were distributed yearly under a testing program to experiment stations, arboretums, and nurserymen. For example, 68,000 ornamental plants were offered for testing in 1913. A number of introductions have become important nursery plants. Among these are the Chinese juniper (*Juniperus chinensis* var. *columnaris*), numerous selections of the Chinese elm (*Ulmus pumila*), *Pinus bungiana, Ilex cornuta* Rotunda, and *Pyrus callery-ana*, an ornamental pear that is being used as a garden and street tree.

Progress in Breeding American Varieties

After 1900, with the rediscovery of the Mendelian laws of inheritance, plant breeders and geneticists in this country began a more systematic evaluation of the germ plasm present in horticultural species and varieties in many parts of the world. Although most of the kinds from foreign sources were not suitable to our needs without further improvement, it was recognized that such plant materials possessed desirable characters that could be incorporated into the kinds that could be grown here.

With the backlog of new varieties developed by breeding, we might ask, "Where do we stand today relative to the need for germ plasm in horticulture?" We might consider that we have all the variations in fruit, vegetable, and ornamental plants that could be provided by the progenitors of our modern horticultural crop plants. If we have reached the ultimate in quality and economic requirements that our present-day society demands, there is little reason to seek additional germ plasm or to preserve other than the known best varieties as either seed or vegetative stocks. The goal, however, has not been reached and there is even more need today to examine diverse stocks of wild genetic variants and foreign culti-vated varieties than there was sixty years ago, when the federal plant introduction office was established.

As fruits and vegetables have been grown on large acreages over an extended area in the various regions of the country, they have been subject to various production hazards of disease and insect attacks, cold or frost injury, and drought. The losses from patho-genic fungi and bacteria, viruses, insects, and nematodes have been high. Some of the insects and diseases can be controlled by spray-ing, but generally virus diseases cannot. Chemical sprays are expensive to use. Scientists in the publicly supported institutions of this country are giving major attention to breeding new disease-resistant varieties of fruits, vegetables, and ornamental plants. If resistance to certain diseases can be found in our present-day varieties, progress in the development of new varieties is relatively rapid. Where germ plasm of disease-resistant varieties is not avail-able, progress is delayed. Past experience indicates that the best source of disease resistance is found in the native habitat among cultivated kinds and wild relatives of the fruit or the vegetable variety under study. A few examples of vegetable varieties will illustrate this point.

In the twenties, when cantaloup varieties in the Imperial Valley of California were attacked by powdery mildew, a disease that could not be satisfactorily controlled by fungicides, plant breeders began a search for disease-resistant material. In three years of care-ful testing several resistant varieties were discovered among melons imported from India. The melons were of poor quality but were an excellent source of germ plasm carrying resistance to mildew. By suitable crosses and backcrosses, resistance to powdery mildew was bred into good American types and in another four years the first of the hybrids was released to California growers. Four more years of selection gave a powdery mildew resistant cantaloup called Number 45, which has superior shipping qualities in addition to disease resistance. This variety was released to growers in 1936.

Similarly, there was only moderate resistance to fusarium wilt in the germ plasm of tomatoes being grown in this country. A speci-men of a wild type of *Lycopersicon pimpinellifolium*, identified as P.I. 79532, was introduced from Peru in the late 1920's. This is a small-fruited tomato of no value commercially, but it has the intrinsic value of having germ plasm carrying very high resistance to fusarium wilt. After only four years of crossing and back-crossing with American varieties and selections, the genes for high wilt resistance were successfully introduced into the first of several new varieties for use in this country. The first of these, called Pan America, was introduced in 1940.

Spinach is another vegetable that has been improved through the use of germ plasm from the wild. A wild type of spinach from Manchuria that carried genes resistant to cucumber virus was crossed with several spinach varieties grown in this country, and a disease-resistant Virginia Savoy spinach resulted. A higher type of resistance was found a few years ago in lines obtained from Belgium. Genes for resistance to blue mold and downy mildew were obtained from Iran and for resistance to white rust from India.

The new anthracnose-resistant watermelons that now dominate the eastern markets trace their anthracnose resistance to an introduction from the Belgian Congo.

To combat downy mildew of lima beans in the Middle Atlantic States, a bush variety, Thaxter, was recently developed. Its resistance came from a pole variety from India. More recently resistance to two races of mildew has been found in a type of lima bean from Guatemala, the original home of the species.

Valverde lettuce is a recently introduced variety that is highly resistant to downy mildew. Its resistance comes from a wild form of lettuce introduced from Russia about 1930.

Scores of vegetable species are widely grown over this country and with the increase in severity of insect and disease attacks, plant breeders are faced with the problem of developing improved varieties resistant to these pests. Parenthetically, it may be said it is not the objective of these breeding programs to make two heads of lettuce or other vegetable grow where only one grew before but rather to keep *that one* growing.

Greater progress is now being made in developing new varieties by use of new techniques helpful in the breeding operations. Here again characteristics of germ plasm play an important part. The discovery in 1925 of an all female plant of the Italian red onion opened the door to new techniques in plant breeding. The study

of the inheritance of cytoplasmic male sterility and the incorporation of this character into present-day onion varieties grown in this
country have made possible the rapid development of hybrid
onions. Breeders are interested in finding male sterilities in other
vegetables, and these characters are now being sought.

The occurrence of virus diseases in our fruit and vegetable
varieties has of necessity compelled the breeder to develop new
resistant varieties. The cultivated strawberries developed by
planned breeding during the past fifty years are a good example of
the progress made in developing new fruit varieties. The strawberry of today is derived from two American species, the wild
meadow type of eastern North America, *Fragaria virginiana*, and
F. chiloensis found along the Pacific Coast from Alaska to California and along the coast of Chile in South America. The strawberry is another example of a fruit obtained from Europe after it
was improved there. Germ plasm of the Red Chilean strawberry
was taken to France early in the eighteenth century, hybridized
there with our native eastern North American meadow strawberry,
and gave us our common garden variety. Quality in the new
varieties comes largely from the meadow strawberry. Since the
strawberry plant is propagated vegetatively rather than by seeds,
virus diseases may be disseminated into new plantings unless methods are used to ascertain that nursery stocks are free of the causal
viruses. In recent years we have found that many of our strawberry
plants were infected with a virus complex. It has been necessary
for breeders to find means of eliminating these viruses from plant
material used in propagation because the viruses seriously affect
growth and production. *F. vesca* shows good symptoms of the
virus complex when grafted to cultivated varieties; thus it is useful
in determining the presence of viruses in cultivated varieties.
Another strawberry disease that has taken heavy toll is the red
stele root rot. The finding of additional strawberry germ plasm
growing in the wild that carries resistance to this disease would be
very valuable.

Breeding to develop new varieties of fruits except peaches,
nectarines, berries, grapes, and blueberries has been slow in this
country. There has not been the development of a number of new
varieties of apple as a result of breeding, as has been the case with

other fruit varieties, partly because chance superior seedings have arisen and have been discovered by individuals in many parts of the country, and partly because fruiting of breeding progeny seedlings requires a long time. Thus breeding is slow. Breeding for cold hardiness in apples was started in the North Central States in the late nineteenth century by using varieties from Russia as a source of genes for hardiness. Work in other locations was for the purpose of developing early and late maturing high-quality hardy varieties. Since apples, like strawberries, can be propagated vegetatively it is possible to distribute a new kind rather quickly.

Apple varieties have given rise to a number of color sports which have satisfied the market requirements for fruits of high color. Some of these sports have been from varieties that already possessed high quality, and the red color added another desirable characteristic. The commercial apple industry in the United States is largely made up of varieties propagated on seedling stocks. The trend in other parts of the world is toward the use of varieties propagated on vegetative dwarfing stocks. Fortunately virus diseases have not yet been a serious problem on apples, but we should know sources of germ plasm that carry resistance to virus diseases.

Citrus varieties and species were introduced into this country in the late nineteenth century. These fruits were grown in the Orient many centuries previously. Citrus is a relatively new crop here as compared with some other fruit crops. The Washington navel orange, which came from Brazil, was planted in California in 1873. Improvement has been largely through bud selection and bud mutations from the original strain. The Valencia orange was introduced into Florida and California between 1870 and 1872. The successful culture of this new crop had a marked impact on the agriculture and economic growth of these two states.

Recently the orange crop has been threatened by a virus complex involving the rootstocks on which the varieties are propagated. The Tristeza disease of citrus, which is a virus disorder, may be severe when infected sweet orange (*Citrus sinensis* L.) is budded on sour orange (*Citrus aurantium* L.) rootstock. Fortunately we have many citrus rootstocks that were brought in as a part of our introduction program. Some of these appear resistant to known viruses. All introduced stocks are now being evaluated to determine which rootstocks are more resistant or tolerant to the virus complex.

Another problem currently threatening citrus production in Florida, called spreading decline, is associated with attacks on the roots by the burrowing nematode. Control of this trouble may also be possible through use of tolerant or resistant rootstocks.

These problems illustrate again the need for a reservoir of germ plasm of rootstocks and varieties to meet disease emergencies that may threaten the continued culture of important fruit crops.

Some Trends Requiring Improvement of Existing Varieties

Present trends in vegetable production in this country require the development of new varieties to meet changed harvesting operations—machine harvesting rather than hand picking. The need is for varieties to develop their edible parts so that most of the harvesting can be done at one time. The bean processor, for example, prefers a variety that can be harvested by machinery, with a large percentage of the pods picked in one operation. This will require the development of new varieties that possess this characteristic. Similarly, with corn-picking machines now a part of the operation for harvesting corn, it is necessary to have varieties that produce the ears of uniform degree of maturity at approximately the same level on the stalk so that they can be harvested more easily.

Market varieties of vegetables are changing with consumer demands. Consumers are demanding better quality. Another trend in the handling and processing of vegetables is the increase in prepackaging. Varieties that lend themselves to quick freezing are in greatest demand by processors. This change will mean tailoring new varieties to meet this demand. Some varieties are satisfactorily reconstituted after freezing and hold the shape of the fresh product; others are not.

The need for higher quality in our fruits is equally important. New varieties of citrus must be developed to meet the demands of the juice concentrate industry. Better flavored varieties with high solids content that would add more consumer acceptance to the frozen concentrates are now desired. As long as oranges were marketed fresh, the older original varieties were considered satisfactory.

New Horticultural Crops

An accelerated research program on the evaluation of plant material as possible new crops was begun in 1956. A number of horticultural crops grown in other parts of the world but not now economically feasible in this country could be grown here. Most of our present-day horticultural crops were new crops at some time in the past.

For example, interest has been expressed from time to time in snow peas (edible pod), chick peas (garbanzos), and southern peas (edible varieties of cowpeas). The imported pistachio nut is consumed in large quantities in this country. Varieties of this nut are under preliminary test at the Plant Introduction Station at Chico, California, and show possibilities as a nut crop for the West and Southwest.

Some of the older crops present opportunities for improvement as new crops. Among the fruits, the avocado and mango, which are relatively new, can be further improved. Blackberries were largely abandoned as a fruit because the large spines on commercial varieties make picking hazardous. Genes for thornlessness are now available for the development of improved varieties that could become a new crop.

The New Crops Research Branch, of the Agricultural Research Service, is currently cooperating with the Longwood Gardens Foundation in a search for new and promising ornamentals. Since 1956 five collecting expeditions were undertaken, to Japan, southern Europe, Brazil, Australia, and northern Europe. Some of the plants are totally new to our gardens and were selected with the possibility that they would produce new forms for foundation plantings, shade trees, and other needs for ornamental plants.

The utilization of horticultural crops for industrial use also offers possibilities. Some of these are in the ornamental groups. The genus *Dimorphotheca*, or the Cape marigold, made up of about twenty species of herbs and subshrubs native to south Africa, is a source of unusual seed oil. Some of the chrysanthemum and veronica species, as well as members of the mustard, rape, and carrot families, may prove sources of special oils.

The bamboos that have been grown in this country for some years as ornamentals have a possibility as a source of paper. In their native Japan and Taiwan they are recognized as a valuable source of raw material for pulp and paper.

FEDERAL AID TO PLANT INTRODUCTION

The United States Department of Agriculture has aided in the introduction and dissemination of new kinds of fruits, vegetables, and ornamental plants since it was established in 1862. Previously many new plants were brought into this country by travelers and government representatives stationed in other countries. Early in this century the Department set up four plant introduction stations where germ plasm of all plants that might have potential value for use in this country could be grown. These stations were established in four geographical areas: (1) at Miami, Florida, where the tropical and subtropical plants principally could be grown for observation and preliminary evaluation; (2) at Chico, California, for stone fruits, such as peaches, plums, nectarines, and cherries; (3) at Glenn Dale, Maryland, that served not only as an introduction station for tree fruits that might have promise in the Northeast, but also as a quarantine station where plants could be observed to determine that no unwanted insects or diseases were introduced; and (4) at Savannah, Georgia, where the station became a center for species of bamboo, blight-resistant chestnuts, and other crops. Germ plasm maintained at these stations provided source materials for the breeders of many new horticultural crops. Some varieties of fruits have been introduced directly after a preliminary evaluation. In most cases, however, the introduced fruits and vegetables were not adapted for use as commercial varieties under our conditions.

With the growing interest in the need to import additional germ plasm for the improvement of American agriculture, funds were made available by Congress in 1946 for the establishment of four additional introduction stations. These are under federal-state cooperative management and are located in four geographic regions of the United States where plant material sent to each of these stations can be preliminarily evaluated. One of these is located in the

South at Experiment, Georgia; the second, at Geneva, New York, for the northeastern region; another at Ames, Iowa, for the North Central States; and a fourth at Pullman, Washington, for the Western States. These state-federal cooperative stations, along with the four federal stations established earlier, are centers for the accumulation of germ plasm for a large number of crops. As another aid to the preservation of germ plasm, the federal government has recently constructed a National Seed Storage Laboratory at Fort Collins, Colorado. In this facility seeds of varieties and species embodying new or improved germ plasm may be stored.

These stations will serve their purpose only in so far as the material can be used and evaluated by the breeders, but it is important to American and World agriculture to have these centers where germ plasm can be preserved for future use. They are currently serving not only American agriculture but also agriculture in other parts of the world. Exchange has been going on for centuries and should continue so that the most valuable kinds can be studied and preserved. A survey of plant breeding stations in western Europe was made in 1959 by a geneticist of the United States Department of Agriculture. Arrangements have been made for the exchange of breeding lines showing resistance to some diseases that occur in this country, as well as to other diseases that are not currently present.

Another aid to the location of valuable germ plasm as improved varieties or wild seedlings in Europe or Asia may come through Public Law 480. Through the use of counterpart funds from this government, assistance can be given to foreign exploration.

Need for Evaluation of Introduced Plant Material

One of the great needs at present is for more careful examination of the plant material accumulated so that it can be catalogued as to gene makeup. This is now possible through genetic studies that can be made. It is also important before wide dissemination of clones or vegetatively propagated material to study it for the presence of known or unknown viruses. This can best be done at the plant introduction station where the material is held in quarantine. The virologist of the Plant Quarantine Division of the Department will make the necessary studies before new material is released. For the past thirty years a federal-state cooperative program of potato breeding has been carried on. Scientists in the several states who are developing and testing varieties cooperatively can now maintain a large number of species among which they can hunt for the plant characters in which they are interested. At present potatoes are being evaluated at the Inter-Regional Potato Introduction Station at Sturgeon Bay, Wisconsin, where genetic, cytogenetic, and pathological studies are being made on a number of *Solanum* species collected in many parts of the world, principally in Mexico and South America. With this information, which is a more intensive evaluation than has been possible in the past, plant breeders and geneticists are made aware of the genetic makeup and behavior of these *Solanum* species, such as crossability, disease and insect resistance, chromosome content, and other needed information. Similar work needs to be done with other vegetables and fruits where they may be maintained and genetically evaluated, and their characters catalogued. Only in this manner can we make the most rapid progress in solving some of the agricultural problems of production and in the reduction of production hazards brought about by insects, diseases, weather and other hazards that confront the American farmer.

Field Crops

Martin G. Weiss

Agricultural Research Service, United States Department of Agriculture, Beltsville, Maryland

Germ plasm of the plants that supply our food, feed, and fiber ranks high in importance among world resources. We can only speculate upon its real value, particularly in the distant future. Long after man has exhausted certain of our natural resources, such as fossil fuels, he will be dependent on living plants to feed and clothe him.

As compared with other resources, germ plasm of living plants is highly unstable. Through millions of years its instability has permitted the evolution of characters that facilitated the survival of plants in their native habitat. In a comparatively short period, man has changed the habitat of many plants, either by introducing into new areas those with presently greater potentials to feed or clothe him or through management practices. Vast quantities of germ plasm have been lost and are still being lost.

The future potential of this vast world resource of germ plasm rests to an alarming degree upon man's ability to recognize which germ plasm available today will be of value in generations to come and upon his ability to preserve such germ plasm for posterity. In examining our gigantic responsibility, let us consider some of the immediate needs of the presently economically important field crops.

Intensive cultivation of any species of plants almost invariably has created an environment more favorable for the multiplication of diseases and insect enemies than occurred when the species grew dispersed in its natural habitat. Let us first consider the problems in the protection of field crops from the ravages of disease-producing organisms. Because of the extensive acreages upon which field crops are grown, and because the gross value per unit acre is less than that of many other crops, it generally has not proved economically feasible to control pathogens through large-scale application of chemicals. Greatest success has been achieved by finding and incorporating natural genetic resistance into these crops and through the use of improved management practices.

GENETIC RESISTANCE TO DISEASES AND PARASITES

Germ plasms introduced into this country have unquestionably made vast contributions to the control of diseases caused by fungus and bacterial pathogens. Research workers in cereal grains have been singularly successful in finding and incorporating resistance to new races of rust as they evolve. Resistance contributed by wheat varieties introduced from Palestine and Russia made possible the reestablishment of Durum wheat in its area of adaptation. Similarly, germ plasm from South America and Australia made possible the development of oat varieties resistant to virulent races of crown and stem rusts. In most cases, however, resistance to these diseases is conditioned by a single gene. Furthermore, the genes available do not impart a broad type of resistance. The narrow genetic base poses certain problems. It requires a continuous concerted research effort to develop varieties resistant to new races of the pathogen. Further, it necessitates frequent changeover of varieties. In oats, for instance, a complete changeover of varieties was necessary three times during the past two decades. Broader types of resistance are needed and are being sought.

Certain fungal diseases, particularly those caused by some of the non-obligate fungi, do not lend themselves as readily to control through host resistance. In the cereal grains, such diseases include Septoria disease of oats and scab of barley; in cotton, verticillium wilt and Phymatotricum root rot; in flax, pasmo; in soybeans, stem canker and brown stem rot; in peanuts, cercospora leaf spot and southern blight; in sugar beets, Rhizoctonia root rot. Higher types of resistance are needed for each of these diseases.

Forage crops are attacked by a host of leaf, stem, and root diseases caused by fungi and bacteria. It is difficult to measure disease losses accurately in forage crops that are utilized and harvested in so many different ways. In addition to causing losses in quality and yield, diseases reduce the longevity of a number of the perennial forage plants. However, excellent progress has been made in isolating germ plasm with resistance to a number of serious diseases. The contribution of Turkistan alfalfas in providing wilt resistance is well known. Introductions have provided smut-resistant rescuegrass and good sources of crown rust resistance in annual ryegrass. Among hundreds of perennial ryegrass introductions screened, three from Cyprus recently proved to have a high type of resistance to Helminthosporium blight. The inadequate breadth of the genetic base, a significant limitation of many crops, is particularly evident in a number of forage species. Thus, a very substantial percentage of the intermediate wheat grass acreage in the United States is planted with strains that trace to a single introduction. Seed production by some forage species is curtailed by diseases affecting the seed, roots, and leaves. To this end, we need resistance to ergot in dallisgrass, to rust in ryegrass and Kentucky bluegrass, and to root-rot complexes in birdsfoot trefoil and several of the wheatgrasses. Several exploration trips have been made in areas where prominent forage species are indigenous, but considerably more planned exploration is needed to accumulate an adequate diversity of germ plasm.

Progress in obtaining resistance to diseases caused by viruses has frequently been slow. When germ plasm is adequate, however, intensive screening has resulted in finding high levels of resistance. In rice, for instance, an intensive program has resulted in the discovery of an introduction from Taiwan that is highly resistant to hoja blanca. Development of wheat varieties resistant to soilborne mosaic is credited with saving that crop in much of Illinois and adjacent states. Sources of resistance to many virus diseases are presently not available. Such diseases include yellow dwarf of oats, curly top of flax, virus yellows of sugar beets, yellow patch of whiteclover, and ratoon stunting and forms of mosaic caused by new virus strains in sugarcane.

Success also is not as spectacular in finding resistance to nematodes as in finding resistance to diseases caused by fungi and bacteria. The encouraging exceptions include the contribution of Turkistan alfalfas in providing a source of resistance to the alfalfa stem nematode, and the immunity from the soybean cyst found in three introductions of soybeans among thousands screened.

Higher types of resistance are needed to the cyst nematode of sugar beets, to several species of root knot nematodes in peanuts and many forage legumes, and to the sting and meadow nematodes of peanuts and other legumes.

Another parasite that recently came to the United States should not go unnoticed. The parasitic weed *Striga asiatica* has become established in a localized area of the Southeast. Research workers feel that resistant germ plasm in corn, sorghum, and sugarcane is a distinct possibility.

Genetic Resistance to Insects

The search for resistance to insects is not of so long standing or intense as that pertaining to diseases. The potential success of this effort can be well illustrated by several promising developments. Resistance to the Hessian fly by recently developed hard red and soft red winter and western club wheats gives indication that clear-cut resistance is available. Similarly, the resistance to the spotted alfalfa aphid contributed by certain Turkistan alfalfas is highly effective; in fact, these alfalfas appear to be a promising source of resistance to the pea aphid also. The absence of nectar glands in cotton, as induced by genetic factors obtained from a wild cotton in Hawaii, gives promise of greatly reducing the reproductive rate of certain lepidopterous insects. The potentialities of insect control through plant resistance seem equal to those for disease control. Like disease resistance, resistance to insects frequently is not associated with any visible plant character. Success, therefore, depends upon adequate sampling of germ plasm, particularly in those areas where greatest diversity of germ plasm occurs, and the development of techniques that will permit accurate and rapid screening of large populations of plants.

Adaptability to Climatic Factors

Failure to persist or maintain vigorous growth during periods of climatic extremes limits the usefulness of many of our major crops. In many crops requiring a full growing season, ability to germinate and make growth during relatively low temperatures would greatly expand their range and usefulness. Such potentialities have not been fully explored. Andean corn, for instance, is reported to germinate and grow at temperatures considerably below those required for United States strains. Damage from early cold periods could be alleviated in such normally subtropical plants as sugarcane by the use of early maturing varieties that would attain maximum yields prior to the occurrence of low temperatures.

In forage crops in which duration of grazing period is of great economic importance, vigorous growth during periods of low temperature and of drought would greatly enhance the usefulness of many species. A German team is reported to have conducted an exploration into the high reaches of the Himalaya Mountains in search of forage plants during the 1930's. Many of their introductions, lost during World War II, are reported to have had the ability to grow relatively rapidly during periods of low temperature. In some cases, grazing periods can be extended through the incorporation of germ plasm that induces later maturity. New introductions of Persian and ball clover give promise of extending the spring grazing season by as much as three weeks with much higher total productivity than that of strains presently grown. Similarly, the introduced and newly released Israel annual sweetclover extends the grazing season over that of Hubam clover by some six weeks in the Gulf Coast area of Texas.

Many of the forage species have inadequate tolerance to drought and ability to persist during lengthy dry periods. It has been conjectured that a broader germ plasm base could improve many grasses in this respect, such as the wheatgrasses, Russian wildrye, timothy, orchardgrass, and tall oatgrass. In many of the leguminous crops, persistence during hot, dry periods is of even lower degree; in fact, lack of persistence is a major limitation to their use on ranges.

The potentialities of crop improvement through greater winter hardiness has been well illustrated in the winter grains and alfalfa. Greater winter hardiness in such species as big trefoil and the palatable hardinggrass would greatly improve their usefulness.

Stand Establishment and Maintenance Factors

The possibilities of eliminating the hazards associated with the establishment of plants through acquirement of seedling vigor have scarcely been touched. The development of the Nordan variety of crested wheatgrass with its large seed and increased seedling vigor is one of the few examples that can be cited. Seedling vigor is less than desirable in many of the native and introduced range grasses. Lack of such vigor is a serious limiting factor in such grasses as Russian wildrye. Seedling vigor is also needed in some of the forage legumes such as big and birdsfoot trefoil. The potentialities for improvement can be illustrated by the recent introduction of a new biennial yellow sweetclover with seed size and vigor more than twice those of the presently grown varieties.

Establishment of many forage crops also would be enhanced by more vigorous spreading characteristics. The creeping habit in alfalfa obtained from introductions of *Medicago falcata* serves to illustrate the potentialities. Individual plants of many grass species vary greatly in spreading ability, and variants with maximum spread are sought.

Adaptation to Mechanization

Economical production of field crops necessitates a high degree of mechanization. Spurred by this necessity, a great deal of progress has been made in adapting crops to machine culture and harvesting. However, much more can be done. Resistance to lodging has been given major attention in the development of new varieties of many crops. With the current increase in use of fertilizers, however, lodging resistance in many of the seed-producing crops, such as rice, barley, and oats, is presently inadequate.

Adaptation of seed crops to high fertilizer rates usually requires germ plasm that produces shorter, stiffer straw or stalks. A notable illustration is found in the introduction of wheat germ plasm with dwarf straw from Japan. The introduced character results in reducing internodal length of the straw without influencing internodal length of the spike. Several undesirable characters have been found to be associated with the factor for dwarf straw. Wheat breeders, however, have been successful in isolating the desired character and the first improved dwarf-strawed variety will be released shortly in the Pacific Northwest. Unfortunately, germ plasm of this type is currently not available in collections of many of our crops.

Germ plasm conditioning dwarfness in species that normally grow tall or have long branches has permitted the development of crops that lend themselves to culture and harvest by conventional equipment. One of the outstanding achievements in this line was the development of the triple dwarf grain sorghum that can be harvested with combines developed primarily for the harvest of small grains. In castor beans, notable achievement in restricting stem elongation also is in progress. This species, with its normally lengthy branches and profuse growth, long has vexed the engineer in the development of an efficient harvester. Slightly more than a decade ago certain tropical forms that bore a character resulting in the drastic shortening of the plant internodes were introduced from Brazil. Further, the branching habit is greatly reduced, and capsules are largely borne on spikes at the seventh to the ninth internode of the plant. This character has been transferred successfully to early types suitable for growing in this country, and the first variety, Dawn, has been released. The dwarf form has greatly facilitated the development of an efficient harvester for this crop.

In the evolution of many species now used as economic crops, characters that assured dissemination and dropping of the seed to the earth's surface were developed. In many species various modes of seed shattering still persist and plague the seed producer. In many grass species, such as tall oatgrass and buffalograss, adequate germ plasm variability for seed-holding capacity has not been found. Similar problems confront the seed producer of several legumes such as birdsfoot trefoil and crimson clover. In fact, the difficulty of seed production is one of the limiting factors in the growing of certain forage legumes. In some crops, such as sesame, susceptibility to shattering has been a major factor in its not becoming an important crop to date. It is not unreasonable to believe that adequate genetic variability exists in each of these crops to minimize appreciably the problems of seed production.

Still other plant characters affect the ease with which a crop can be mechanized. Leaf and stem pubescence, which protects certain crops such as soybeans and clovers against leafhoppers, lowers the quality of cotton picked mechanically in that it increases the amount of trash in the fiber. A smooth-leaf character found in a wild diploid cotton from Mexico is being incorporated into commercial cotton. It is estimated that this character will raise the quality of machine-picked cotton by one grade.

Seedling vigor was mentioned earlier in conjunction with stand establishment. It is also of importance in the development of precision planting for certain crops. The discovery of the monogerm character in a seed field of sugar beets in Oregon opened the possibility of precision seed planting and elimination of the expensive process of hand thinning and weeding. More vigorous single-germed embryos are needed, however, to insure the emergence of singly planted seeds. Greater seedling vigor will aid in reducing costly hand operations in a number of crops.

IMPROVEMENT OF QUALITY

The introduction and incorporation of germ plasm that imparts high quality to agricultural products produced by the various crops have received attention in varying degrees. The milling and baking qualities of flour produced from wheat have been given considerable attention by plant breeders and, with refinement of techniques, progress in producing high-quality varieties will accelerate. Improvement of cotton fibers with respect to strength, length, and fineness has been a major objective of the cotton breeder, and recent instrumentation that facilitates accuracy of measurements will permit further improvement in this character. Breeders of oilseed crops have been singularly successful in increasing the quantity of oil borne by seeds and in a few cases its quality. The qualities of certain crops, such as the forages, have not received concerted attention. As a consequence, many of the important forage grasses are defective in that elusive character called palatability. The cool-season grass, tall fescue, widely grown because of its adaptability to various soils and climates, ranks low in palatability. Some warm-season grasses, such as the weeping lovegrasses and bluestems, also are deficient in this character. In some cases adequate genetic variability may not be available within the species. On the other hand, in species not indigenous to this country, it is suspected that the germ plasm base introduced into the United States is very narrow compared with that in existence.

Quality of an agricultural product can in some cases be enhanced by removal of objectionable constituents. An objectionable factor is found in cottonseed meal in the form of an alkaloid called gossypol, which is secreted by glands normally found in the cotyledon. Several genetic characters that virtually eliminate the gossypol-bearing glands from the cotyledon have been isolated from Hopi cotton, formerly grown by the Pueblo Indians. Another classical illustration is afforded by the development of low-coumarin varieties of sweetclover through interspecific hybridization. At present toxic alkaloids render castor bean meal completely unusable as feed. It seems entirely possible that germ plasm which will not produce this toxic principle can be located.

The addition of specific constituents may enhance quality. Increase of the carotinoids, particularly xanthophyll, in corn, for instance, would make it a more desirable feed for intensifying skin coloration of broilers.

During periods of agricultural production beyond our food, feed, and fiber needs, particular attention is focused upon the use of agricultural products in industry. Compared with materials synthesized from petroleum, agricultural products frequently have serious disadvantages such as chemical nonuniformity. In many crops there is a potentiality for tailoring agricultural products for industrial usage. A prime example occurred during World War II when the waxy gene of maize was incorporated into commercial hybrids, and production of waxy corn was initiated. In this case, the task of converting a commercial crop to one with specialized uses was relatively simple. A single gene causes the corn plant to produce only branched starch molecules. In contrast, the present attempts to produce high-amylose corn are of interest. Cornstarch with only straight-chain molecules would have potential usage in the film and fiber field. Several genes that will raise the straight-chain fraction considerably above the 27% of normal cornstarch have been found. Combinations of these genes have, in fact, resulted in the experimental production of lines with starch having more than 80% amylose. It is not known presently whether starch with such constitution has commercial usage in the film and fiber industry. Attempts are being made to find germ plasm that will provide still higher amylose fractions. The work in maize points the way to the potential of tailoring agricultural products for industrial usage.

Maximizing Productivity

The search for germ plasm to increase production per se is not being stressed in this presentation. Maximum productivity is universally sought in all crops; in fact, it is a determining factor as to whether the crop can be grown economically. Furthermore, all the factors discussed herein have a bearing upon the productivity of the crop involved. The potentialities of further usage of heterosis should, however, be mentioned briefly.

The successful utilization of heterosis through hybridization permitted by the discovery and use of male sterility has been amply demonstrated in grain sorghum and sugar beets. Many research workers believe that cytoplasmic male sterility factors and genetic fertility-restoring factors, when needed, are available in the germ plasm of most of the naturally cross-pollinated crops or their wild relatives. Potentialities for increased production in crops such as cotton and many of the forage grass and legume species seem great enough to justify an intensive search for sterility factors. Further, in some species that reproduce largely through apomixis, such as dallisgrass, diploid, sexually reproducing strains are needed for plant improvement.

Wild Relatives of Cultivated Species

Potentialities for the increase of germ plasm diversity within our cultivated plants through hybridization with wild ancestral forms and relatives have long been recognized but have been explored only to a limited extent. A classic example of potential usefulness of wild species is found in tobacco. Resistance to three serious diseases, wildfire, black root rot, and mosaic, was incorporated into commercial tobacco from three different wild species. Still another example of successful use of wild crosses is found in the increase in lint strength of cotton. *Gossypium thurberi*, a wild diploid species with lintless seeds, native to northern Mexico and Arizona, was crossed with G. *arboreum*, a wild Asiatic diploid species. The resulting sterile hybrid was treated with colchicine, which doubled the chromosome numbers and thus produced a tetraploid plant known as an amphiploid. The amphiploid was in turn crossed with normal upland tetraploid cotton. The lint strength incorporated from the lintless wild species is presently widely used in cotton-breeding programs as a source of germ plasm for this character.

In many crops, serious barriers have limited the extent to which interspecific or intergeneric crosses can be utilized. Many crosses fail to develop viable hybrid seed, whereas the hybrid plants produced by others are completely sterile. The use of colchicine as an agent to double chromosomes in some instances has provided a solution to sterility. In fact, it has been possible to synthesize a number of polyploid crop plants, such as certain of the allo-tetraploid wheat species, commercial tobacco, and upland cotton.

Recent refinements in the technique of culturing excised embryos give promise of overcoming the difficulties involved in obtaining viable hybrid seeds. In certain crops the use of growth regulators also gives promise of overcoming this problem.

Still another barrier in the use of diverse germ plasms is the frequent close linkage of undesirable genetic factors with desired ones. Incomplete chromosome pairing often prevents the occurrence of crossovers between the genes involved. In a few instances, irradiation has been useful in causing breakage of the chromosomes between the desirable and the undesirable genes. The possibilities of solving this problem are shown by accomplishments in wheat. A wild diploid relative of wheat, *Aegilops umbellulata*, known to carry a high type of resistance to leaf rust, was crossed with a tetraploid wild wheat, *Triticum dicoccoides*. The chromosomes of the resultant sterile hybrid were doubled to give an amphiploid which in turn was crossed with the common bread wheat. Although the leaf rust resistance was successfully transferred to bread wheat, it was found linked with reduced vigor and fertility. Irradiation consequently was used to cause breakage within the desired chromosome. After screening many resultant progenies, a type in which a translocation had occurred between the *Aegilops* chromosome and one of the wheat chromosomes was found. In effect, a small segment of the wild type chromosome had been substituted for a corresponding portion of a wheat chromosome. The leaf rust resistance acquired is considered to be the broadest type presently available.

In still another instance, irradiation was used in wide crosses. *Agropyron elongatum,* one of the forage wheatgrass species, was observed to carry excellent resistance to bunt. The wheatgrass, which carries 70 chromosomes, was crossed with common wheat, which has 42 chromosomes. The resultant 56-chromosome hybrid was successfully backcrossed to wheat. The segment of *Agropyron* chromosome carrying bunt resistance was transferred to a wheat chromosome through an irradiation-induced translocation.

With the new techniques at hand, a vast new source of germ plasm is available in many commercial crops. In oats, for instance, recent successful hybrids involving a wild diploid oat, *Avena strigosa,* have resulted in the successful transfer of the broadest type of resistance to crown rust yet available. This wild species also carries excellent resistance to a number of other major oat diseases, such as stem rust, loose and covered smuts, Septoria disease, yellow dwarf, and anthracnose. In such crops as barley, in which presently only a single gene protects the crop from stem rust, it would seem particularly desirable to survey wild relatives in a search for a broader base of resistance.

Broadening the Range of Adaptation of Present Field Crops

With additional diversity of germ plasm, many of the present economically important crops have the potential of being grown throughout a wider range. The past histories of many major crops well illustrate this potentiality. After soybeans became established as an oilseed crop in the United States, available germ plasm permitted their production on a large scale as an oilseed crop only through the southern portion of the north-central region. The acquisition of germ plasm adapted to the longer days of more northerly regions permitted development of new varieties which pushed the soybean belt north considerably. In Minnesota, for instance, soybeans increased within a ten-year period from a crop of little significance to the secondmost cash crop of the state. Since World War II, the production of soybeans for beans has been extended throughout the South, particularly in the Mississippi Delta region. The expansion into this region was made possible through the acquisition of high-oil types adapted to the shorter days of this region. In winter oats, the expansion permitted by germ plasm diversity is nearly as striking. Over a forty-year period the belt in which winter oats are grown has moved northward approximately 200 miles.

A few of the potentialities relative to crop expansion will be mentioned. Grain sorghums have become a major crop in the Great Plains region, particularly in the central and southern Great Plains. Earliness and laxness of head would permit considerable expansion into the northern Great Plains. Expansion into the humid regions, particularly in the southeastern United States, would also be permitted by acquisition and incorporation of resistance to leaf diseases.

The potentialities of safflower have not been realized. Development of earlier varieties would permit expansion into the northern Great Plains and the intermountain regions. Disease resistance would permit expansion in the irrigated regions of the Southwest and into more humid areas. Capsule mold has been a serious limiting factor in the production of castor beans in humid regions. Acquisition of resistance to this mold and certain leaf diseases would widen the range of adaptation of this crop, particularly in the humid regions of the Southeast.

The potentialities of production of most of the world's major food, feed, and fiber crops in the United States have been determined in at least a general way. The potentials of many, of course, must occasionally be reexamined in the light of current economic conditions and in consideration of newly acquired germ plasm. In certain groups of crops, such as the forage grasses and legumes, and crops with special uses, many species have not been adequately evaluated.

In this presentation we have reviewed a few improvements of the nation's field crops that have come about through the introduction of germ plasm. Consideration has been given to inadequacies of some field crops and the potentialities for improving them through the acquisition of germ plasm not now available in the United States breeding programs. The illustrations and considerations clearly substantiate the premise that germ plasm of our economic crops is one of the world's greatest natural resources. The responsibilities of man in recognizing and preserving this resource cannot be overemphasized.

Small Farm Animals[*]

A. W. Nordskog

Department of Poultry Husbandry, Iowa State University, Ames, Iowa

For purposes of this discussion "small farm animals" will be defined as including chickens (*Gallus domesticus*), turkeys, ducks, geese, guinea fowl, and fur-bearing animals. Our definition embraces three major agricultural industries, namely the egg industry, the broiler industry, and the turkey industry with a total annual production valued at 3½ billion dollars in the United States alone with lesser industries producing furs, rabbits, ducks, geese, and guinea fowl.

Need for additional sources of animal germ plasm might be justified in order to develop a new product, to improve the quality of an existing product, to increase the efficiency in producing a product, to obtain better utilization of land, facilities, or by-products, and to make possible an increasing supply of a product for an expanding human population.

In order to consider the problem of the need for additional sources of germ plasm, it seems logical to attempt some evaluation of the present state of progress in each industry separately and then to consider the problems peculiar to each. Only those problems of a genetic-economic nature are relevant to this discussion. Also, all genetic problems may be translated into economic problems of three types: (*a*) consumer acceptance and demand, (*b*) efficiency of production, and (*c*) quality of product.

Poultry Industry

The poultry industry in the United States consists of three major segments, concerned separately with the production of

[*] Journal paper No. J-4027 of the Iowa Agricultural and Home Economics Experiment Station, Ames, Iowa, Project 1039.

eggs, broilers, and turkeys. It is unique because it has exploited the sciences of genetics, nutrition, and disease control for the production of poultry products far greater than elsewhere in the world. It has been quick to make applications of modern breeding methods, including inbreeding and hybridization, the theory of quantitative inheritance and even blood typing techniques, for the possible improvement of performance. The poultry industry is the first livestock industry that has created a moderate demand for the employment of trained geneticists for commercial research and development.

The extent to which modern science of breeding and genetics has contributed to the high performance of egg laying strains, broilers, and turkeys in the country cannot be easily evaluated for the reason that genetic improvement is quite thoroughly confounded with improvements due to better feeding practices, management, and disease control. We do know, however, that modern egg laying strains today average better than 200 eggs per bird per year, compared with 104 eggs per bird per year in 1909, or fifty years ago (8). Eggs are now produced on at least 45% less feed than birds required fifty years ago. Thus, today one dozen eggs can be produced on 4 pounds of feed compared with a requirement of almost 8 pounds of feed for a dozen eggs fifty years ago.

The growth of the broiler industry is a remarkable episode in the history of livestock production, and is only about thirty-five years old. In 1934, the first year records were kept, 34 million broilers were produced in the United States (8). In 1959, production was close to the 2 billion mark. More than 80% of the chicken meat we consume today is produced by the broiler industry. This is contrasted with only 1.4% in 1934, the balance of our chicken meat at that time being a by-product of our egg industry.

The high level of efficiency obtained by broiler producers today is indicated by the fact that only 6 to 7.2 pounds of feed are required to produce a 3-pound broiler ready for market in 8 to 9 weeks (8). This is in contrast to meat chickens in 1930 when 15 pounds of feed were required to produce a 3-pound bird in 14 to 15 weeks. The modern broiler today consumes fewer pounds of feed per unit of gain in weight than any other farm animal. It has been estimated that to produce 100 pounds of broilers requires 72% of the labor required to produce 100 pounds of hogs and 53% of the labor necessary to produce 100 pounds of milk (9).

Expansion of our turkey industry so far has not matched the growth of the broiler industry. Yet rapid progress has been made in the past twenty years. Since 1940, the time required to get a turkey ready for market has been cut by more than 20% (8). Feed efficiency has been improved at least 35%. Mortality is less than one-fourth of what it was. Turkeys are one of our best converters of feed into human food. In fact, they are generally considered the most efficient producers of pounds of protein per pound of feed. Annual turkey production in the United States has climbed to some 80 million birds, or a fivefold increase since 1930, and is 2.5 times the number raised just ten years ago.

This is not to say that problems possibly genetic in origin do not exist in the poultry industry. For example, there is reason to believe that selection by the usual methods of intrastrain breeding is less effective today than some years ago and that we are approaching a plateau in rate of egg production. Still, we have not reached the theoretical physiological limit in egg production of one egg per day. If the average high-producing strains produce 200 eggs per bird per year, this would represent about two-thirds of the physiological limit, assuming that such a limit exists.

Another important problem of our egg producers today has to do with disease. Mortality rates in pullet flocks of 30 to 50% are not uncommon (5). The most important single disease appears to be leukosis. Veterinarians have given little help in controlling this disease as yet. Control through breeding still seems to be a possibility, but little has been accomplished on a national basis.

A potentially important problem is one of longevity. Almost all breeders today have concentrated on the improvement of strains and crosses for maximum yield in the first year of production. Essentially no attention in the past has been given to developing strains which would be efficient egg producers the second and third year. This is a problem that could be of increasing importance when one considers that the cost of replacement of an egg laying chicken is the second most important cost item in producing a dozen eggs today, and exceeds labor costs which were in second place just a few years ago. In terms of the concept of agriculture adjustment for the future, it appears that breeders may need to reevaluate the problem of longevity in our egg laying strains.

What are the possibilities of using new sources of germ plasm to hasten the solution of these problems of our egg producers? In the United States, the Leghorn breed is preeminent. Heavy breeds or so-called general purpose breeds such as the Rhode Island Red and the Barred Rock which were especially common just a few years ago appear to be losing out, even in the New England States, in favor of the Leghorn type chicken. One question is whether breeds or stocks exist in other parts of the world which might supplement the germ plasm available in this country, making possible a higher level of performance by correcting especially the high mortality problem and perhaps partially solving the longevity problem.

As an example, a breed of chickens native to Egypt known as the Fayoumi appears more resistant to leukosis than the existing United States strains. Experiments carried out at the Iowa State University over the past ten years indicate that this breed might be useful commercially for crossing purposes (7). Although it is clear that this breed would need to be corrected for obvious faults including small egg size, crosses between the Fayoumi and the Leghorn, as well as the Rhode Island Red and White Rock, demonstrate that such crosses produce at a fairly high rate, yet with a low rate of mortality. Likewise, Jull (6) reported that crosses between the Fayoumi and the Leghorn carried out in Egypt at the Ministry of Agriculture Experiment Station showed superior egg production compared with the pure lines. A number of commercial breeders in this country are experimenting with this breed. It seems reasonable to believe that there would be stocks of useful genetic material (the Fayoumi is one example) in other parts of the world which could improve the productivity and utility of the chickens in this country.

On the other hand, there are those who wonder whether the chicken, after all, is the best choice of species for the production of man's egg supply. Hutt (4) reported that the Jansen strain of

Khaki Campbell ducks developed in the Netherlands far exceeds the best production obtainable in chickens. These ducks averaged 320 eggs per bird per year, representing about 90% of the physiological limit of egg production, as compared with 66% in our better strains of chickens today. Moreover, the Khaki Campbell ducks laid larger eggs, and adult mortality was only about one-third that found in chickens. Thus, as Hutt put it, "These phenomenal results with ducks demonstrate what can be accomplished when the right methods of selection are applied to the right species by the right people."

There is, of course, the problem of consumer preference and consumer acceptance. If we are accustomed to having chicken eggs for breakfast, we might resist duck eggs as a substitute. Another factor which will keep duck eggs from replacing chicken eggs has to do with feed efficiency. Chickens apparently will convert feed into eggs as efficiently as ducks (4).

Most of us today eat chicken at least once a week and frequently more often. Broiler meat has been criticized because it is rather bland and requires a great deal of seasoning for satisfactory flavor. This explains, I suppose, the popularity of charcoal braziers and barbecues for the preparation of chicken today. Quite possibly, more attention might be paid by nutritionists to types of feed which would add greater flavor to our broiler chickens. On the other hand, there might be opportunity to produce broiler-like birds with more natural flavor from species other than *Gallus domesticus*. The guinea fowl, for example, which is used only occasionally today in hotels and restaurants as a special delicacy, might be amenable to greater commercial exploitation. Guinea fowls are said to dress into attractive carcasses, and when young are tender and fine in flavor resembling wild game. It seems to me that we are missing something in our highly organized modern civilization when, for example, we go into a supermarket and find a wide choice of breakfast cereals, fruits, or vegetables, but the choice in chickens is limited to young broilers. Perhaps if the guinea fowl or even pheasants were bred intensively for greater growth rate and reproductive performance, these might well supplement our weekly ration of broiler chicken.

The duck and goose industry, especially the latter, has suffered a considerable decline over the past twenty to thirty years. The principal difficulty apparently is the high percentage of fat in ducks and geese which, for most people today, is undesirable. The duck industry in this country is mainly represented by the several large farms located on Long Island that cater to the foreign element of the New York metropolitan population. The breed used is almost exclusively the White Pekin.

The high fat content characteristic of most domestic breeds of water fowl is due in part to diet, but this apparently also is a genetic characteristic. Ducks and geese, even when fed almost exclusively on grass, are said still to have a high fat content. A Long Island duck of only 8 weeks of age but weighing 6 pounds will have about 30% fat in its carcass (10). Perhaps we are using the wrong breed. Some duck breeders believe that the Muscovy, either as a purebred or when crossed with the Pekin, produces carcasses much lower in fat content. It would appear that more experimental work might be done to verify this contention which might lead to a more substantial duck industry and which would add greater variety to our choice of poultry meats.

According to the 1950 census, something like one million geese were raised in 1949 on less than 2% of the farms in the country. This is only about one-third the number of geese raised in 1929. Goose farming appears to be held in check because of the limited demand for goose meat, the high fat content of the carcass, and also because of the low reproductive rate of geese. The latter tends to keep the price of goslings too high to permit competition with the turkey industry. Geese, however, have been used for grazing and weeding strawberry beds and cotton fields. They, therefore, would have value in reducing labor costs in connection with truck farming, in addition to the meat value of the carcass.

According to Delacour (2) the common European breed of goose known as the Toulouse in general appearance is almost identical to its wild ancestor the Greylag. In fact, Charles Darwin (1) called attention to the small amount of variation between the wild and domestic varieties of geese. He said, "The amount of variation which it has undergone as compared with most other domesticated animals is singularly small. This is probably because selection has not been heavily resorted to." Yet geese have evidently been domesticated for thousands of years.

Perhaps other species of geese might better serve the purpose of man than those we now have domesticated. Certain species of so-called Sheldgeese found in South America are considered by ornithologists to be better adapted to grazing than our presently domesticated species (2). They are essentially land birds and can progress in water only rather slowly according to Delacour. They are of rather large size with long legs and have been referred to as the "ungulates" of the water fowl family. Most water fowl authorities state that wild species can be kept under confinement readily, and of course, many wild species may be found in aviaries today.

FUR INDUSTRY

The fox and the mink may be taken as examples of our most recent domesticated or partially domesticated species. These are the "big two" in the fur farming industry, although the first farm-raised fur was produced some 100 years ago from the Karakul sheep used in the production of Persian lamb fur. Toward the end of the last century, fox farming became established on Prince Edward Island in Canada. Since that time, both fox farming and mink farming have attained considerable prominence both in Canada and in the United States as well as in other countries, including Russia.

It would appear that much greater exploitation is yet possible in the fur industry from the standpoint of fur farming. In a recent report, Edwards and Cowan (3) showed that in British Columbia 19 square miles of trapping area produced on the average only one mink pelt per year. A marten pelt was produced for every 13 square miles, and one otter pelt was obtained for every 1298 square miles. Although the fur harvest of the wilds of Canada remains an important source of income to some 47,000 trappers, it is evident that as our population increases fur bearing animals will become less important as a part of our natural resources. Because of the fact that our fur industry does not compete with our agricultural food industries, expansion in this direction would seem desirable.

A considerable body of information is becoming available concerning genetic factors influencing color variations in mink and fox. Production of color mutants such as platinum, silver sable, blue sapphire has tended to keep prices of mink pelts fairly good.

One of the main problems of the fur farming industry is that its stability is greatly influenced by fashion. Thus, today, long furs such as fox are not fashionable, while mink fur and martens are fashionable. As a result fox farming today is only a small fraction of what it was in 1940.

The use of imported animals for fur production appears to have possibilities, such as the chinchilla, native to South America, which was introduced into this country some years ago. In 1950, an estimated 500,000 animals were in existence in the United States which so far have been used mainly for breeding purposes.

Another imported animal from South America is the so-called nutria or coypu, sometimes called the South American beaver. They were first introduced into this country to be raised in captivity, but some animals escaped or were released and have become established as wild colonies especially in Louisiana. They have increased in rather large numbers and have spread to other adjoining states. In 1955, over 370,000 pelts were taken from the wild animals released in Louisiana. This species seems better adapted to wild conditions than to being raised in confinement.

In summary, new germ plasm or new species for purposes of strengthening small animal agriculture might conceivably be used in the pure form to supplement or replace existing domestic species, or to cross with existing domestic species, or to synthesize a new form from a cross. Perhaps greater efforts should be made on an experimental basis to domesticate wild but potentially useful species of gallinaceous birds, water fowl, and fur bearing animals. Although higher efficiency of production would be an important goal in the domestication and development of such species, especially through better disease control, it would appear that greater emphasis should be placed on developing foods with greater variety and flavor. This might be accomplished by using feral species with certain distinct and desirable characteristics or by exploiting already domesticated species so far not extensively exploited.

References

1. Darwin, Charles. *The Variation of Animals and Plants under Domestication.* London, 1885. (Cited by Brown, *Poultry Breeding and Production,* Vol. 1, p. 11. John Wiley and Sons, New York.)

2. Delacour, Jean. *The Waterfowl of the World,* p. 203. Country Life Ltd., London.

3. Edwards, R. Y., and I. McT. Cowan. Fur production of the Boreal Forest Region of British Columbia. *J. Wildlife Management, 21,* 257-267 (1957).

4. Hutt, F. B. The Jansen Khaki Campbell ducks. *J. Heredity, 43,* 277-281 (1952).

5. Hutt, F. B. *Genetic Resistance to Disease in Domestic Animals,* p. 107. Comstock Publishing Associates, Ithaca, New York, 1958.

6. Jull, Morley A. *World's Poultry Sci. J., 14,* 202 (1958).

7. Nordskog, A. W., and R. E. Phillips. Heterosis in poultry. V. Reciprocal crosses involving Leghorns, heavy breeds and Fayoumi. *Poultry Sci., 39,* 257-263 (1960).

8. Science and Service. Published by *Feedstuffs,* The Miller Publishing Company, Minneapolis, Minnesota, 1959.

9. U. S. Department of Agriculture, 1955. Citation in Morley A. Jull, *World's Poultry Sci. J., 14,* 204 (1958).

10. Wooster, Harold A., and Fred C. Blanck. *Nutritional Data,* p. 86. H. J. Heinz Company, Pittsburgh, Pa., 1950.

Large Farm Animals

J. L. Lush

Department of Animal Husbandry, Iowa State University, Ames, Iowa

The practical need for additional sources of breeding stock depends in part on whether sources do actually exist which would help to improve our farm animals more rapidly if we had access to those stocks.

Under five sets of circumstances getting breeding stock from additional sources can be desirable. First, a stock may now exist somewhere abroad, already so well suited to some of our needs that it should be imported and multiplied for commercial use as a pure stock or for very high grades. Most of our pure breeds in the United States came that way, although some breeds have been developed here out of various crosses or unpedigreed descendants of previously imported stock. Second, some important ecological niche may be empty in the sense that no existing breed or stock fills it at all well, but several different stocks, some of them not in North America, may among them seem to possess all the qualities needed. Then the task is to combine those qualities into a single stock. Third, one stock may seem to be much nearer to the ideal than any other and may possess somewhere within it at a low frequency all the qualities needed, but this stock may not actually be improving further, i.e. the stock may appear to have "plateaued." Then a mild outcross, perhaps to a stock from another land, might offer the best prospect of breaking through that ceiling. Fourth, some one stock may appear to have all but one or two of the qualities needed for some important niche, and those missing qualities may exist in some stock which is, however, inferior in most other qualities. This has happened often in breeding plants for disease resistance, although the conspicuous and oft quoted cases nearly all concern self-fertilized or asexually propagated species and most of the effect is from a single pair of genes. Fifth, some stock not particularly meritorious when bred

127

pure may nevertheless produce enough heterosis in some crosses that importing it to be used in a rotation crossbreeding system would be worth while.

Actual experiment, often replicated several times and in several places, is needed before we can be reasonably sure of the outcome of a specified cross or breeding method. These experiments cost so much in money and time that only a few of the infinitely many possible ones can actually be conducted. However, at least two rules seem well enough grounded in genetic principles and in actual experience to make our advance estimates something better than mere guesses.

First, when two stocks are crossed, the offspring are generally somewhere near a metrical average of the parental stocks but their qualities closely related to "fitness," such as vitality, reproductive rates, and growth rates, usually show at least a little heterosis. The exceptions to this rule are numerous, especially if we confine our attention to single characters as Mendel did. But the rule is dependable enough to be generally useful when we consider complex characters such as net merit of the whole animal or stock. In using this rule, it also should be remembered always that the net usefulness of the animal *for our purposes* may not be at all proportional to the linear measurements of its constituent characters. An example is backfat thickness in pigs. The optimum is an intermediate, nearer the lower than the upper end of the range found among presently existing stocks of swine. Thus if we cross a stock too thin with one which is too thick and we get offspring which are a metrical average of the parental stocks (as our general rule would lead us to expect), yet on the scale of net merit to us the offspring would be distinctly superior to both parental stocks. The surprises engendered by net merit not varying linearly with each character and (perhaps more importantly still) by net merit not always being proportional to the sum of net merit in the individual characters are enough at times to limit severely the average utility of this first rule in actual practice.

Second, the improvement resulting from selecting within a rather freely interbreeding population is the product of three factors: (*a*) the accuracy of selection, (*b*) the intensity of selection, and (c) the amount of additively genetic (genic) variation present in the stock. This rule is helpful when trouble-shooting to find why progress is slow, or when the population may seem to have "plateaued."

Most of this article concerns the needs when improvement seems to be slow or zero, but a few remarks about the other situations may be in place. The case where stock well fitted to some of our needs already exists in some other land was common in pioneering times. For example, the pioneers had to import horses and sheep, as no animals native to America could come near to serving the same purposes as those. This situation is much rarer now, largely because so much pioneering and exploratory importing was done before it was stopped by quarantine regulations. On moderately rare occasions, this need may still rise. For example, when standards of merit in swine swung so hard and so suddenly against lard in recent decades, this created a real place for some breeds of the Landrace type from northwestern Europe.

If market demands for beef should likewise change to cause a prejudice against overfatness as extreme as that against lard in swine, possibly the need for breeds like the Charollais might increase suddenly. Even in such cases, actual experimenting is needed because the stock which looks so promising in its home surroundings may turn out for one reason or another not to be well adapted to our conditions.

The need for importing and crossing several existing stocks to produce a new stock, with a combination of characters that will fit our needs well, likewise occurs moderately rarely. Examples are the need for dairy cattle well adapted to the tropical regions, and for beef cattle well adapted to such subtropical regions as our own Gulf Coast.

The need to introduce one or a few rare genes not present at all in our own stocks is probably comparatively rare in animals. The process of introducing such a stock and then grading back toward the original improved stock, but selecting among the crosses and their descendants for those individuals which had the valuable genes from the introduced stock, while letting the breeding system dilute out the undesirable genes which were in the introduced stock, is difficult to do successfully if the desired genes are more than one or two pairs. Such genes must have effects recognizable with a rather high degree of accuracy or we shall lose the genes during the backcrossing. If the quality we desire to introduce requires the presence and joint action of many pairs of genes, the combination scatters so many ways in the backcrossing process that trying to keep these genes by selecting for them while backcrossing to the native stock is but little more effective than trying to scoop up dry sand with one's bare hands while the fingers are spread wide apart. Even in plants, this has been a highly successful operation only in the self-fertilized plants which were so prolific that progeny tests are moderately simple and cheap and highly accurate.

Finding stocks which are individually mediocre but would produce valuable heterosis when crossed with other stocks would require an enormous amount of experimenting to test each such possible stock in each and every cross.

Evidence on Rates of Improvement

Evidence, dependable in varying degrees, on time trends in productiveness is scattered in many places. For all of them, the trend of productiveness has generally been upward. This is unmistakable over any long period of years, although the irregular year-to-year variations are sometimes large. We have no wholly satisfactory way of determining how much of this trend was due to genetic improvement and how much to improvement in such environmental things as nutrition, health, and sanitation. In some cases we have clear evidence that genetic changes were being produced. There are examples in the backfat and belly thickness in the Danish Landrace pigs and some data from experiments where selection was in both the high and the low direction. Even in the latter cases, the controls were not adequate to show whether the genetic changes in the high and in the low directions were at the same rate. The whole problem of controls adequate to show us exactly what is happening genetically in selection experiments is still wide open. A statistical method of fitting constants to years and birth year groups seems useful, but appears to need exploring still more under all sorts of conditions.

Many possibilities for muddled thinking surround this question of whether a trend was genetic or environmental. For instance, dairy cows produce more than they did twenty years ago, and they also eat more. If we ask whether the increase in production is due to the increase in food consumption or to genetic improvement, we need first to know *why* the cows eat more feed now. We advise dairymen to feed according to production. Doubtless many of them do. When they do, a cow who volunteers to produce more is given more feed, and if she produces still more, she is given still more feed. Under such a system, the amount of feed she gets is really a *result* of her production rather than a cause of it! If one were to insist that only the extra production not explainable by the extra feed can be considered as genetic, he would have changed definitions so that he would be discussing improvement in *economy* rather than in *amount* of production. Genes are not disembodied ghosts that act in a vacuum nor are they like the constants of physics which are practically the same everywhere. They are *potentialities for reacting* in a given way *with a given environment*. It is thinkable that the limiting factor on dairy production twenty or thirty years ago was the cow's capacity to consume feed. If so, and if we have since then improved genetically her capacity to consume feed, which, in turn, has permitted more production, then the genetic effect on feed consumption which causes more production can be considered as a bit of genetic improvement. Likewise, the undoubted fact that we know considerably more about nutrition and that veterinary and sanitary practices have certainly improved does not of itself mean that the environment for the individual cow has thereby improved. We may have offset that by keeping cows under more crowded conditions where the opportunities for infection, etc., are greater. It is even possible that the net environment may have deteriorated for the individual cow, although not for her owner, even while our knowledge of and ability to control nutrition and sanitation were undoubtedly increasing. Many other pitfalls of interpretation beset attempts to separate trends into genetic and environmental portions. The plain fact remains that the trends have been rather unanimously and distinctly upward.

Some of these trends suggest that a plateau is being reached.

Others, however, suggest that improvement is still accelerating. Theoretically, plateaus seem possible in all populations. Some laboratory experiments where the selection has lasted for thirty to forty generations seem rather certainly to have encountered them. As a rule, such populations then are still far from being entirely homozygous. Instead they have reached some sort of metastable equilibrium between opposing forces, as if the genes which are still segregating had multiple effects, some favorable and some unfavorable.

Plateauing because selection is knowingly or unknowingly for a genetic intermediate seems especially likely for complicated characters, where the net functioning may depend upon the proper balance of many participating processes. Another plausible genetic interpretation for plateaus is that when we select for a multitude of goals, some of these are mutually exclusive. A negative correlation is another name for that. Under such circumstances, if we start selecting more intensely for one character we change it rapidly at first but other characters, which we may not at first even suspect were related to it, will deteriorate rapidly enough that soon we must divert our attention to repairing them. This then decreases or even stops improvement in the first character. Haldane says somewhere that most species are most of the time in some kind of metastable equilibrium and that the major, but irregular, advances in evolution have followed the rupture of such equilibria.

Some of these plateauing mechanisms might be overcome by introducing breeding stock from distinctly different sources, but we will not be sure of the outcome of that without actually trying it. To try all possible kinds of crosses in all possible ways obviously is impossible. I do not see any useful chart to guide us in breaking through these plateaus although we will be more likely to find a way through if we know the genetic causes of the plateau.

At all times we must weigh the costs of a given procedure against its probable gains. We cannot start out to try everything, because the possibilities outnumber so vastly our resources, either financial or in personnel and time. Although we cannot be wholly certain of the probable gains nor absolutely certain of the costs, yet we simply *must* do some such advance estimating of the procedures to help us choose which few of the many possible alternatives seem most worth pursuing.

Utilizing an Introduced Stock

If the introduced stock is to be maintained pure or nearly so and is to be used for many generations, either directly for commercial purposes or occasionally as a source for future crosses on other stocks, the numbers need quickly to be made large enough that the inbreeding effect, or random genetic drift, becomes unimportantly small. Probably the original importation should have included at least 6 or 8 different males, not very closely related to each other, and 30 or more females. To guarantee the indefinite preservation of the stock in this country without material genetic changes occurring against the breeders' intentions seems to require that it be quickly expanded to something over 20 males and over 200 females of breeding age. A subordinate question, which may at times be important, is whether such an introduced stock should be kept as one large and rather freely interbreeding population or should be subdivided considerably, so that it would have permanently some kind of a *reticulate* breeding structure. The latter would generally have several advantages. If the introduced stock is to be used only a few times in making some initial crosses, as under the second and fourth purposes, a much smaller number in the initial importation might be satisfactory, and the importation may not need to be maintained pure for more than one or two generations.

In all matters of importation, as well as in the breeding of stock already here, the desirability of revising the goals or standards of excellence from time to time needs always to be kept in mind. As markets change and as farming methods change, that which was ideal at one time may cease to be so. Striking examples from the past are the conditions under which the corn belt breeds of American swine were originally developed and the need to change them in recent decades. Likewise the early breeds of light horses which developed in the United States more than a century ago did so under conditions not likely ever to recur. The extreme development of Merino sheep in the Vermont region before the Civil War and the swing later toward more mutton qualities constitute another conspicuous example. Rapid changing of standards is conspicuous in pet and fancy stock and in some fur animals, such as mink. Novelty itself often has some selective value in such breeds or species.

SUMMARY

Needless barriers to importation of genetically different stocks should be removed, even though we cannot write with great assurance a long list of all the stocks we would ever need to import and for what purposes. The difficulties and expense of importations are such that no large numbers of all kinds and varieties of stock will ever be imported indiscriminately, just for the sake of importing.

Importations certainly carry some risk of introducing diseases. Modern rapid transportation by airplane or fast steamship has made the risk greater than it was when animals came by sailing ship. Then any latent diseases the animals carried had a good chance to become obvious in the long weeks at sea. However, veterinary techniques for detecting diseases and for inspecting the incoming stock have likewise improved tremendously, thus diminishing the risk that an importation might introduce some disease not now in the United States. We are surely in a better position now to import without introducing disease than we were 100 years ago when, it is to be remembered, many diseases did not arrive, in spite of importations from many parts of the world and without quarantine.

No one wanting to import breeding stock can object seriously to a reasonable period of quarantine and inspection nor indeed to passing animals through a succession of quarantines on different islands if the risk is high. They can rightly object to regulations which make importation practically *impossible* no matter what precautions or inspections are taken. Smuggling is more difficult with large animals, such as cattle, than it is with the eggs of birds, yet the smuggling of frozen semen is by no means impossible. Surely it is more in the public interest to establish legal and reasonably effective systems of inspection and quarantine which, even though tedious and expensive, will still permit importation of supposedly valuable stock by American citizens eager to do so, than to establish rules which practically prohibit all importations. Such rules automatically tend to encourage smuggling. Surely something should have been learned from our experience with the prohibition of alcoholic drinks through the 1920's.

For the most part the potentialities of improvement by using only the stocks already in the United States have by no means been exhausted. But certainly such improvement could occasionally be made more rapid if sources of genetically different stocks were made available, even though the importing process were hedged in with expensive and tedious inspections and quarantines.

No genetic basis exists for estimating *the ultimate limits* to which a stock can be improved from within itself. But we can estimate the present *rate* of improvement and that can usually be extrapolated four or five generations without serious error. For the larger farm animals, this is long enough for most practical purposes, because we usually need to reappraise the situation every two or three animal generations, if we keep in reasonably close touch with the changing goals.

Discussion of the Need
for Additional Sources
of Germ Plasm

H. A. Rodenhiser

*Agricultural Research Service, United States Department
of Agriculture, Washington, D. C.*

It is clearly evident from the information presented by contributors to Part II that there is need for acquisition and utilization of additional sources of plant and animal germ plasm. Numerous examples have been cited in the crops field, of varieties developed through recombination and selection utilizing germ plasm available in our world collections of seed and vegetatively propagated plant stocks. In many instances these new varieties have been outstanding and have met the immediate needs of the farmer, the trade, and the consumer. It is generally recognized, however, that success may be temporary and that the future value of a new variety depends on the breadth of its genetic base. For instance, it may or may not be adequate to resist the attack of new parasitic races or biotypes of pathogens and strains of insects which repeatedly appear in the United States and limit the usefulness of otherwise desirable varieties. Furthermore, there is the added menace of diseases and virulent races of pathogens as well as insects and insect vectors present in other countries of the world for which we must be prepared in the event they become established in this country.

So far, the current world collections have been fairly adequate in meeting our needs for germ plasm with which to keep abreast of many of the major crop problems in the United States. Both Dr. Weiss and Dr. Cullinan emphasized the need, however, for additional germ plasm and more effective and widespread screening of our current collections to supply us with additional stocks in order that we may more effectively combat our various production hazards of disease and insect attacks, cold or frost injury, and drought.

In the crops field significant progress is being made in screening and evaluating germ plasm in the world collection of small grains, particularly for disease reaction, through the cooperative efforts of the United States Department of Agriculture, the ministries of agriculture in many foreign countries, The Rockefeller Foundation, and to a limited extent the Food and Agriculture Organization and the International Cooperation Administration. From a modest beginning in 1950 in seven Latin American countries and Canada, the project has been expanded to include this year sixty nurseries in twenty-six countries, on five continents. Varieties and promising selections of wheat, oats, and barley are thus subjected to the many parasitic races and biotypes of pathogens that occur in other parts of the world. Data obtained are summarized and annual reports made available to those concerned with small grain improvement in the United States and to cooperators in foreign countries. The results obtained with wheat stem rust will illustrate the general pattern of data obtained. As expected, many lines resistant in the United States have been susceptible in other countries, while others resistant there have been susceptible in North America. Fortunately, a few have been resistant in all areas, including Peru, where the lines were subjected, among others, to the virulent wheat stem rust race 189. Most outstanding has been a Frontana — K58 × Newthatch selection (Minn. II-50-17) in which is combined a broad base of germ plasm from wheat from Brazil, Kenya, and the United States. Almost equally useful germ plasm has been identified in these tests from Canada, the United States, Mexico, Colombia, Peru, Egypt, and Ethiopia.

I would like to expand on Dr. Weiss's reference to the utilization of our world collection of rice in the search for resistance to the Hoja blanca virus disease. In 1956 this disease caused estimated losses of 40 and 60% of the crop grown in Cuba and Venezuela, respectively, and was known to occur in Panama. This disease was found in Colombia, Costa Rica, and in the United States in 1957. From the screening tests of some 3000 varieties and selections in Cuba and Venezuela, 281 were identified as resistant in 1957. Fortunately, some were from crosses already made for other purposes and, in what might be termed a crash program for seed increase, about 40,000 bushels of a medium grain variety are now available for further increase and control of the disease which has now been found in Florida, Mississippi, and in the intensive rice-growing area of Louisiana.

There is a long list of diseases indigenous in foreign countries which, if established in North America, would be a menace to many of our crops. Among these of immediate concern is the "enanismo" virus disease of cereals in southern Colombia and northern Ecuador, the sugarcane smut *Ustilago scitamenia*, which some years ago was extremely destructive to cane in Argentina and Brazil, and the yellows disease of sugar beets in Chile and Argentina of which we have no current knowledge of sources of resistance. A screening and evaluation program similar to the small grain project would aid materially in combating these hazards and those of many other crops that could be cited. Some, in fact, have been initiated, as with the enanismo disease in Nariño, Colombia, Dr. Niederhauser's project with late blight and virus diseases of potato, and Dr. Ricker's current project with forest tree species.

Admittedly, personnel and regularly appropriated federal and state funds are presently inadequate to meet our needs for a comprehensive screening program of our world collections. However, research of this nature, which will be conducted in foreign countries under Public Law 480 for the exploration of valuable germ plasm and the screening for sources of disease and insect resistance, hardiness and drought resistance, and other valuable characters, should help overcome our deficiencies and current hazards. No program of disease control in either plants or animals can be complete without placing equal emphasis on the study of the pathogenic organisms.

Identification of the resistant germ plasm in the crops international testing programs, as suggested above, is only one big step toward the successful solution to the over-all problem. Microorganisms are as variable as their host plants—they hybridize and mutate and produce, in some instances, races more pathogenic than the parent stocks. Coordinated with the germ plasm screening program, there is, therefore, urgent need for more extensive projects on the identification of races on an international scale, expanded basic research to determine the limits of pathogenicity or, in other words, to determine how much virulence nature can put into plant pathogens, and lastly, an intensified program on host parasite relationships and nature of resistance.

Advances in productivity levels have frequently been limited because of inadequate germ plasm. It has been found, for example, that lodging limits the use of fertilizer on small grains in our humid and irrigated areas or on highly productive soil under a fallow system. Beneficial yield responses generally stop at the point where lodging occurs.

High plant populations associated with high productivity management systems introduce, or accentuate, a different microclimate in the crop canopy. Sometimes this is evident in greatly increased disease problems. For example, mildew and the rusts are much more troublesome in the semi-dwarf wheats under test in the Palouse region and under irrigation in Mexico than in wheats of standard height or at lower productivity levels. Head blights likewise appear to be more serious diseases in the short-strawed wheats being developed in the eastern soft winter wheat area. It is apparent that increased attention must be given to germ plasm that is adequate to meet problems created by other advances in technology.

Whereas new technology may put greater demands on germ plasm, we should not forget that technological advances may also permit the use of germ plasm in ways not considered practical before. The dwarf tomato, for example, has been of but limited practical value. However, with mechanical harvesters showing promise, a new type of dwarf-determinate habit tomato plant will be required. Picker-sheller-dryer equipment has put new interest in dwarf types of maize, genetic curios known for many years.

From predetermined needs of industry new species and genetic variants of common ones might be sought to fill such needs instead of relying almost solely on chemical modification as is done at present. For example, waxy corn and sorghum were utilized to meet a need in industry for starch having special properties. High amylose corn is another example.

There is only limited technique for evaluating germ plasm. We think we do a pretty fair job with the self-pollinated species.

Actually we do not. We are repeatedly surprised at the variant forms arising from cross combinations, often exceeding the entire range of parental forms. Many accessions merely duplicate the important genes, but which are duplicates and which are different? Only a minute effort on a few characters has ever been undertaken. How should an open pollinated variety of corn be preserved and evaluated? What size of sample is adequate for preserving collections representing forage species, vegetables, etc., and how should they be evaluated? And finally, where is there a guide to ways to perpetuate the complex unstable genotypes, structural hybrids, aneuploids, and other such forms except by annual, or at least frequent, vegetative propagation? Imaginative research is required in all these areas to provide future generations with the great wealth of germ plasm that nature has given us and to make effective use of it.

The problems and prospects of using additional sources of germ plasm in livestock breeding have been ably presented by Dr. Nordskog and Dr. Lush.

One important emphasis in Dr. Nordskog's discussion of small farm animals was on the economic benefits that might be realized by development of more varied sources of poultry meat and eggs, and by expansion of fur farming as an agricultural enterprise.

In Dr. Lush's discussion of large animal breeding, on the other hand, the emphasis was on long-term fundamental research questions, such as determining to what extent genetic factors contribute to higher levels of livestock productivity, and to what extent plateaus of productivity have been or are likely to be reached.

Certainly it seems that the different emphasis in these two presentations appropriately reflects a difference in the practical problems facing breeders of small and large farm animals. But at the same time, there were points in both discussions that have application to all classes of livestock.

For example, most of Dr. Nordskog's five justifications of the need for additional sources of germ plasm seem to apply to large animals as well as to small animals. We might well review them. They are: (*a*) to increase the supply of animal products for our increasing population; (*b*) to improve product quality; (*c*) to increase the efficiency of livestock production; (*d*) to obtain better utilization of land or other agricultural resources; and (*e*) to develop new livestock products.

Dr. Nordskog gave examples of these five points in terms of small animals, but additional examples in the large animal area come readily to mind. For instance:

1. Increased supplies of beef, milk, and pork products, as well as increased supplies of poultry, meat, and eggs, will surely be required to feed our future population.

2. Improved product quality to meet consumer demands is already a recognized need in large animal agriculture, as indicated by the interest in tenderer beef, leaner pork, and milk with a higher content of non-fat solids.

3. Increased feed efficiency, higher percentage calf and pig crops, and other improvements in production efficiency are certainly needed for large animals as well as for small.

The opportunities for better use of agricultural resources and for development of new products are more difficult to visualize in the case of large animals, but perhaps these justifications of the need for additional sources of germ plasm also may apply to cattle and other large animals, as well as to small animals such as geese and new types of poultry and fur animals.

In the same way, much of the discussion on large animals by Dr. Lush is pertinent to small animal breeding. The extent to which genetic factors have contributed to past increases in livestock productivity and may be counted on for further advances in productive efficiency is important for all phases of animal agriculture. The same is true of the questions raised concerning how we can make best use of additional germ plasm, and the need for continually revising the goals or standards of excellence that we establish to guide our breeding programs.

Not only small animal breeders, but also a great many other people, including supermarket operators and a sizable group of consumers, should be much heartened at the prospects suggested by Dr. Nordskog for a substantial increase in the variety of poultry products that could be made available. I am not sure how big a market there may be for duck eggs, but the efficiency of the duck as an egg producer, as well as a meat producer, may well appeal to farmers. And no doubt many of us would welcome a greater variety of poultry, including guinea fowl and pheasant, at reasonable prices in our grocery stores, along with leaner ducks and geese. In the U.S.S.R. ducks and geese are held in great esteem as foods.

Dr. Lush has discussed how the introduction of outside blood has in the past hastened progress in large animal breeding, and he has called attention to several crucial considerations in obtaining worth-while use of introduced stock. In discussing the points he has raised, we may wish to consider the possibilities involved in present-day techniques for the storage and use of germ plasm in livestock breeding.

In cattle especially, it is now possible to obtain very large numbers of sperm from male animals, which can be diluted in such a way that several hundred matings can be made from a single collection. Remarkable progress has been made also in germ plasm storage. Some samples of frozen bovine semen, for example, have remained fertile for as long as five years. Some persons now working on this problem seem hopeful that successful storage of semen for ten years or more is a distinct possibility. The transplantation of fertilized ova and of frozen ovarian tissue, though still in the developmental stage, offers further possibilities.

At any rate, it appears that animal geneticists may be in a position to approach their problems from entirely new directions. For example, it may be possible to plan, months or years in advance, (a) matings of a large number of animals at several different locations simultaneously, using a single sire, or (b) a series of matings.

In this connection, there is now under consideration a proposal to establish, as an interregional project, a National Bank for Farm Animal Germ Plasm. Although the preservation of breeding stock through storage of germ plasm is to be considered in later papers, I believe it may be pertinent to our own discussions to summarize briefly this proposal for a germ plasm bank.

It provides for a facility to acquire, preserve, and distribute frozen semen as a service to federal and state agricultural experiment stations cooperating in regional breeding projects.

The staff of the bank would devote considerable time to the

investigation and further development of methods for extending the length of time semen of the different classes of farm animals can be preserved with satisfactory fertility.

A bank of this kind would provide opportunities now unavailable for the study of new and improved methods of preserving germ plasm. I understand that commercial firms in the business of processing and selling frozen semen are doing only a limited amount of such research, and they are not likely to expand their efforts in this field until the commercial usefulness of long-term semen storage has been demonstrated to a greater degree than is now the case.

The proposed germ plasm bank would store semen in six main categories:

1. Sires now in use and designated as controls or testers. Semen from sires in this group would have two main uses: (*a*) for future matings, to provide a comparison with semen of sires then in use, as a means of evaluating progress in selection programs; and (*b*) for matings in which semen of certain sires would be used at different locations, so that the relative importance of genetic and environmental factors in breeding programs can be evaluated.

2. Foundation sires used in the formation of inbred lines.

3. Sires of exotic breeds not now used in the United States, which appear to offer possibilities for animal improvement in this country. Stockpiling semen of foreign breeds when disease situations abroad would permit its importation would facilitate the orderly use of this germ plasm in research.

4. Sires representing older seed stocks of important pure breeds and native strains with potential usefulness. The purpose of storing semen from these sires is primarily to guard against extinction of the strains.

5. Sires carrying hereditary defects, such as dwarfism, which are or may become problems for breeders. Semen from these known carrier animals would be valuable for making test matings in research herds.

6. A few outstanding proved sires. Semen from these sires would be used (*a*) for upgrading animals in experiment station herds when considered desirable and (*b*) for propagation in industry.

Thus, it seems clear that maintaining such banks of germ plasm could be of great value in (*a*) maintaining adequate genetic controls in experimental herds and flocks; (*b*) determining the importance in breeding programs of genetic-environmental interactions; (*c*) establishing and maintaining inbred lines; and (*d*) in the introduction of foreign germ plasm.

Semen stored in the bank might also be used for (*a*) more economical and effective progeny testing of larger numbers of sires; (*b*) use of selected sires in breeding *after* an evaluation of their carcasses; (*c*) maintenance of genetic material known to carry hereditary defects; and (*d*) maintenance of germ plasm that might otherwise be lost to the nation.

In the papers presented many illustrations have been cited of the value derived from the use of stocks from our germ plasm banks. We should be reminded, however, that in food and feed crops we still suffer an estimated average annual loss from plant diseases of 3 billion dollars, from insects of 4 billion dollars, and in some years 10 to 25% from unfavorable weather conditions. In my opinion, more intensive research in the evaluation of our current stocks, together with added germ plasm from foreign areas, is essential if we are to improve the productive potential of our farm crops to meet the constantly changing conditions brought about by diseases and insects. Screening, storing, and evaluation of large and small animal germ plasm banks are more costly and present difficulties not encountered in farm crops. However, the economic benefits which might be derived would seem to justify intensification of research in this field.

III. Developmental Programs in Crops and Livestock

Use of Diverse Germ Plasm in the Improvement of Some Forage Legumes

H. J. GORZ

Agricultural Research Service, United States Department of Agriculture, and Department of Agronomy, University of Nebraska, Lincoln, Nebraska

and

W. K. SMITH

Departments of Agronomy and Genetics, University of Wisconsin, Madison, Wisconsin, and Agricultural Research Service, United States Department of Agriculture

Plant improvement by breeding depends upon the availability of abundant genetic diversity. When genetic variability within cultivated varieties exists at a sufficiently high level, improvement consists in deriving from this pool the gene complexes that produce a strain superior to those already being grown. The productive hybrids of *Zea mays* now in use in the corn belt illustrate the improvement possible by bringing together lines of different origin derived from adapted local varieties. When sufficient favorable genes are not available within adapted cultivated varieties, an increase in genetic diversity within a breeding population may be obtained by hybridization with wild forms or by the induction of mutations.

As the need arises for genes not found in the varieties under cultivation, improvement may involve the utilization of germ plasm from related species. When the species are very closely related, transfer of desired genes to the cultivated varieties often proceeds without difficulty. But if the species to be intercrossed are more distantly related, special techniques may be necessary to effect the transfer. Two genera of the Leguminosae, *Medicago* and *Melilotus,* provide contrasting illustrations of the successful transfer of germ plasm from wild forms to improved varieties.

ALFALFA

Alfalfa (*Medicago*) is adapted to a wide range of climatic and soil conditions and is worldwide in distribution. The species *M. sativa* is typically blue-flowered, but the varieties of alfalfa that are winterhardy and adapted to northern latitudes tend to have variegated flowers ranging in color from blue to yellow. It is generally considered that North American varieties such as Grimm, Ontario Variegated, Cossack, and Ladak derived their distinctive flower color, prior to introduction into North America, by introgression of yellow-flowered, tetraploid strains of *M. falcata*, and that, along with flower color, they derived at least a portion of their winterhardiness from this species. The remarkable cold resistance and drought tolerance of *M. falcata* were recognized many years ago by Hansen (10) and by Oakley and Garver (18). All strains have deep-set crowns and a slow recovery after cutting, characteristics presumably associated with winterhardiness. But there is a great diversity in habit of growth, ranging from erect types to those that are prostrate or spreading (18). There is diversity also in productivity, with some collections nearly as vigorous as cultivated varieties whereas others have a very limited growth.

The species *M. sativa* and *M. falcata* appear to be closely related. Interspecific crosses are readily made between strains having the same chromosome number, and the F_1 hybrids have viable pollen, good fertility, and essentially normal chromosome pairing at pachytene (29). In addition, the hybrids are generally more vigorous than the parents (23). Waldron (34) noted that F_1 hybrids of the cross *M. sativa* × *M. falcata* yielded 59% more than the *sativa* parent, whereas in the reciprocal cross the hybrid yielded 43% more than the *falcata* parent. The variegated strains of alfalfa that presumably have arisen after interspecific crossing tend to be intermediate between the two species and are sometimes referred to as *M. media*. Nevertheless, the typical *M. sativa* is clearly differentiated from *M. falcata*, both morphologically and physiologically.

Plant breeders have now been able to incorporate some desired genes from *M. falcata* into cultivated varieties. Included among the various strains of the species are two distinct forms, the so-called diploid ($n = 8$) and the tetraploid ($n = 16$). The diploid forms are typically small plants, with prostrate, fine-stemmed growth, and are not productive when compared with cultivated alfalfas. Nevertheless, three winterhardy, productive, and widely adapted varieties have derived a part of their parentage from these small wild forms. One of the diploid strains of *M. falcata* was included in the stocks used in a breeding program begun in 1920 by G. G. Moe in British Columbia. The diploid, which was introduced into the United States in 1906 by N. E. Hansen of South Dakota State College, traced back to a collection obtained from the Don Province of southeastern Russia. It was growing in the breeding nursery along with the alfalfa varieties Grimm and Ontario Variegated. Seed collected on the Don strain gave rise to six plants that appeared to be natural crosses with tetraploid alfalfas. Four were later found to be tetraploid, and two were apparently triploid. These hybrids were the parent stocks of the variety Rhizoma (17), and selections from the progeny of the hybrids were used as parents in the breeding of the variety Narragansett (20).

The hardy and widely adapted variety Vernal has another strain of wild diploid *M. falcata* in its parentage (4). When *M. falcata* is used as the pistillate parent in crosses with *M. sativa*, slow-growing triploid embryos are usually formed, followed by abortion of the ovule when they are two weeks old (16). But from this cross several tetraploid hybrids, presumably arising from fertilization of unreduced eggs, were obtained. Chromosome behavior in the hybrids was usually regular and the hybrids were interfertile. Several F_2 plants of the intercross were included in the Vernal synthetic.

Two varieties of substantial merit have also recently been developed from crosses involving *M. falcata*, but tetraploid forms of this species were probably involved. The variety Teton was released by the South Dakota Agricultural Experiment Station in 1958 (1). It was derived from a surviving population of plants descended from an interspecific cross made by N. E. Hansen in 1914. Both parental stocks had been introduced by him from southern Russia. One was a hardy Turkestan strain of *M. sativa* from Tashkent, whereas the other was a very hardy strain of *M. falcata* from Semipalatinsk. The Teton variety is outstanding in winterhardiness, frost resistance, and persistence under grazing. A similar type of breeding program was begun in western Canada at Swift Current, Saskatchewan, in 1938, to develop an alfalfa with greater hardiness and drought resistance than the varieties of alfalfa available at that time (12). Selections from cultivated alfalfa, primarily Ladak, and selected plants of a Siberian strain of *M. falcata* were intercrossed in various combinations. After re-selection and testing, seven superior clones were combined in a synthetic named and released in 1955 as the variety Rambler (13). It is superior in drought resistance and winterhardiness to Ladak and Grimm, and approximately 65% of the plants are so-called creeping-rooted. Adventitious stems arise from lateral roots that may grow out several feet from the center of the plant. This characteristic was noted as early as 1912 by Garver and described by Oakley and Garver (18) as occurring in four of the collections of *M. falcata* introduced by Hansen. The characteristic apparently is not found in *M. sativa*.

Thus, germ plasm from *M. falcata* has played an important role in the improvement of alfalfa in the northern part of North America. Alfalfa is the most important leguminous forage in this area and much breeding work is in progress. It is noteworthy that five varieties released for commercial use during the past fifteen years have all been derived, at least in part, from crosses between *M. sativa* and *M. falcata*. On the basis of the accomplishments to date, it is likely that strains of *M. falcata* will make additional contributions to alfalfa improvement.

SWEETCLOVER

Diverse germ plasm has also been successfully utilized in the improvement of sweetclover (*Melilotus*). Breeding work with this forage legume dates back approximately thirty years. Prior to this time, sweetclover was legislated against as a weed in some states, but its outstanding superiority as a soil-improving crop and its ability to produce a good yield in the moisture-deficient areas of the Great Plains have promoted its use over a wide area of the United States and Canada. Four species of *Melilotus* have been grown commercially, but most of the acreage is composed of *M. officinalis* and *M. alba*. All species studied are diploids with a somatic chromosome number of 16.

Prominent among the undesirable traits of sweetclover as a forage crop is the high content of coumarin that is found in commonly grown varieties. Young leaves contain an average of approximately 5% of coumarin, calculated on a dry weight basis (11). Coumarin in sweetclover is harmless to livestock, but it imparts to the forage a stinging, bitter taste that markedly lowers palatability until the animals become accustomed to it. Coumarin also will taint wheat when stems of sweetclover pass through the combine with the grain. The main objection to coumarin, however, is the transformation of coumarin or closely related compounds into the anticoagulant compound dicumarol, which occurs in sweetclover hay that is not cured thoroughly before being stored, or in poorly preserved sweetclover silage. Dicumarol weakens the clotting power of the blood, and animals feeding on poorly preserved sweetclover forage often develop fatal internal hemorrhages.

A description of the sequence of major events from the discovery of the coumarin problem to the present stage of varietal development is of interest. The pioneer work of Schofield (24) and Roderick and Schalk (21) established the fact that the mysterious bleeding disease of cattle was associated with feeding from stacks of sweetclover hay. It also was pointed out that coumarin probably was associated with the malady, and unsuccessful attempts were made to isolate the toxic principle.

Smith and Brink (28) established the fact that development of the toxic principle in poorly cured sweetclover hay depended upon the presence of coumarin. After the development of a reliable bioassay for the determination of the toxic principle (6), Campbell and Link (5) succeeded in isolating and crystallizing the pure anticoagulant, which was subsequently identified as 3,3'-methylenebis(4-hydroxycoumarin), and synthesized (30).

It was soon discovered that the new compound, given the common name of dicumarol, could save human lives by guarding against the formation of blood clots after surgery. By slowing the clotting time of blood, dicumarol was also effective in reducing the incidence of coronary thrombosis. More recently, several synthetic derivatives of dicumarol have been used as anticoagulants in human therapy (14). A sister compound, with the trade name Warfarin, is effective in controlling rats and mice by causing internal hemorrhages and death in animals ingesting it.

The development of a low-coumarin variety was one of the major objectives in sweetclover breeding programs initiated by 1930 at several experiment stations in the United States, in Canada, and on the European continent. Initially, attempts were made to isolate a coumarin-free plant of *M. alba* or *M. officinalis*. Obermayer (19) was the first to develop a method for the determination of coumarin in sweetclover, but several refined methods of testing have been reported since 1935. Ufer (33) reported that more than 900,000 sweetclover plants had been tested for coumarin. This work and studies in other countries indicated that plants varied widely in coumarin content, but a low-coumarin variety was not developed in this way. Suvorov (32) reported that *M. dentata* contained an insignificant amount of coumarin, and Brink (3) independently reported the discovery of a low-coumarin strain of *Melilotus*, which was later also identified as an annual form of the typically biennial *M. dentata*. Many accessions of both annual and biennial forms of *M. dentata*, collected in their native habitat in eastern Europe and western Asia, were subsequently tested (Smith and Brink, unpublished), and all strains of this species were low in coumarin content. Attempts to cross *M. dentata* with *M. alba*, *M. officinalis*, and *M. suaveolens* were unsuccessful at first, because all F_1 hybrids obtained were chlorophyll-deficient and died soon after emergence.

In Canada, Stevenson and White (31), using a method of testing based on alcohol extraction, reported the selection of a low-coumarin line of *M. alba*, and from this line the variety Pioneer was developed. However, it was soon discovered that Pioneer contained an appreciable amount of coumarin, all of which was in a bound form, not extractable with alcohol without previous hydrolysis.

Smith (25), continuing efforts to transfer the low-coumarin

character from *M. dentata,* an agronomically undesirable species, to *M. alba,* conceived the idea of promoting the growth of the albinistic hybrids by grafting them on normal plants. Three hybrids were reared to maturity, and two backcrossed progeny were derived by applying *M. alba* pollen to the flowers of the albinistic F_1 hybrid. Probably all low-coumarin strains in the process of development at this time trace to these two plants. It was subsequently determined (7, 26) that the low-coumarin character is conditioned by a single pair of recessive genes and that an independent pair of recessive alleles prevents the formation of free coumarin,* although plants of this second class contain a high level of bound coumarin. Backcrossed progenies, derived by the use of *M. alba* as the recurrent parent, segregated for various levels of chlorophyll deficiency (2) and low-coumarin segregates were lacking in vigor.

Subsequent studies by Smith (27) disclosed that the chlorophyll deficiency barrier to interspecific transfer of genes discovered in *M. alba* and *M. dentata* was not uncommon in the genus *Melilotus,* since a number of other interspecific matings gave chlorophyll-deficient hybrids. It was also noted by Smith (27) and by Greenshields (8) that the reproductive cycle was interrupted at an earlier stage in some interspecific crosses, and resulted in aborted ovules or dark brown, aborted seeds. This type of interspecific barrier is found particularly in crosses with the yellow-flowered species, *M. officinalis,* which is grown extensively in the Great Plains region of the United States. Since viable seeds could not be obtained, Webster (35) excised the hybrid embryos from the cross of *M. officinalis* × low-coumarin *M. alba* and grew them on nutrient media until they were sufficiently vigorous to transplant to soil in the greenhouse. By this means, the low-coumarin gene from *M. alba,* originally obtained from *M. dentata,* was transferred to *M. officinalis.* The hybrids, which contain germ plasm from three different species, were pale green in color, but a normal green branch arose on one plant, presumably as a result of somatic

---

* Recent investigations have disclosed that free coumarin is virtually absent in intact plants of sweetclover, regardless of the genotype of the plant, although free coumarin is formed readily as a consequence of any disruption of the normal cellular organization in plants carrying the dominant alleles.

mutation. All backcross progeny from this branch have been normal green in color.

M. officinalis and *M. alba* have recently been hybridized without the use of embryo culture (15). Since there was considerable variation in embryo development among specific plant combinations, it was possible, by excising and observing the size and condition of the embryos, to select one plant in each species that gave maximum embryo development. A number of viable seeds were produced, and one F_1 hybrid was grown to maturity.

The principal problem in the development of agronomically adapted, low-coumarin strains of sweetclover has been the lack of vigor in the low-coumarin lines. However, productive stocks are now being obtained. Two low-coumarin varieties of *M. alba* were recently released (9, 22), and another is nearing release. In the development of a low-coumarin variety of *M. officinalis*, five backcrosses have been made between low-coumarin segregates and adapted selections of *M. officinalis* (Gorz, unpublished).

Thus, with the development of low-coumarin varieties, we see another step in the guided evolution of what was once regarded as a roadside weed into a useful forage plant. In solving the many phases of the over-all problem of coumarin in sweetclover, major contributions were made by specialists in several distinct scientific disciplines. The present state of development probably would not have been achieved without this cooperation.

Larger size of seed is another important objective in sweetclover breeding programs, particularly in the Great Plains region. Four species of *Melilotus* in the subgenus *Micromelilotus* have extremely large seed, but crosses of these species with cultivated sweetclover have not been successful. However, two recent introductions of *M. officinalis*, one from Turkey (P. I. 178985) and the other from Tunisia (P. I. 227594), have unusually large seed and are being used in crosses with low-coumarin selections.

A major deterrent to the use of sweetclover at present is the sweetclover weevil, *Sitona cylindricollis*. An intensive effort is being made to find resistance or tolerance to the weevil among the various species and strains of *Melilotus*. No evidence of true resistance has yet been found.

Conclusions

Alfalfa and sweetclover have been used to illustrate the successful transfer of germ plasm from wild forms to cultivated varieties. In the case of alfalfa, the transfer was made without difficulty, whereas in sweetclover, grafting and embryo culture were necessary before the transfer could be effected. Future breeding programs in all crops will undoubtedly place greater emphasis on the utilization of diverse germ plasm. Many of the genes in these diverse forms are readily available, but the breeding systems and the methods of selection employed have not always been effective in isolating the most desirable combinations. Perhaps new methods of sifting out the desired genes or gene complexes are needed. Other potentially valuable genes are presently unavailable because of various types of barriers to gene transfer. Since transfers made between distantly related stocks increase the possibility of introducing characters not present in the cultivated species, radical approaches to the problem of crossing widely divergent strains will greatly increase the available genetic variability. Thus, progress in the utilization of diverse germ plasm depends not only upon the accumulation of additional materials but also upon the development of new methods of utilizing genetic mechanisms.

References

1. Adams, M. W., and G. Semeniuk. Teton alfalfa—a new multipurpose variety for South Dakota. *S. Dakota Agr. Expt. Sta. Bull. 469*, 1958.

2. Bringhurst, R. S. Genetic analysis of chlorophyll deficiency in *Melilotus alba* × *M. dentata* hybrids with some observations on meiotic irregularities. *Summaries of Doctoral Dissertations, Univ. of Wisconsin, 11*, 96-97 (1951).

3. Brink, R. A. A non-bitter variety of *Melilotus. Science, 79*, 301 (1934).

4. Brink, R. A., F. R. Jones, Dale Smith, and L. F. Graber. Vernal alfalfa. *Wisconsin Agr. Expt. Sta. Spec. Circ. 37*, 1934.

5. Campbell, H. A., and K. P. Link. Studies on the hemorrhagic sweet clover disease. IV. The isolation and crystallization of the hemorrhagic agent. *J. Biol. Chem., 138*, 21-33 (1941).

6. Campbell, H. A., W. K. Smith, W. L. Roberts, and K. P. Link. Studies on the hemorrhagic sweet clover disease. II. The bioassay of hemorrhagic concentrates by following the prothrombin level in the plasma of rabbit blood. *J. Biol. Chem.*, *138*, 1-20 (1941).

7. Goplen, B. P., J. E. R. Greenshields, and H. Baenziger. The inheritance of coumarin in sweet clover. *Can. J. Botany*, *35*, 583-593 (1957).

8. Greenshields, J. E. R. Embryology of interspecific crosses in *Melilotus*. *Can. J. Botany*, *32*, 447-465 (1954).

9. Greenshields, J. E. R. Note on Cumino sweet clover. *Can. J. Plant Sci.*, *38*, 507-508 (1958).

10. Hansen, N. E. The wild alfalfas and clovers of Siberia, with a perspective view of the alfalfas of the world. *U. S. Dept. Agr.*, *Bur. Plant Ind. Bull.* *150*, 1909.

11. Haskins, F. A., and H. J. Gorz. The fluorometric assay of free and bound coumarin in sweetclover. *Agron. J.*, *49*, 493-497 (1957).

12. Heinrichs, D. H. Developing creeping-rooted alfalfa for pasture. *Can. J. Agr. Sci.*, *34*, 269-280 (1954).

13. Heinrichs, D. H., and J. L. Bolton. Rambler alfalfa. *Can. Dept. Agr. Publ. 1030*, 1958.

14. Hunter, R. B., and D. M. Shepherd. Chemistry of coumarin anticoagulant drugs. *Brit. Med. Bull.*, *11*, 56-61 (1955).

15. Lang, R. C., and H. J. Gorz. Factors affecting embryo development in crosses of *Melilotus officinalis* × *M. alba*. *Agron. J.*, *52*, 71-74 (1960).

16. Ledingham, G. F. Cytological and developmental studies of hybrids between *Medicago sativa* and a diploid form of *M. falcata*. *Genetics*, *25*, 1-15 (1940).

17. Nilan, R. A. Rhizoma alfalfa: chromosome studies of the parent stocks. *Sci. Agr.*, *31*, 123-126 (1951).

18. Oakley, R. A., and S. Garver. *Medicago falcata*, a yellow-flowered alfalfa. *U. S. Dept. Agr. Bull. 428*, 1917.

19. Obermayer, E. Quantitative Bestimmung des Kumarins in *Melilotus*-Arten. *Z. anal. Chem.*, *52*, 172-191 (1913).

20. Odland, T. E., and C. R. Skogley. The origin of Narragansett alfalfa. *Agron. J.*, *45*, 243-245 (1953).

21. Roderick, Lee M., and A. F. Schalk. Studies on sweet clover disease. *N. Dakota Agr. Expt. Sta. Tech. Bull. 250*, 1931.

22. Rudorf, W., and P. Schwarze. Beiträge zur Züchtung eines cumarinfreien Steinklees und Untersuchungen über Cumarin und verwandte Verbindungen. *Z. Pflanzenzücht.*, *39*, 245-274 (1958).

23. Schaeffler, H. Untersuchungen an Bastardluzernen. *Z. Zücht.*, *A17*, 485-562 (1932).

24. Schofield, Frank W. A brief account of a disease in cattle simu-

lating hemorrhagic septicaemia due to feeding sweet clover. *Can. Vet. Record*, *3*, 74-78 (1922).

25. Smith, W. K. Propagation of chlorophyll-deficient sweetclover hybrids as grafts. *J. Heredity*, *34*, 135-140 (1943).

26. Smith, W. K. Transfer from *Melilotus dentata* to *M. alba* of the genes for reduction in coumarin content. *Genetics*, *33*, 124-125 (1948).

27. Smith, W. K. Viability of interspecific hybrids in *Melilotus*. *Genetics*, *39*, 266-279 (1954).

28. Smith, W. K., and R. A. Brink. Relation of bitterness to the toxic principle in sweetclover. *J. Agr. Research*, *57*, 145-154 (1938).

29. Sprague, E. W. Cytological and fertility relationships of *Medicago sativa*, *M. falcata*, and *M. gaetula*. *Agron. J.*, *51*, 249-252 (1959).

30. Stahmann, M. A., C. F. Huebner, and K. P. Link. Studies on the hemorrhagic sweet clover disease. V. Identification and synthesis of the hemorrhagic agent. *J. Biol. Chem.*, *138*, 513-527 (1941).

31. Stevenson, T. M., and W. J. White. 1940. Investigations concerning the coumarin content of sweet clover. I. The breeding of a low coumarin line of sweet clover. *Sci. Agr.*, *21*, 18-28 (1940).

32. Suvorov, V. V. [*Melilotus.*] *Rastenievodstvo S.S.S.R.*, *1*, 431-436 (1933).

33. Ufer, M. Wege und Ergebnisse der züchterischen Arbeit am Steinklee. *Züchter*, *6*, 255-258 (1934).

34. Waldron, L. R. First generation crosses between two alfalfa species. *J. Am. Soc. Agron.*, *12*, 133-143 (1920).

35. Webster, G. T. Interspecific hybridization of *Melilotus alba* × *M. officinalis* using embryo culture. *Agron. J.*, *47*, 138-142 (1955).

Effectiveness of Selection
for Animal Improvement

GORDON DICKERSON

Kimber Farms, Inc., Fremont, California

Two widely differing approaches might be considered in attempting to evaluate response to selection in animal populations, the *historical* and the *analytical*.

The historical approach is based upon gross time trends in performance of livestock populations and includes effects of time changes in a wide variety of environmental influences, in addition to changes of any sort in the genetic composition of the population. To illustrate, the increase in productivity, which Dr. Lush mentioned, of roughly 70 eggs per hen since 1935—nearly 3 eggs per year—has included effects of such diverse *genetic* changes as: (*a*) ever widening distribution of chicks from improved "pure" strains, replacing home-multiplied stocks; (*b*) gradual but continuous elimination of poorer strains, including shifts from dual purpose to specialized egg production strains; (*c*) increasing use of hybrid vigor from crossbreeding and from crossing of selected strains or inbred lines; (*d*) increasing control by breeders over the genetic quality of chicks reaching poultrymen, achieved through associated commercial hatcheries; and (*e*) finally, the genetic improvements accomplished by breeders of specialized egg production strains.

However, the most severe limitation of time trends for evaluating the effectiveness of selection is the uncertainty concerning the magnitude, and perhaps even the direction, of changes in *environmental* influences over the 25-year-period, in such factors as (*a*) nutrition, from use of largely unsupplemented home-grown grains to the modern "complete" laying mash formulas; (*b*) disease control, as affected by exposure, isolation, immunization, and medication; (*c*) housing and other management, from the farm-

161

yard flock to the highly specialized facilities and procedures of present-day egg production units.

Clearly the historical approach, although certainly useful as a general barometer of progress in an industry, is a clumsy instrument for evaluating the effectiveness of selective breeding as such. A much more experimental and analytical approach is required if we are to obtain useful answers to the questions:

1. How much of past improvement in performance can be attributed to *genetic* change in animal populations?

2. What rates of further *genetic* improvement reasonably can be expected from various methods of continued selective breeding within long-selected, highly improved stocks?

It will be our purpose here (*a*) to review briefly the theoretical basis for predicting response to selection, but more especially (*b*) to suggest, with examples, some experimental ways of testing the validity of selection theory.

PREDICTION OF RESPONSE TO SELECTION

Genetic change expected per unit of time may be expressed as (Fig. 1):

$$\Delta G = \frac{\bar{s} \cdot H - \sum a_i}{t} \tag{1}$$

where $\bar{s}$ = mean phenotypic superiority of the parents selected *in a single quantitative trait*

 t = mean age of parents, or generation interval

 H = fraction of $\bar{s}$ which represents superiority in average gene effects, in a *given complex of environmental influences* ($\sigma^2_{G_i}/\sigma^2_{X_i}$ or $b_{G_iX_i}$), usually estimated from twice the regression of progeny on one parent ($2b_{OD}$) or from the correlation among paternal half sibs ($4S/\sigma_X{}^2$)

 $\sum a_i$ = summation of factors which contribute to reduction of net response to selection (ΔG) below that predicted from $\bar{s} \cdot H$ for single traits

Forces which potentially reduce net response to selection may be classified as follows (4):

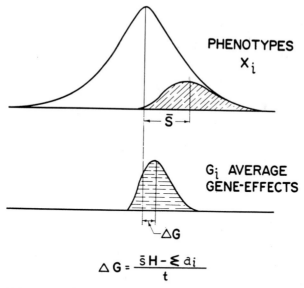

PHENOTYPES
X_i

$\bar{S}$

G_i AVERAGE
GENE-EFFECTS

ΔG

$$\Delta G = \frac{\bar{s}H - \xi\, a_i}{t}$$

Fig. 1. Diagram of selection differential ($\bar{s}$) and expected response (ΔG).

1. *Intraenvironmental.* (*a*) Negative pleiotropic relations among components of performance, causing effective heritability to be lower for total performance than for the average of its components. This amounts to heterozygote superiority or overdominance for total performance, and leads to equilibrium or plateau in response to selection. (*b*) Recurrent loss each generation of epistatic combinations favored in selection, through crossing-over segregation and recombination. (*c*) Inbreeding depression, from random loss of useful genes, inversely related to effective size of the population. (*d*) Mutations, prevailingly deleterious.

2. *Interenvironmental.* (*a*) Genetic-environmental interaction, causing part of the intraenvironmental selection response to become useless when the population moves into an altered environment. This leads to "ebb and flow" (unstable equilibrium) in gene frequencies and, in effect, to average heterozygote advantage, or overdominance, in net adaptive merit over a number of generations during which environmental conditions have fluctuated. (*b*) Adverse "treadmill" environmental change is really a special

case of genetic-environmental interaction, in which, for example, evolution of virulence in pathogens and parasites forces continuous natural selection for resistance in animal populations merely to maintain satisfactory levels of viability.

The problem is to determine, as quantitatively as possible, the importance of these several sources of genetic slippage and the means by which such handicaps may be minimized in selection programs.

Techniques for Testing Selection Theory

Solid evidence that actual response in livestock is appreciably less than would be predicted from $\bar{s}H/t$ for single traits is scarce, because most selection experiments have not been designed to measure absolute response to selection in one direction, independent of environmental trends. For example, in the experiments with selection in mildly inbred strains of swine (35), one would have had to assume either a steadily deteriorating environment or underestimation of inbreeding effects, in order to conclude that reasonably intense selection for litter size and growth-rate had been effective at all. Similar conclusions were reached concerning response to selection for egg production in the Kimber flock over a 22-year period (4), although response in egg size and incidence of blood spots "looked" more encouraging.

More recently, Gowe *et al.* (9) reported results from five years of selection for egg production in a long closed Ottawa Leghorn flock in comparison with those from an unselected control strain started from the same base population. When results are expressed in volume of eggs laid per pullet housed (i.e., the product of adult viability $\times$ sexual maturity $\times$ rate $\times$ egg size, Fig. 2), the selected Ottawa and control strains did not diverge. However, the "New" strain, combining seven presumably unrelated Leghorn stocks, did show evidence of substantial gains during four years of selection.

When hen-housed production, egg size, and body weight were included in an economic rating (Fig. 3), again there was no divergence between the Ottawa and the control strains during five years. If the control strain actually remained genetically constant, as intended, then the Ottawa strain showed evidence of plateau

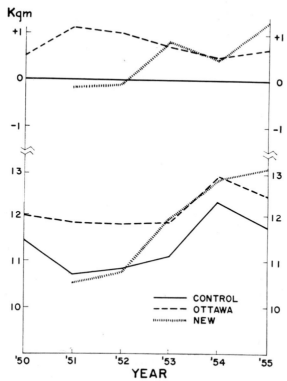

Fig. 2.   Selection response in total egg volume per pullet housed. (Computed from Gowe *et al.*, 1959.)

under continued selection. If the control strain actually was deteriorating genetically under the relaxed selection, then the evidence for plateaued response in the Ottawa strain would be even stronger, unless, of course, the level of inbreeding was increasing faster in the Ottawa than in the control strain.

From laboratory experiments there is now a considerable body of evidence that continuous selection for multigenic traits within a closed population gradually becomes ineffective relative to the total genetic variability in the selected trait (2, 7, 18, 19). Plateau in response is reached more quickly when deliberate and natural selection are in the same direction for a trait which has long been closely related to productive fitness in the population studied (2, 7, 18). Almost by definition, one would expect, as Bell (1)

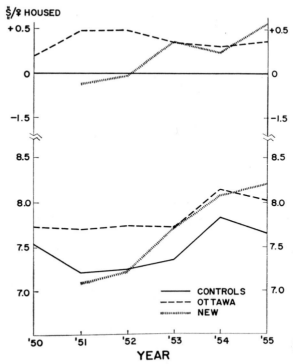

Fig. 3.   Selection response in an economic rating [$0.025 (egg numbers per pullet housed) + $0.050 (grams per egg in March) − $0.136 (kilograms body weight in March)]. Computed from Gowe *et al.*, 1959.)

found, a decline in the additive genetic variance (i.e., from *average* effects of genes) of the trait under artificial selection corresponding to the decline in actual response realized provided that most of the selection applied was for that trait alone. However, this need not hold for component traits in selection for multiple objectives, especially when there is genetic-environmental interaction between generations (4).

This background evidence that actual improvement from selection is much slower than would be expected from the product of selection differential and heritability is ample justification for more critical studies of both the magnitudes and the causes of the discrepancies. Lush's question (14) as to whether "witches really can turn milk blue" has been answered, and it is now high time we learned more about how! A few examples of possible approaches follow.

Negative Pleiotropic Relations among Components of Performance

To the extent that each gene influences, directly and indirectly, a number of different biochemical reactions, physiological functions or stages of development, the expected accumulative result of selection, natural or deliberate, is to retain at intermediate frequencies chiefly those genes with dominant favorable and recessive unfavorable effects on reproductive fitness (12).

This leads to heterozygote superiority or overdominance which means lower heritability for reproductive fitness than for its components, as a consequence of negative genetic correlations among the components of the total performance index.

For example, in chickens bred for efficient production of eggs, there appears to be a negative relationship of egg size, thick albumen, and shell strength with the total numbers of eggs laid. The estimates in Table I were based on regression of progeny on dam,

TABLE I   Genetic correlations among components of egg production (estimated from regression of progeny on dam's family)[a]

	Adult Viability	Early Maturity	Rate, %	Total Eggs	Small Body	Large Eggs	High Albumen	Thick Shells
Early maturity	0.77							
Per cent rate 1st egg-60 wks	0.44	0.62						
Total eggs to 60 wks (per pullet housed)	0.42	0.88	0.82					
(Small) body size	0.02	0.27	(0.08)	(−0.02)				
(Large) egg size	(−0.18)	−0.35	−0.37	−0.53	−0.66			
(High) albumen score	−0.21	−0.21	−0.11	−0.18	−0.27	0.48		
(High) specific gravity (shell thickness)	−0.09	0.13	0.00	(0.15)	−0.01	(−0.05)	0.34	
Oval shape (W/L)	(0.06)	(0.08)	0.12	0.31	−0.31	0.47	0.31	0.06

[a] Correlations in italics represent genetic antagonisms between desired traits. Those in parentheses are arithmetic averages of reciprocal estimates which differed in sign.

within sire and strain cross combination, and the body weights and egg quality measures were taken at 32 weeks of age, early in the laying year. Note that no negative relationship of egg numbers with specific gravity (shell strength indicator) is evident at 32 weeks. When shell strength, albumen score, and egg size are measured later in the laying period (4), the negative relationship with egg numbers is heightened particularly for shell strength, as would be expected from physiological depletion. Note also that the smaller body size, desired for more efficient egg production, is genetically associated with smaller egg size, poorer albumen, and longer-shaped eggs.

Of course, some of the relationships among components are positive and others are independent. Also, if the gross phenotypic correlations among components tend to be more positive than the genetic correlations, heritability of the index will be lowered, since the total variance of the index will be inflated more than the genetic portion by correlation among the components.

The net effect of all genetic and environmental correlations among components on the response to selection may be tested independently by comparing the heritability of the selection index directly, in the same data, with the average of the heritabilities of all components, each weighted according to its direct contribution to the variance of the index, omitting the contribution of the convariances (Table II). In this particular example, the effect of the positive genetic correlation ($r = 0.44$, Table II) between the two major components of the index, adult mortality and rate of production, completely overshadows the effect of the negative correlations with less important traits, and the heritability of the index is higher than would be expected if components were entirely independent (0.37 vs 0.25).

The importance and direction of correlated response also can be evaluated more rigorously by means of selection experiments (6, 15). However, so many components are included in any real selection program for domestic animals, that selection experiments can be used to estimate only some of the potentially more important relationships.

Enough is known already concerning pleiotropic relationships between traits to make it abundantly clear (*a*) that meaningful selection experiments must take into account total genetic response of the organism and (*b*) that estimates of the genetic and phenotypic correlations among traits must be utilized to obtain the index

TABLE II. Comparative estimates of heritability for
selection index and its components

Trait	Per Cent Heritability[a]	$b_{I\bar{X}_i}^2 \, \sigma_{\bar{X}_i}^2$
Fertility	8 ± 5	0.02
Ferti-hatch	-4 ± 5	0.06
Cull chicks	11 ± 6	0.02
Mortality		
0-10 weeks	-19 ± 11	1.10
11-60 weeks	22 ± 10	16.95
Broodiness	39 ± 29	2.12
Body size	63 ± 9	1.84
Age 1st egg	27 ± 9	0.10
Rate of production	26 ± 9	37.53
Egg size	70 ± 7	0.39
Specific gravity	52 ± 6	0.12
Shell shape	100 ± 15	0.30
Albumen score	51 ± 5	0.14
Shell texture	14 ± 8	0.01
Shell color	-0.3 ± 17	0.03
Blood spots	18 ± 18	8.16
Selection Index		
Calculated[b]	25	
Actual	37	

[a] From twice the intrasire regression of progeny on dam's full sib family average, with standard errors.

[b] From sum of (heritability $\times b_{I\bar{X}_i}^2 \, \sigma_{\bar{X}_i}^2$) divided by sum of ($b_{I\bar{X}_i}^2 \, \sigma_{\bar{X}_i}^2$), omitting all covariances between components.

weightings which will yield most nearly maximum genetic response in the index.

Genetic-Environmental Interaction

An appropriate measure of genetic-environmental interaction is the repeatability or genetic correlation between performances of identical genotypes in different environments (r_G). This genetic repeatability for the same trait in altered environments is merely an extension of the concept of genetic correlation between two *different* traits of the same animal, because the same trait will be influenced by different genes and differently by the same genes as environment is changed. The difference is only in the *degree* of environmental change, since environment will be different for two traits of the same animal if they are expressed or measured at a different time or stage of development.

Response to intraenvironmental selection (i.e., based upon performance within the restricted sample of environmental influences among contemporaries at a single location) will be reduced to $r_G = G/G + GE$ of the intraenvironmental response as the population moves into other environments, as shown in Fig. 4. Increasing the number of environments (k) over which performance is averaged in making selections between strains or progenies improves the effectiveness of selection for "general adaptability" (ΔG in Fig. 1) to the extent that genetic-environmental interaction is important as a source of error in estimating general adaptability (G). Error from variance among individuals within the

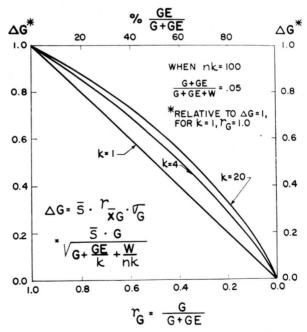

Fig. 4. Interenvironmental slippage from gene-environmental interaction ($r_G = 1$ to 0).

same strain and environment (W) is reduced as numbers per strain (nk) are increased. We have assumed $H_m = 0.05$ and $n \cdot k = 100$ for all values of r_G and k in Figs. 4 and 5.

Estimates of the importance of genetic interaction with representative intrayear environmental variations among commercial poultry farms in California are shown in Table III. These are pooled estimates of intrayear variances among individuals due to strain (G), strain $\times$ location interaction (GE), and within location-strain (W). There were 79 strains at each of 13 loca-

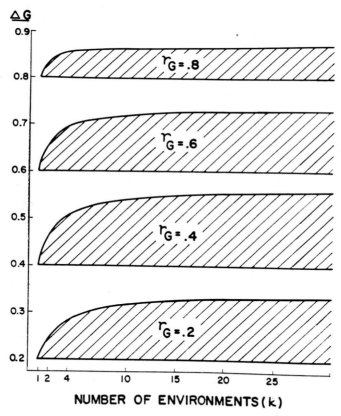

Fig. 5. Increase in ΔG from testing in sample of k environments when r_G varies from 0.2 to 0.8 [relative to $\Delta G = 1$, for $k = 1$, and $r_G = 1.0$ when $(G + GE)/G + GE + W = 0.05$, $r_G = G/G + GE$), $n \cdot k = 100$].

TABLE III. Heritability within locations (H_m) and genetic repeatability between locations (r_G) for strain differences in several traits of chickens

	$H_m = \dfrac{G + GE}{G + GE + W}$	$r_G = \dfrac{G}{G + GE}$
Per cent mortality, 21-72 wks	2.1	0.39
Age at 1st egg, wks	6.7	0.67
Per cent production, 1st egg, 72 wks	3.3	0.82
Eggs per pullet housed, 72 wks	3.0	0.69
Body weight, 32 wks, lb	20.4	0.97
Egg weight, 32 wks, oz/doz	16.0	0.91
Specific gravity, 32 wks	6.6	0.66
Albumen score, 32 wks	7.1	0.92
Shell shape (length/width)	4.7	1.12

tions in 1957 and 59 strains at 12 locations in 1958, with a total of 29,494 pullets housed. Egg production data were obtained at 22 of the locations for 19,739 pullets, and body weights and egg quality measurements were taken at 32 weeks of age at 16 locations for 15,080 and 12,920 pullets, respectively. A full report will be given elsewhere.

Note that interaction (GE) is likely to be somewhat overestimated, and genetic repeatability between locations (r_G) is underestimated, in any such analysis of actual performance data, because any strain or location effects that are not strictly additive (i.e., multiplicative or proportional deviations from additive effects) will contribute to the estimates of interaction variance (GE). Strain differences ($G + GE$) were largest, relative to total variation within locations, for body size and egg size and repeatability of genetic ranking was very good between locations. However, repeatability was only 0.4 for adult mortality and about 0.7 for the all-important egg production per pullet housed and for shell strength.

Enhancement of selection response in general adaptability (ΔG) from testing in a representative sample of k environments is shown in Fig. 5 for various levels of genetic environmental interaction. Naturally, the *relative* advantage of testing in many environments is greatest when there is much strain $\times$ location interaction (i.e., r_G small, as for mortality). But notice, also, that the *absolute* gain is greatest for intermediate degrees of interaction with environment, and nearly as great when interaction accounts for as little as 20 to 30% of the intraenvironmental genetic variance ($r_G = 0.7$ to 0.8 as for hen-housed egg production, sexual maturity, rate, and shell strength). The *absolute* gain from increasing k also would be greater for the more highly heritable traits (i.e., higher H_m in Table III). It would appear that 5 to 10 randomly chosen environments might be justified, although fewer might suffice *if* one knew what environmental variations should be included and could supply them in a well-controlled fashion.

Genetic-environmental interaction is significant as another mechanism which leads to an *average* advantage for heterozygotes, or overdominance, with consequent lower interenvironmental than intraenvironmental selection response. Hence, variance in general adaptability (G) would be expected to contain larger contributions from gene interaction (G_i) and less of average individual gene effects (G_g) than intraenvironmental genetic variance ($G + GE$). This places a premium on breeding methods which are effective for the non-additive gene effects.

Recombination Loss between Generations

By recombination loss we mean any deterioration in performance between generations caused by the breaking up, through crossing over and the segregation and recombination of chromosomes, of favorable "balanced" gene combinations whose frequencies are maintaned at higher than "coupling-repulsion equilibrium" levels by selection. If real and of sufficient magnitude, such recombination decay would *recur each generation* and thus offset some of the response to selection *each generation*. This could lead to plateau in response even though substantial variation from average gene effects remained.

Interpopulation Recombination

Some evidence that recombination-loss is real has been provided by Wallace and Vetukhiv (22) and by King (13). The former found that F₂ fruit flies obtained by crossing different locally adapted populations were definitely poorer in viability, under a restricted food supply, than the parental populations, even though the F_1 crosses were superior to the parental stocks. Similarly, King found F_2 poorer and more variable in DDT resistance than either the parental lines or the F_1 crosses.

In corn, the linear relationship between degree of heterozygosity and yield among P_1, F_1, F_2, and backcross populations has been interpreted as excluding important interallelic gene combination effects (16, 20, 21). Pollak et al. (17) found similar results in comparing P_1, F_1, and F_2 for three open-pollinated varieties of corn. The larger numbers of independently segregating chromosomes in corn than in Drosophila may account in part for the difference in results. Also recombination and level of heterozygosity are confounded in this approach.

Direct comparison of four-way or three-way crosses with their constituent two-way crosses offers a means of measuring the effect of recombinations of chromosomes from different parental lines, with no difference in either average or dominance effects. Results from an experimental test of accuracy in predicting double-cross performance from single-cross tests (11) indicated that the yields of four-way crosses averaged about 1.5% lower than the constituent two-way crosses, but the difference was not significant ($P < 0.10$).

TABLE IV.   Comparison of 3-way ($3w$) and 2-way ($2w$) crosses

Trait	$\overline{3w}$	$\overline{3w} - \overline{2w}$	P^a
Viability 0-20 wks	93.2	−1.0	∼0.05
Per cent, 21-60 wks	85.5	−2.0	<0.01
Age 1st egg, wks	22.5	0.22	<0.01
Per cent rate, 1st egg, 60 wks	67.3	−1.81	<0.0001
Total eggs to 60 wks	184.8	−7.0	<0.0002
Body weight, lb	3.90	−0.01	N S
Egg weight, g	53.4	0.13	N S
Albumen, height, mm	77.7	0.22	N S
Specific gravity, score	4.42	0.066	N S
Egg shape, L/W	1.443	−0.003	N S
Per cent blood spots	3.08	−0.91	∼0.05

[a] N S = non–significant, $P \gg 0.05$

Results of a two-year experimental comparison of three-way with constituent two-way crosses in chickens are shown in Table IV. Here the crosses compared were:

$$A(B \cdot C) \text{ vs } \tfrac{1}{2} (A \cdot B + A \cdot C)$$
$$A(D \cdot B) \text{ vs } \tfrac{1}{2} (A \cdot D + A \cdot B)$$
$$A(D \cdot C) \text{ vs } \tfrac{1}{2} (A \cdot D + A \cdot C)$$

Details of design and results will be given elsewhere. It was interesting to find that there was a rather consistent ($P < 0.01$) decline of nearly 3% in viability, especially among adults, a highly consistent decline of 2% in rate of lay ($P < 0.0001$), and hence of nearly 4% in total egg numbers per pullet housed ($P < 0.0002$).

Apparently the genotypes of strains B, C, and D each were organized to complement A in a somewhat different manner, so that gametes from BC, BD, and CD parents included crossovers and recombinations of whole chromosomes from different strains which did not complement A gametes as well.

Intrapopulation Recombination

"Decay" in recombinations of chromosomes from different populations suggests but does not prove that similar decay occurs between generations of the same population. This possibility may be tested by utilizing the repeat mating control strain technique of Goodwin et al. (8). The necessary matings are shown in Fig. 6. To measure the *regression* from intrapopulation recombination, including perhaps some effects of natural selection, depending upon technique, it is necessary to make an intrayear comparison of:

$C_3{}^r$ = progeny from *unselected* matings of C_2 parents, brooded in year 3, with

C_2'' = replication of the C_2 generation from same C_1 sires and from C_1' pullet dams which are full sisters, similarly selected, of the C_1 dams.

In other words, $\dot{C}_3{}^r - \bar{C}_2''$ is an *intrayear* comparison of mean performance for a generation with the mean performance of progeny from unselected matings of that same generation.

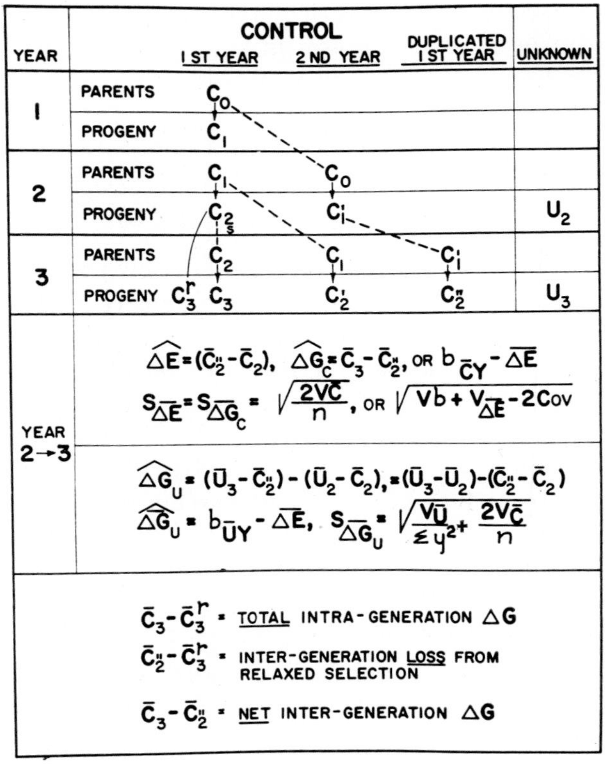

YEAR		CONTROL 1ST YEAR	CONTROL 2 ND YEAR	DUPLICATED 1ST YEAR	UNKNOWN
1	PARENTS	C_0			
1	PROGENY	C_1			
2	PARENTS	C_1	C_0		
2	PROGENY	C_2^r C_2	C_1'		U_2
3	PARENTS	C_2	C_1	C_1'	
3	PROGENY	C_3^r C_3	C_2'	C_2''	U_3

YEAR 2→3
$\hat{\Delta E} = (\bar{C}_2'' - \bar{C}_2)$, $\quad \hat{\Delta G}_c = \bar{C}_3 - \bar{C}_2''$, OR $b_{\bar{C}Y} - \Delta E$ $S_{\hat{\Delta E}} = S_{\hat{\Delta G}_c} = \sqrt{\dfrac{2V\bar{C}}{n}}$, OR $\sqrt{Vb + V_{\Delta E} - 2\text{Cov}}$
$\hat{\Delta G}_u = (\bar{U}_3 - \bar{C}_2'') - (\bar{U}_2 - \bar{C}_2) = (\bar{U}_3 - \bar{U}_2) - (\bar{C}_2'' - \bar{C}_2)$ $\hat{\Delta G}_u = b_{\bar{U}Y} - \Delta E$, $\quad S_{\hat{\Delta G}_u} = \sqrt{\dfrac{V\bar{U}}{\Sigma y^2} + \dfrac{2V\bar{C}}{n}}$
$\bar{C}_3 - \bar{C}_3^r$ = TOTAL INTRA-GENERATION ΔG $\bar{C}_2'' - \bar{C}_3^r$ = INTER-GENERATION LOSS FROM RELAXED SELECTION $\bar{C}_3 - \bar{C}_2''$ = NET INTER-GENERATION ΔG

Fig. 6. Mating plan for measuring genetic and environmental change separately.

The *total* intrageneration response is estimated from $\bar{C}_3 - \bar{C}_3^r$, comparing in the same year, the C_3 progeny from selected C_2 parents with C_3^r progeny from unselected C_2 parents.

The *net* response ($\bar{C}_3 - \bar{C}_2''$) is *total* ($\bar{C}_3 - \bar{C}_3^r$) less *regression* ($C_2'' - C_3^r$). The one-year comparisons for 1958 (Table V) are given only as examples. Sampling error would be considerably less for the ($\bar{C}_3 - \bar{C}_3^r$) difference than for those involving $\bar{C}_2''$. However, there is a possibility of bias due to differences in health of selected and unselected dams being reflected in direct maternal influence through the egg (C_3 vs C_3^r).

The *total* responses are in the direction intended except for egg weight and specific gravity, but comparison with the per-

TABLE V.   Intrapopulation selection response,
one-year sample

Trait	$(\bar{C}_3 - \bar{C}_3{}^r)$ Total	$(\bar{C}_2{}'' - \bar{C}_3{}^r)$ Regression	$(\bar{C}_3 - \bar{C}_2{}'')$ Net
Age 1st egg, wks	−0.56	−0.44	.12
Per cent production, early, 60 wks	1.65	3.88	−2.23
	1.02	2.13	−1.11
Total eggs, 60 wks	2.31	4.81	−2.50
Egg weight, g	−0.61	−0.49	−0.12
Egg volume, 60 wks, g	59.4	94.6	−135.2
Body weight, lb	−0.21	−0.10	−0.11
Albumen, height, mm	1.28	−1.79	3.07
Specific gravity, score	−0.034	0.100	−0.134

formance of the repeated previous generation indicated that much of the total intrageneration gains $(\bar{C}_3 - \bar{C}_3{}^r)$ were canceled by regression in performance under relaxed selection $(\bar{C}_2{}'' - \bar{C}_3{}^r)$. Slight net gains were indicated for sexual maturity and body weight, but there were net losses for egg production, egg weight, and specific gravity. Both deliberate selection and regression appeared to improve thick albumen score. With sufficient replication and care to avoid bias, this approach should help us to learn to what extent selection must overcome recombination loss before it can accomplish a net gain.

Measuring Environmental Change in Selection Experiments

In the absence of evidence, one can find reasons for believing that the net time trend in environmental influences has been either improving, static, or deteriorating. In domestic animals, certainly, there have been innumerable applications of advances in nutrition, physiology, and disease control. However, there also have been other possibly adverse environmental changes with time, in density of animal population, in economic pressures affecting feed formulation and housing practices, as well as new or more virulent pathogens. We need to know how much of the intravironmental response to selection is required merely "to make one head of cabbage grow where one grew before."

One means of estimating environmental change is by repeating the same generation (from same sires, sister dams of same age) in successive years (8) as indicated in Fig. 6. As shown, the estimate of environmental change is:

$$\Delta E = (\overline{C}_2'' - \overline{C}_2)$$

and the estimate of average environmental change per unit of time is

$$\overline{\Delta E} = \sum_n (\overline{C}_i'' - \overline{C}_i)1/n$$

with standard error

$$S_{\overline{\Delta E}} = \sqrt{2V(\overline{C})/n}$$

A variation which allows samples of two generations of the control strain to be produced readily over a long hatching season each year, without interference from selection and "ped" matings within the control strain, is as follows. Each year an unselected sample of cockerels and pullets of the current (C_2) and of the repeated (C_1') generations are segregated for flock or inseminated matings, independently of the rest of the control strain. The $C_2 \male \times C_2' \female$, whose C_1 sires and dams have survived and are being used to produce C_2' progeny, are used to produce C_3^r progeny. Similarly, the $C_1' \male \times C_1' \female$ produce C_2'' progeny. The same process is repeated each year, making available the ($C_2'' - C_2$) comparisons between years, but produced from unselected matings.

Comparing Alternative Selection Schemes

Some methods of selection are designed to be more effective than others in utilizing non-additive genetic variation and in improving general adaptability. For example, closed flock index selection based on family and individual performance at a single location each year is not expected to be effective in utilizing over-dominance variation or in overcoming errors from genetic-environmental interaction in selecting for general adaptability. On the other hand, a program of index selection for cross performance over a considerable range of environmental variation is designed to be handicapped less by overdominance and genetic-environmental interaction.

The *difference* in response from two or more selection methods can be measured readily and efficiently, simply by making intra-environmental comparisons of the population, over a suitable range of environments, each year. However, the *relative* effectiveness of several methods cannot be estimated unless the *absolute* response to each method is measured. This can be accomplished by an experimental design which either (*a*) measures and corrects for environmental change or (*b*) permits some type of intra-environmental (intrayear) comparison of different generations of each selected population.

Adjustment for Environmental Change

One method of removing the environmental component from the gross time trend in a population under selection is to measure performance for the control strain and the selected population in the same environments, as indicated in Fig. 6. The estimate of *absolute* genetic change in the selected population then is:

$$\Delta G_u = (\bar{U}_3 - \bar{U}_2) - (\bar{C}_2'' - \bar{C}_2)$$

Over a period of years an estimate of linear genetic response would be the regression on years (b_{uy}), less the mean environmental change per year ($\overline{\Delta E}$):

$$\overline{\Delta G_u} = b_{\bar{u}y} - \sum_n (\bar{C}_i'' - \bar{C}_i)1/n$$

with standard error:

$$S_{\overline{\Delta G_u}} = \sqrt{(V(\overline{U})/\sum y^2) + (2V(\overline{C})/n)}$$

One limitation of this approach is the possibility that environmental changes will affect performance of the selected population and the control strain differently. To the extent that such interaction is random, it would only inflate the experimental error. However, interaction with a consistent environmental trend would lead to bias in the estimate of ΔG. Probably the best solution would be to use a portion of the selected population itself for measuring environmental change.

The results shown in Figs. 7-12 illustrate the use of a "repeat mating" control strain in chickens to measure environmental change, and thereby obtain estimates of *absolute* genetic change, in the control strain itself and in pedigreed and commercial cross

populations. Pullets of all populations were tested, in propor-
tionate numbers, on thirty to forty California poultry farms
each year in 1956 through 1958. These estimates of absolute
response are for only two years of selection and hence should be
regarded primarily as illustrations.

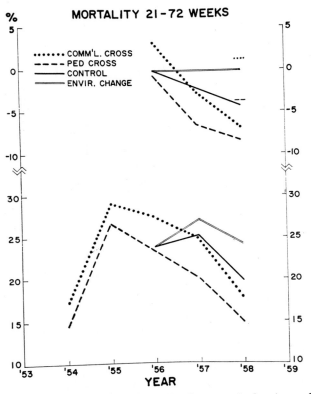

Fig. 7. Gross and environmental change (below) and genetic
change alone (above) for mortality, 21 to 72 weeks of age.

Notice that adult mortality (Fig. 7) declined in all three strains
from 1956 to 1958, but environment worsened in 1957 and improved in 1958. After adjustment for environmental change (upper lines), two-year genetic improvement in mortality was about
5% in the control and about twice that much in the crosses, with
the commercial cross lagging behind the pedigreed cross.

In egg production (Fig. 8), the environmental trend was slightly negative and absolute gains were greater in the commercial cross than in either the control strain or ped cross.

Egg weight at 32 weeks of age (Fig. 9) appeared to be declining in the crosses and even more so in the control strain, but

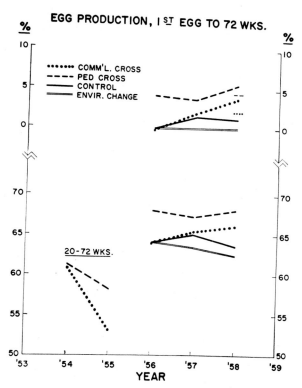

Fig. 8. Gross and environmental change (below) and genetic change (above) in per cent egg production.

when corrected for environmental trend no genetic change was evident in the crosses and little after 1957 in the control strain.

Gross time trends in specific gravity (shell strength indicator, Fig. 10) were favorable in the crosses but not in the control. Adjustment for environmental trends indicated greater genetic gains for crosses in 1957 and 1958 but greater losses in 1959.

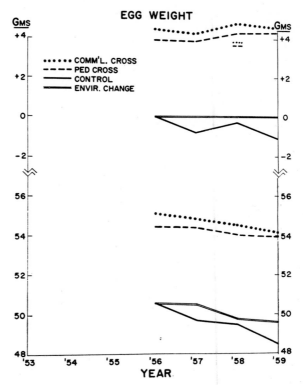

Fig. 9. Gross and environmental change (below) and genetic change (above) for egg weight at 32 weeks of age.

When changes in all components of performance were converted to economic equivalents and summed (Fig. 11 and Table VI), the environmental trend was negative in both years, and the absolute genetic gain appeared to be roughly twice as great in crosses as in the control strain. The importance of looking at total performance in assessing response to selection is emphasized by the results for ped crosses, shown in Fig. 12. On the basis of intra-year estimates of error, the two-year genetic gain in economic rating was highly significant ($P < 0.01$) for both ped and commercial crosses. Among the component traits, genetic changes in the crosses were significant for adult mortality, body size, and specific gravity. Response in percentage production was significant

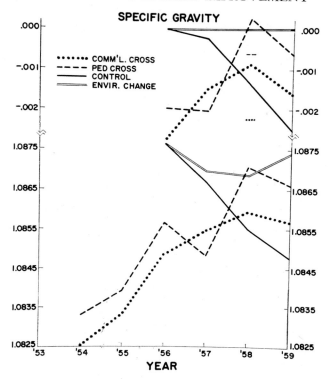

Fig. 10. Gross and environmental change (below) and genetic change above) for specific gravity (shell thickness indicator) at 32 weeks of age.

only for the commercial crosses. The only significant changes in the control strain (from intraenvironmental closed flock index selection) were the intended reductions in body size and blood spots, and the unintended reduction in specific gravity. The statistical significance of gains is overestimated in Table VI, since the standard error did not include year-response interaction. Only many more years of results will tell the story with certainty.

In the larger farm animals, measurement of environmental trend is more difficult, but not hopeless. For example, if a cattle population is reproduced by selecting two young sires each year, and using each sire for three years, mating each age group of sires to a representative cross section of females, the difference between

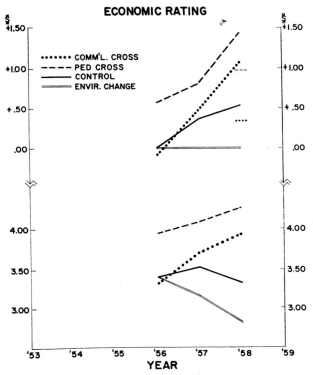

Fig. 11. Gross and environmental change (below) and genetic change (above) for economic rating, including all traits shown in Table VII.

progeny of the same sires (i.e., paternal half sibs), at an interval of t years will contain

$$\overline{D'} = t\left(\frac{\Delta G}{2} + \Delta E\right)$$

whereas the mean difference between the same years for the whole population contains

$$\overline{D} = t(\Delta G + \Delta E)$$

Subtracting one difference from the other leaves

$$\overline{D} - \overline{D'} = \frac{t(\Delta G)}{2}$$

as an estimate of absolute genetic change.

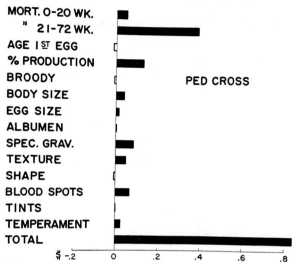

2-YEAR ΔG IN ECONOMIC RATING

Fig. 12. Two-year genetic change in components of performance for pedigreed crosses, expressed in economic equivalents.

TABLE VI. Two-year genetic change ($2_{\Delta G}$) and intrayear standard errors ($S_{\Delta G}$)

Trait	Ped Cross $2_{\Delta G} \pm S_{\Delta G}$		Commercial Cross $2_{\Delta G} \pm S_{\Delta G}$		Control $2_{\Delta G} \pm S_{\Delta G}$	
Per cent mortality,						
0-20 wks	−1.7	± 1.5	−0.9	± 2.2	−2.1	± 1.9
21-72 wks	−7.7	± 2.2	−10.5	± 4.1	−4.7	± 2.9
Age 1st egg, wks	0.14	± 0.18	0.42	± 0.96	0.27	± 0.17
Per cent production	1.4	± 1.02	3.9	± 1.60	1.2	± 0.95
Body size, lb	−0.13	± 0.039	−0.11	± 0.045	−0.26	± 0.034
Egg weight, g	0.36	± 0.33	0.21	± 0.48	−0.28	± 0.25
Albumen score	0.13	± 0.49	1.65	± 0.89	0.87	± 0.67
Specific gravity	0.57	± 0.11	0.47	± 0.17	−0.33	± 0.11
Shell texture	−0.07	± 0.025	−0.04	± 0.050	0.01	± 0.047
Shell shape	0.05	± 0.039	−0.05	± 0.060	0.09	± 0.045
Shell color	−0.004	± 0.016	0.000	± 0.013	−0.009	± 0.029
Per cent blood spots	−0.90	± 0.82	−0.92	± 1.79	−2.2	± 1.05
Temperament	−0.03	± 0.05	−0.20	± 0.10	−0.01	± 0.04
Economic rating	0.84	± 0.22	1.24	± 0.38	0.40	± 0.26

Of course the errors of the $\overline{D}$ values (but not the $\overline{D'}$) for successive *pairs* of years are negatively correlated as are the errors of the $\overline{D}$ and $-\overline{D'}$ values within pairs of years. These negative correlations among errors serve to reduce the error of the average estimate of genetic change:

$$\overline{\Delta G} = \frac{2}{n \cdot t} \sum_n (\overline{D} - \overline{D'})$$

Contemporary Comparisons of Generations

Any experimental design which permits unbiased contemporary comparisons of different generations of a population can be used to estimate absolute genetic response to selection. In chickens, the complete matings of the previous year may be replicated for comparison with the current selected matings (8) as indicated in Fig. 6. Rate of response may be estimated by averaging n successive intrayear differences:

$$\overline{\Delta G} = (\sum_n \overline{C}_{i+t} - \overline{C}_i)1/tn$$

with standard error:

$$S_{\overline{\Delta G}} = \frac{1}{t} \sqrt{2V(\overline{C})/n}$$

where t = number of years difference in age of parents in the repeated and the current matings

$V(\overline{C})$ = error variance of intrayear means for progeny from repeated or from current matings, including year $\times$ response interaction.

A somewhat more efficient alternative estimate is linear regression of "current" generations on time, less average environmental change per year (see Fig. 6):

$$\overline{\Delta G} = b_{\overline{C}_y} - \overline{\Delta E}$$

with standard error,

$$S_{\Delta G} = \sqrt{V(b) + V_{\overline{\Delta E}} - 2\text{Cov}}$$

In large farm animals, greatest hope for efficient estimates of absolute genetic response of selection seems to lie in contemporary comparison of progeny from sires selected from different birth years (Table VII). Such comparisons can be made in at least two ways.

TABLE VII. Intrayear comparison of sires selected
from different birth years

Year	At 2 years	Repeated[a]	Dams
1956	1954		
1957	1955	—	Distributed randomly,
1958	1956	1954	or paired, between
1959	1957	1955	sire groups
1960	1958	1956	

$$\Delta G_s = \frac{\sum_n 2(\overline{X}_{i+t} - \overline{X}_i)}{n \cdot t} \qquad S_{\Delta G} = \frac{2}{t}\sqrt{\frac{2V\overline{X}}{n}}$$

where t = years between generations of sires
n = number of intrayear comparisons averaged

[a] Repeated sires must be *unbiased* sample of those used in the earlier year.

1. *Within the selected population itself.* In this case it is essential that the two age groups of sires be mated to groups of dams which are equalized as to generation, age, etc. Also, of course, the repeated group of sires should be the same sires, or a thoroughly representative sample of the sires first used t years earlier. Since genetic change in only the sires' contribution is measured, the average estimate of $\overline{\Delta G}$ over a period of n years is:

$$\overline{\Delta G} = \frac{2 \sum_n (\overline{X}_{i+t} - \overline{X}_i)}{n \cdot t}$$

with standard error,

$$S_{\overline{\Delta G}} = \frac{2}{t}\sqrt{2V(\overline{X})/n}$$

Notice that the standard error is reduced directly as the time interval between uses of a group of sires (t) is increased. The same level of reliability is achieved with contemporary comparison of sires differing by $t = 2$ in age as when the comparison is for sires *and* dams born in years differing by $t = 1$.

The distinct possibility of maintaining fertility in cattle sperm stored for five or more years opens up the exciting prospect of measuring absolute genetic change in cattle just as efficiently as could be done *if* it were possible to maintain a *genetically constant* control strain for comparison with selected populations each year. In the latter case, the estimate of absolute genetic change per year would be:

$$\overline{\Delta G} = b_{(\overline{U}\overline{C})} \cdot y$$

with standard error,

$$S_{\overline{\Delta G}} = \sqrt{\frac{V(\overline{U}) + V(\overline{C})}{\Sigma y^2}}$$

In actual practice, the standard error would have an additional contribution from genetic drift (10).

2. *By using the two age groups of sires each year to mate test herds, independent of the selected foundation population itself.* In this case, the standard error of the estimate of response ultimately could be reduced by one-half, if current sires were always used on the *same half of the cows and their female descendants* in the test herd, and similarly for the repeated sires. Much would depend upon the equality of the initial division, but gradually the two halves of the test herd would come to reflect *twice* the difference between sire sets differing by t years in age, so that

$$\overline{\Delta G} = \sum_{n} \frac{(\overline{X}_{i+t} - \overline{X}_i)}{p \cdot t} \frac{1}{n}$$

and

$$S_{\overline{\Delta G}} = \frac{1}{p \cdot t} \sqrt{\frac{2V(\overline{X})}{n}}$$

where p = proportion of the genetic difference in the two age groups of sires represented in the test progenies (ranging from $\frac{1}{2}$, $\frac{3}{4}$, $\frac{7}{8}$, etc., to 1).

Similar contemporary estimates of absolute selection response could be obtained from intrasire comparison progeny from dams of different birth years, provided there is no selection among dams and unbiased estimates are available for any age change in maternal influence. This approach deserves exploration for possible use in the selected population itself, but it seems likely to be much less useful than comparing generations of sires.

Conclusions

To be realistic, experimental approaches to the study of selection response in animal populations are necessarily concerned with:

1. All important components of performance, as defined by both natural and deliberate selection, including the effects of pleiotropic and environmental relationships among the component traits on weighting for optimum index selection and on the net response to selection.

2. Genetic—environmental interactions and their implications in selecting for general and for specific adaptability.

3. Extent of intergeneration loss in performance from decay of gene combinations favored in selection, through crossing over and recombination, and the consequent reduction in net response to selection.

4. Measurement of time trends in environmental influences, both to assess their importance and to permit estimation of absolute genetic response to selection.

5. Measurement of absolute response to selection to test the adequacy of selection theory.

Some techniques for experimental exploration of selection theory in animals are discussed, with examples.

References

1. Bell, A. E. Results of selection method studies in Drosophila and Flour beetle. *Proc. 6th Poultry Breeders Roundtable*, Hotel Sherman, Chicago, 1957, pp. 81-95.

2. Bell, A. E., C. H. Moore, and D. C. Warren. The evaluation of new methods for the improvement of quantitative characteristics. *Cold Spring Harbor Symposia Quant. Biol.*, 20, 197-212 (1955).

3. Dickerson, G. E. Effectiveness of selection for economic characters in swine. *J. Animal Sci.*, 10, 12-17 (1951).

4. Dickerson, G. E. Genetic slippage in response to selection for multiple objectives. *Cold Spring Harbor Symposia Quant. Biol.*, 20, 213-224 (1955).

5. Dickerson, G. E., C. T. Blunn, A. B. Chapman, R. M. Kottman, J. L. Krider, E. J. Warwick, and J. A. Whatley. Evaluation of selection in developing inbred lines of swine. *North Central Region Publ. No. 38, Missouri Research Bull. 551*, 1954.

6. Falconer, D. S. Validity of the theory of genetic correlation. *J. Heredity*, *45*, 42-44 (1954).

7. Falconer, D. S. Patterns of response in selection experiments with mice. *Cold Spring Harbor Symposia Quant. Biol.*, *20*, 178-196 (1955).

8. Goodwin, K., G. E. Dickerson, and W. F. Lamoreux. An experimental design for separating genetic and environmental changes in animal populations under selection. *Biometrical Genetics*, pp. 117-138. Pergamon Press, New York, 1958.

9. Gowe, R. S., A. S. Johnson, J. H. Downs, R. Gibson, W. F. Moantain, J. H. Strain, and B. F. Tinney. Environment and poultry breeding problems. IV. The value of a random-bred control strain in a selection study. *Poultry Sci.*, *38*, 443-462 (1959).

10. Gowe, R. S., A. Robertson, and B. D. H. Latter. Environment and poultry breeding problems. V. The design of poultry control strains. *Poultry Sci.*, *38*, 462-471 (1959).

11. Hayes, H. K., R. P. Murphy, and E. R. Renke. A comparison of actual yield of double-crosses of maize with their predicted yield from single-crosses. *J. Am. Soc. Agron.*, *35*, 60-65 (1943).

12. Hull, F. N. Recurrent selection and overdominance. *Heterosis*, pp. 451-473. Iowa State College Press, Ames, Iowa, 1952.

13. King, J. C. Evidence for the integration of the gene pool from studies of DDT resistance in Drosophila. *Cold Spring Harbor Symposia Quant. Biol.*, *20*, 311-317 (1955).

14. Lush, J. L. Effectiveness of selection: Summary. *J. Animal Sci.*, *10*, 18-21 (1951).

15. MacArthur, J. W. Selection for small and large body size in the house mouse. *Genetics*, *34*, 194-209 (1949).

16. Neal, N. P. The decrease in yielding capacity in advanced generations of hybrid corn. *J. Am. Soc. Agron.*, *27*, 666-670 (1935).

17. Pollak, E., H. F. Robinson, and R. E. Comstock. Inter-population hybrids in open pollinated varieties of maize. *Am. Naturalist*, *91*, 387-391 (1957).

18. Robertson, A. Selection in animals; synthesis. *Cold Spring Harbor Symposia Quant. Biol.*, *20*, 225-229 (1955).

19. Robertson, F. W. Selection response and the properties of genetic variation. *Cold Spring Harbor Symposia Quant. Biol.*, *20*, 166-177 (1955).

20. Sentz, J. C., H. F. Robinson, and R. E. Comstock. Relation between heterozygosis and performance in maize. *Agron. J.*, *46*, 514-520 (1954).

21. Stringfield, G. H. Heterosis and hybrid vigor in maize. *Agron. J.*, *42*, 145-152 (1950).

22. Wallace, B., and M. Vetukhiv. Adaptive organization of the gene pools of Drosophila populations. *Cold Spring Harbor Symposia Quant. Biol.*, *20*, 303-309 (1955).

Use of Hybrid Vigor in Plant Improvement

Glenn W. Burton

Coastal Plains Experiment Station, University of Georgia, and Agricultural Research Service, United States Department of Agriculture, Tifton, Georgia

and

G. F. Sprague

Agricultural Research Service, United States Department of Agriculture, Beltsville, Maryland

The first systematic studies on plant hybridization were undertaken and published by the German botanist Koelreuter, in 1766 (11). He was also the first person to describe the increase in vigor resulting from some of the hybrid combinations studied. Following these first reports, there were numerous additional observations on intra- and interspecific hybrids and the extent of hybrid vigor in them. Mendel described hybrid vigor in certain of his pea hybrids (13). In the period between Mendel's report and 1900, there was a gradual accumulation of information on plant hybridization, hybrid vigor, and the contrasts between inbreeding and crossbreeding. This background of information and experience undoubtedly played an important role, but the modern concept of hybrid vigor (heterosis) may properly be dated from Shull's publication in 1908 entitled "The composition of a field of maize" (14).

The success of hybrid corn, more than any other factor, has stimulated the present use of hybrid vigor in plant improvement. It is fitting, therefore, to devote some space in the beginning of this paper to a historical résumé of the development of hybrid corn in the United States. Time will not permit a detailed consideration of the papers of Shull, East, and East and Hayes that contributed to this story. However, two quotations will serve

to indicate Shull's grasp of the hybrid vigor concept and its application to the production of hybrid corn. In his 1908 publication,
Shull concluded:

(1) that in an ordinary field of corn, the individuals are very complex
hybrids; (2) that the deterioration which takes place as a result of
self-fertilization is due to the gradual reduction of the strain to a
homozygous condition; and (3) that the object of the corn breeder
should not be to find the best pure line, but to find and maintain the
best hybrid combination.

In his 1909 paper (15) in a discussion of the pure-line method, he
stated further:

The process may be considered under two heads, (1) finding the
best pure lines, and (2) the practical use of the pure lines in the
production of seed corn.
(1) In finding the best pure lines, it will be necessary to make as
many self-fertilizations as practicable and to continue these year after
year until the homozygous state is nearly, or quite, attained. Then all
possible crosses are to be made among these different pure strains and
the F_1 plants coming from such crosses are to be grown in the form
of an ear-to-row test, each row being the product of a different
cross . . . . (2) After having found the right pair of pure strains for
the attainment of any desired result in the way of yield and quality, the
method of producing seed corn for the general crop is a very simple,
though somewhat costly, process.

These studies and the conclusions drawn provided most of the
essential framework for the commercial production of hybrid
corn. Actual utilization, however, was delayed for an additional
twenty odd years by a lack of suitable inbred lines and scepticism
as to the feasibility of hybrid seed production on a commercial
scale. The second of these objections was removed by the development of the double-cross procedure by Jones (10). The first,
lack of suitable lines, was to remain a limiting factor until the late
1920's. Even today, the lines in most extensive commercial use
leave much to be desired.

A few experiment stations and seed companies had inbreeding
programs prior to 1920. However, the big expansion in corn-
breeding programs by both public and private organizations came
after that date. Inbreeding was done on a very intensive scale and
many thousands of lines were started and carried to varying stages

of homozygosity. The great majority of these were discarded because of various undesirable traits such as lack of vigor and disease susceptibility. The surviving sample of lines was combined into hybrids and evaluated in yield trials. This sample was large in terms of number of items tested but it represented only a very small fraction of the lines initially started. Again, a major fraction of the tested sample was discarded because of poor performance in hybrid combinations. The relatively few survivors constituted the parent material for the hybrids entering into extensive commercial production.

The first estimates on the percentage of the corn acreage planted to hybrid corn were made by the Bureau of Agricultural Economics in 1933. At that time, 0.1% of the acreage was planted to hybrids. Ten years later, the percentage for the United States as a whole had risen to 51.6 and the percentage for the corn belt to 78.0. Several of the more important corn-producing states had hybrid corn acreages exceeding 90.0% of their total corn acreages. It is estimated that approximately 95% of the entire 1959 corn acreage was planted to hybrids.

The effect of the substitution of hybrids for varieties, plus other improvements in farm management practices, has had a tremendous effect on production. This can be illustrated by the following comparisons:

	Acreage	Production, bushels	Source of Data
1928-1932	103,419,000	2,554,772,000	Table 38, Agr. Stat. 1937
1938-1947	90,590,000	2,787,628,000	Table 45, Agr. Stat. 1950
1945-1954	84,758,000	3,084,389,000	Table 36, Agr. Stat. 1957
1945-1954 expressed as a percentage of 1928-1932	81.96	120.73	

Thus, during the period from 1928-1932 (prior to the use of hybrids on an important scale) to 1945-1954 (when the bulk of the corn belt acreage was planted to hybrids), there was nearly a 20% decrease in acreage of corn accompanied by a 20% increase in total production. The first hybrids which were distributed commercially have long since been replaced by newer and superior combinations.

During the past thirty years, a large number of investigators have reported on the existence and magnitude of heterosis in a variety of crops of economic importance. Some of this work was summarized by Ashton in 1946 (1). The general conclusion that may be drawn from such research is that heterosis or hybrid vigor is a common phenomenon that occurs widely in economic crop species and is of sufficient magnitude to warrant commercial exploitation if appropriate techniques can be devised. In corn, the desired manifestation of heterosis is an increased yield of grain. In certain other crops, seed yield other than that necessary for propagation is of minor importance, and increased yields of the total plant, or special plant parts, become the objective of the plant breeder. The remainder of this paper will be devoted to a consideration of the various commercial applications of hybrid vigor, some speculation on possible future developments, and a listing of those areas where additional research is needed for further improvement of methods.

The commercial application of hybrid vigor may be divided into two broad groups depending upon whether commercial propagation of the F_1 hybrid is by sexual or asexual means. The opportunities and techniques for the utilization of hybrid vigor will differ in these two classes. Different breeding procedures will also be called for. Whereas there may be reason for inbreeding in the development of sexually propagated hybrids, there would seem to be little need for it in the production of those propagated by asexual means.

COMMERCIAL PROPAGATION BY ASEXUAL MEANS

Vegetative Propagation

Horticulturists, as they have increased superior genotypes by cutting, grafting, budding, layering, etc., have long been able to exploit heterosis. Most of the world's sugar is produced on hybrid canes increased by planting short sections of the stems.

The last twenty years have seen the vegetative propagation of forage and turf grasses become a widely accepted practice. Today one outstanding hybrid plant, Coastal Bermudagrass (4), occupying over 2 million acres in the southern United States, produces over 200 million pounds more beef (liveweight gain) per year than a similar acreage of the common Bermudagrass it has replaced. Suwannee and Midland Bermudagrasses, Merkeron Napiergrass, Colonial Guinea grass, and Pangola grass are examples of other grasses superior largely because of their hybrid vigor maintained through vegetative propagation.

Propagation by Apomictic Seeds

Apomixis is most simply defined as "vegetative reproduction through the seed." Although the mechanics of apomixis may be varied and complex, it results in the reproduction of the female through seed and permits the transmission of heterosis without loss from one seed generation to another. It occurs in many genera of plants including *Citrus*, *Allium*, and *Rubus*. Many pasture grasses exhibit this phenomenon. King Ranch bluestem, Argentine Bahia, and Tucson side oats grama are examples of pasture grass varieties that reproduce by apomixis. As plant breeders learn to manipulate apomixis (breaking it to create hybrids and restoring it to fix them), it will become an increasingly important tool in the hands of breeders who would utilize hybrid vigor.

COMMERCIAL PROPAGATION BY SEXUAL MEANS

The manner in which the commercial F_1 seed is produced will be used to classify this broad group of plants. Appropriate examples will be chosen to cover each method.

Hand Emasculation and Pollination

This method has long been used to produce hybrid seed of ornamentals and tomatoes. Generally, the cost of hybrid seed produced in this way is so great as to restrict its use to high-value crops. Much of this seed is planted by the flower fancier and the home gardener, who do not mind paying high prices in order to add zest to their hobbies.

Hand Emasculations and Natural Pollination

This procedure has been restricted to wind- or insect-pollinated plants. For many years, the hybrid seed corn industry, as it pulled the tassels from plants to make female rows, used this method. Such factors as the increase in yield due to heterosis, the ease of emasculation, the yield of seed per emasculation, the quantity of seed required to plant an acre, and the value of the crop grown from the seed will determine the extent to which this method may be used. Although corn met these requirements unusually well, in recent years cytoplasmic male sterility has come into general use as a technique for avoiding detasseling problems.

Genetic Male Sterility

Genetic male sterility mechanisms are known for many plants. Since they would be self-exterminating in annuals if controlled by dominant genes, only those due to recessive or complementary gene action are available for most commercial uses. The most extensive and successful utilization of a recessive genetic male sterile for the commercial production of hybrids has been with sorghum.

Since sorghum is perfect flowered, hybrid seed production on an extensive scale presented a difficult problem. Genes for male sterility were discovered and procedures were developed for the utilization of genic sterility in the production of hybrid seed. Field plantings of the female parent in such cases consisted of 50% male sterile and 50% male fertile plants. The male fertile plants were rogued before anthesis. This was a necessary, but costly, procedure. Before this mechanism for producing hybrid seed had become firmly established on a commercial basis, a strain having cytoplasmic male sterility was discovered.

Genic male sterility has been reported in barley (16) and pearl millet, *Pennisetum glaucum* (7), and no doubt occurs in many other species. So far, these sterility mechanisms have not been used to produce hybrid seed on an extensive scale.

Cytoplasmic Male Sterility

Cytoplasmic male sterility permits the reproduction through seed of the female without the need for roguing associated with the use of genic male sterility. It results from the interaction of genes for sterility with a cytoplasmic factor. The manner in which it is controlled in grain sorghum will be used to illustrate the mechanisms involved. Maunder and Picket (12) concluded that a single recessive nuclear gene msc interacted with sterile cytoplasm to produce male sterile plants. The inheritance may be shown symbolically by allowing N to stand for normal and S for sterile cytoplasm. According to their theory, the genotypes for the cytoplasmic male sterile line and the sister line used to maintain it will be: S msc msc and N msc msc, respectively. Fertility will be restored whenever S msc msc females are crossed with S MSC MSC or N MSC MSC males.

Although modifying factors have been found to exist and environment has been shown to influence the expression of certain types of cytoplasmic male sterility in corn and other crops, the controlling mechanism has generally been similar to that described for sorghum.

The first commercial use of cytoplasmic male sterility to produce hybrid seed occurred in 1944, when an onion hybrid between strain 13-53 and Lord Howe Island was distributed. Strain 13-53 is cytoplasmic male sterile and this sterility has since been transferred to a considerable number of other onion varieties and inbred lines. One of such cytoplasmic male sterile derivatives serves as the female parent for each of the commercial hybrid onions produced at the present time. It is estimated that 40% of the 1959 crop was planted to hybrid seed which produced a 25 to 30% greater yield than the varieties they replaced. The commercial crop is the bulb, hence provision for pollen fertility restoration is not important.

The greatest economic use of cytoplasmic male sterility is in the production of hybrid corn seed. Although no definite figures are available, it is estimated that as much as 75% of the hybrid corn seed produced in 1959 involved cytoplasmic male sterile stocks. A full seed set is assured in the farmer's field by blending seed of male sterile and fertile versions of the same hybrid or by the introduction of a genetic system which restores pollen fertility.

Hybrid vigor is being utilized in commercial sugar beet plantings. The system used is closely analogous to that for corn and involves both inbred lines and cytoplasmic sterility. Cytoplasmic male sterile female parents have been developed which are adapted to the intermountain or the California areas. Such lines are crossed to nonfertility-restoring inbred males. If the vigor and seed yields of the lines were adequate, such single cross seed could be used for the commercial planting, since the commercial crop is the roots. However, seed yields of existing material is low and three-way cross seed is used for the commercial plantings. Increases up to 30% have been obtained in comparisons involving the best hybrids with standard varieties. It is anticipated that by 1960, approximately one-third of the sugar beet acreage of the United States will be planted with hybrid seed.

Directly or indirectly, cytoplasmic male sterility is involved in all of the present commercial hybrid sorghums. The best of these as a group will outyield standard varieties by approximately 30%. The adoption of hybrid sorghum has been more rapid than was the case for corn. No commercial hybrids were grown in 1956. It has been estimated that in 1958, at least half of the sorghum acreage was planted to hybrid seed and that the percentage may increase to 75% in 1959.

Cytoplasmic male sterility, recently discovered in pearl millet (7), will most certainly furnish the mechanism for the production of hybrid millets in the future. Where the crop is used only for forage, as in the United States, fertility restorers will be omitted in the seed production program. This will help to keep the hybrid in a vegetative condition and will save farmers the losses they experience when they try to harvest and plant seed from the F_1 hybrid. Where grain production is important, as in India and Africa, use of a male parent carrying the fertility-restoring gene will ensure seed in the F_1 hybrid.

Cytoplasmic male sterility mechanisms are known for many crops. Others will no doubt be found as breeding efforts are intensified and the genetics of naturally occurring male sterile plants are investigated. As the importance of the use of the F_1 hybrid becomes more generally recognized, organized efforts may be made to create cytoplasmic male sterile material. Hybridization programs introducing desired genomes into foreign cytoplasm should be fruitful at this point. Cytoplasmic male sterility of wheat, for example, had its origin in the transfer of *T. durum* and *T. vulgare* genomes to *Aegilops ovata* cytoplasm (9).

Dioecious Plants

Some seed plants such as the willows have staminate and pistillate flowers borne on different individuals and are called "dioecious." Where such plants are perennials and may be propagated vegetatively, commercial hybrid seed may be harvested from isolated fields in which a selected pistillate and a staminate plant have been interplanted. Mesa buffalograss, a pasture grass recently released in Oklahoma, is a vigorous F_1 hybrid that may be established from seed. Commercial seed of this hybrid will be produced as outlined above by vegetatively interplanting the two dioecious parents in isolated seed fields.

Self-Incompatibility

Over 20% of the plants in Pensacola Bahiagrass exhibit self-incompatibility, setting less than 2% of seed when selfed. When grouped in pairs to permit cross pollination, most of these plants have set approximately 90% of seed (5). This phenomenon has been used to produce Tifhi-1, a seed-propagated F_1 hybrid of this perennial pasture grass that has given over a four-year test period 69 pounds more beef gain per acre per year than the open-pollinated check (6). Commercial production of Tifhi-1 seed is carried out under the supervision of the Georgia Crop Improvement Association in fields vegetatively planted to alternate rows or blocks of the two parent clones, 14 and 108. Once these spreading clones occupy the soil (15 to 18 months after planting), hybrid seed may be produced for many years merely by harvesting all seed developing within the field.

Alfalfa, tall fescue, bromegrass, orchardgrass, and no doubt other perennial pasture plants produce individuals that are self-incompatible, but set seed readily when given an opportunity to intercross. Testing programs designed to discover two such clones giving the maximum amount of heterosis could lead to the commercial production of hybrids following the procedure successfully used with Pensacola Bahiagrass.

Chance Hybridization of Self-Fertile Cross-Pollinated Plants

Most pasture and forage species are planted at rates that permit only a small percentage of the young seedlings to reach maturity. A six-year study proved that up to 50% of selfed pearl millet seed could be mixed with hybrid seed without significantly reducing its yield, provided it was planted at a rate of 10 pounds per acre in 30-inch rows (2). When seeded at 2½ to 5 pounds per acre, such mixtures yielded in proportion to the selfed and hybrid components in the mixture. In this study, a minimum of 3 to 3½ seedling plants per inch of row were required for the more vigorous hybrids to crowd out the inbreds in the seedling stage and give full hybrid performance. These results suggested that chance hybridization yielding mixtures of parent and hybrid seed could give full hybrid effects if such mixtures were planted and managed properly. Success would require that the parents be highly cross-pollinated, flower at the same time, give reasonably good seed yields, and produce hybrids in all combinations vigorous enough to eliminate most of the parents in the seedling stage. Since the percentage of chance hybrids would increase as the number of parents were increased, the desirability of using at least three or four parents in the seed-producing mixture is apparent. A mixture of four self-fertile lines might be expected to give approximately 75% hybrid seed and 25% selfed and sibbed seed, whereas a mixture of two such lines could only be expected to give 50% of hybrid seed.

Gahi-1 pearl millet is an F_1 hybrid of this annual grass capable of producing up to 50% more forage than the common millet check (8). It is produced by harvesting all seed from a field planted to a mixture of equal numbers of pure live seeds of four inbred lines. Studies of plant populations from this seed show it to contain 68 to 75% of hybrids. Approximately 2000 pounds of seed per acre were harvested in Arizona in 1958, the first year after release. The National Foundation Seed Project is assisting in the seed production program. It is estimated that 1959 seed production will exceed 2 million pounds.

This method has been used experimentally to produce hybrid Sudangrass yielding 27.5% more than the checks (3) and would seem to offer promise for the improvement of many other forage plants.

Amphidiploids

Amphidiploids result when the chromosome numbers are doubled in a hybrid containing genomes of nonhomologous chromosomes from unrelated diploid parents. Here, there is little or no synapsis between the chromosomes in the hybrid, and high sterility is expected. Doubling the chromosomes in such plants should result in fertility and might be expected to fix any heterosis carried in the original hybrid. Many important economic plants including tobacco and wheat have originated in this manner. The extent to which breeders may use this method to fix heterosis awaits further study.

Synthetics

The possibility of utilizing heterosis through the development of synthetic varieties should not be overlooked. It is possible to describe plant material from which synthetics showing considerable heterosis could be developed. Perhaps the ideal situation would call for a number of highly cross-pollinated, high-yielding parents capable of producing high-yielding F_1's (considerably above the checks) in most, if not all, combinations. In most schemes for using synthetic varieties, several generations elapse before the variety reaches the general public. By this time, if F_1's were used in the beginning, some heterosis has been lost and a ceiling has been established. Tysdal et al. (17), commenting on the use of synthetics in a breeding program, said, "Not only would F_1 hybrids have a yield advantage, but it would be easier to 'fix' other desirable characters than in a synthetic. For these reasons, breeders of alfalfa and other forage crops should thoroughly investigate the possibilities of utilizing F_1 hybrid vigor commercially."

NEEDS FOR ADDITIONAL RESEARCH

Expansion in the use of hybrid vigor in plant improvement has been tremendous in the last fifty years. Increased utilization in years to come appears a certainty. In many species, mechanisms such as cytoplasmic male sterility permitting economical hybrid seed production must be found. Much testing will be required in the development of new and better parents, be they inbred lines or clones. Certainly, the ultimate extent and efficiency of hybrid use will depend upon a more adequate understanding of the phenomenon of heterosis and related problems in statistical genetics. The limitations of time preclude a listing and discussion of all the areas in need of further research. A few of the major ones, however, would include:

1. The relative importance of various types of gene action in heterosis.

2. The magnitude of the genotype-environment interaction and its proportionality to estimates of the several components of genetic variance.

3. The nature of genetic differences among varieties.

Such a listing could be extended indefinitely. However, unless critical evidence is obtained on these and other important problems, the commercial usefulness of heterosis will not achieve its full potential.

References

1. Ashton, T. *The Use of Heterosis in the Production of Agricultural and Horticultural Crops.* Imperial Bureau of Plant Breeding and Genetics. Cambridge, England, 1946.

2. Burton, Glenn W. The performance of various mixtures of hybrid and parent inbred pearl millet, *Pennisetum glaucum* (L.) R. Br. *J. Am. Soc. Agr.,* 40 (10), 908-915 (1948).

3. Burton, Glenn W., E. H. DeVane, and J. P. Trimble. Polycross performance in Sudan grass and its possible significance. *Agr. J.,* 46 (5), 223-226 (1954).

4. Burton, Glenn W. Coastal Bermudagrass for pasture, hay and silage. *Georgia Agr. Expt. Stas. Bull.* 2, 1-31, 1954.

5. Burton, Glenn W. Breeding Pensacola Bahiagrass, *Paspalum notatum.* I. Method of reproduction. *Agr. J.,* 47 (7), 311-314 (1955).

6. Burton, Glenn W. Tifhi No. 1—The first hybrid Pensacola Bahiagrass. *Georgia Crop Improvement News,* 9 (50), 3-4 (1957).

7. Burton, Glenn W. Cytoplasmic male-sterility in pearl millet (*Pennisetum glaucum*) (L.) R. Br. *Agr. J.,* 50, 230 (1958).

8. Burton, Glenn W. New millet from Georgia, Gahi-1, outyields Starr. *Progressive Farmer*, April 1958.

9. Fukasawa, F. Studies on restoration and substitution of nucleus in *Aegilotricum*. I. Appearance of male sterile *durum* in substitution crosses. *Cytologia, 18,* 167-175 (1953).

10. Jones, D. F. The effects of inbreeding and crossbreeding upon development. *Conn. Agr. Expt. Sta. Bull. 207,* 5-100, September 1918.

11. Koelreuter, J. G. Vorlaufigen Nachricht von einigen das Geschlecht der Pflanzen betreffenden Versuchen und Beobachtungen. Leipzig, 1766.

12. Maunder, A. B., and R. C. Pickett. The genetic inheritance of cytoplasmic male sterility in grain sorghum. *Agr. Abstracts,* 48-49, 1958.

13. Mendel, Gregor. Versuche über Pflanzen-Hybriden. *Naturf. Ver. in Brunn Verh., 4,* 3-47 (1865).

14. Shull, G. H. The composition of a field of maize. *Rept. Am. Breeders Assoc., 4,* 296-301 (1908).

15. Shull, G. H. A pure line method of corn breeding. *Rept. Am. Breeders Assoc., 5,* 51-59 (1909).

16. Suneson, C. A. A male sterile character in barley. *J. Heredity, 31,* 213-214 (1940).

17. Tysdal, H. M., T. A. Kiesselbach, and H. L. Westover. Alfalfa breeding. *Research Bull. Neb. Agr. Expt. Sta. 124,* 1942.

Extent and Usefulness
of Hybrid Vigor in
Animal Improvement

L. N. Hazel

*Department of Animal Husbandry,
Iowa State University, Ames, Iowa*

The concept of crossing strains and breeds for animal production frequently has been attended by emotional reactions which distract attention from the large body of evidence available on this subject. Almost from prehistoric times, one can find many self-admitted experts on crossbreeding in animals. For example, in Leviticus 19:19: "Thou shalt not let thy cattle gender with a diverse kind; thou shalt not sow thy field with two kinds of seed; . . . " But this attitude has not been unanimous, as indicated by Buffon's statement in the eighteenth century: "Only through crossing and mixing of the good qualities present in every animal and in every locality can complete perfection be obtained." But Darwin evidenced a more balanced viewpoint with respect to the concept: "Although free crossing is a danger on the one side which everyone can see, too close inbreeding is a hidden danger on the other." Crosses of distinct genetic groups are made either for direct production of commercial animals, or to develop new seed stocks which will be used eventually as parental strains. The genetic principles involved in the two applications are so distinctly different that the two practices should be considered separately.

Summary of Evidence

Although efforts to understand the mechanisms which result in hybrid vigor are just beginning to bear fruit, crossing to produce commercial animals has so proved its usefulness that the majority of the pigs, sheep, commercial layers and broilers in the United

States are currently some sort of more or less systematic cross. Many of the early results of crossbreeding experiments with swine were summarized by Winters and co-workers (13) and Lush and co-workers (8). A more recent summary has been given by Craft (3). The heterosis associated with the crossbred pig was measured separately from that which resulted from the mothering ability of the crossbred sow (7). Their results summarized in Table I indicate that a rotational system of crossbreeding which utilizes the advantage of the crossbred sow is considerably superior to that of a single cross of two pure breeds.

TABLE I.   Sources and amounts of heterosis as percentages of purebred performance in swine

Trait	First Cross Minus Purebred		Later Crosses Minus First Cross		Multiple Crosses Minus Purebred
	Pig	Sow	Pig	Sow	
Litter size at birth	0	0	0	12	12
Livability to 8 weeks	7	0	0	7	14
154-day weight	14	0	0	0	14
Total production per litter to 5 months	22	0	0	19	41

Inbred lines of swine generally have tended to deteriorate in some items of performance regardless of the relatively intense selection practiced for those traits (6). While complete restoration to the original productive level of non-inbred foundation stock was noted immediately upon outcrossing, only a few of the crosses appeared noticeably superior to the original stock. Crosses of Indian and European dairy breeds have been generally superior in milk production to the average of the parental breeds where extreme tropical or poor sub-tropical conditions exist. As summarized by Shrode and Lush (12), "Too little Zebu blood leads to poor adaptation while too much leads to low production, but the optimum proportion and the best method of keeping the dairy population near that optimum were still a matter of considerable doubt."

The utility of Yak-domestic cattle crosses for extreme conditions in Asia was pointed out by Phillips and co-workers (10). Planned experiments to measure heterosis for milk production in crosses of European breeds have been conducted or are now under way at the Beltsville Research Center, Purdue University, and the University of Illinois. The Zebu strains have been used widely for developing crossbred strains and for crossing with European breeds to produce beef animals adopted to hot climates.

Rhoad (11) demonstrated that Zebu cattle and their crosses were distinctly superior to Aberdeen-Angus in maintaining normal rectal temperatures when exposed to extreme heat. Limited experiments have been conducted to measure heterosis for beef production in crosses of European breeds, with measurements usually being restricted to the F_1 offspring. Phillips and co-workers (9) found heterosis for more rapid gains with fewer digestive upsets and lower variability in 57 crossbred steers as compared with 67 purebred steers. Heifers in this same experiment were reported to be heavier, particularly at weaning and at later ages (2). Such crosses have long been popular in the British Isles, a high percentage of the feeder steers produced in Ireland and Scotland which are shipped to England for fattening being crosses of this kind.

In the search for more productive animals, established genetic groups have frequently served as the foundation animals for crossing and subsequent interbreeding to develop more productive strains. This has been particularly true of the breeds of swine and light horses in the United States. Especially in cases where the final commercial animal is likely to be a crossbred, as with swine and sheep, the process of making new breeds by crossing the established ones may have a detrimental long-run effect. To the extent that heterosis depends upon genetic diversity, repeated crossing of the foundation strains to make new ones must reduce the heterosis that can be attained in the final cross. Anderson and Brown (1) demonstrated that the commercial inbreds of the corn belt were derived from early crosses of Northern Flint and Southern Dent strains of corn. Modern inbred lines differing most markedly in Flint-Dent characteristics tended to yield the most productive hybrids.

These many demonstrated examples of hybrid vigor may be categorized as follows:

1. The parental strains are approximately equal in productivity and the hybrid exceeds the parental average in one or several important traits.

2. The parental female has been especially developed to fit one ecological or economic niche and is crossed to a special male strain which confers to the progeny characteristics notably lacking in the female parents.

3. The two parental strains are on different sides of an economic optimum and the genetically intermediate hybrid is intermediate between the two parents.

Although the commercial advantage of the second and third categories may be as great as that of the first, the first category is of greatest genetic interest.

Genetic Basis for Heterosis

It is not sufficient to list examples of heterosis and to demonstrate empirically its existence. At least some speculation concerning the genetic nature of heterosis seems in order. At first glance, it seems more than surprising that genetic stocks, each subject to apparently intense selection, but maintained as separate populations with pedigree barriers to prevent transfusion of genes, should manifest heterosis upon crossing. Yet this occurs so frequently that a common widespread phenomenon must be responsible.

Davenport (5) was one of the earliest to realize the implication of dominant gene action in causing heterosis, pointing out that the dominant trait is usually beneficial to its possessor. Thus distinct strains, each containing some recessive genes, but differing in frequency, would produce crosses which inherited at least one dominant gene at most loci. As pointed out by Crow (4), the dominance hypothesis seems inadequate to explain more than an advantage of from 1 to 5% in crosses as compared with the parental stocks. In cases where more marked advantages exist, overdominance for a single trait or pleiotropic effects upon several traits, with complete dominance for the beneficial effects, provide a more logical explanation.

Complex gene interactions involving several loci provide a scarcely tenable hypothesis for explaining the widespread occurrence of hybrid vigor. First, selection has not been notably successful in fixing or bringing to high frequency the genes involved in such interactions, or the parental stocks would have attained already the vigor found in the crosses. Second, crosses should tend to deteriorate and go to pieces as compared with the parental stocks, due to the mixing of complexes which had been selected to operate smoothly within each strain. Third, the most fundamental characteristic of the mechanism of inheritance is the segregation which precedes gamete formation. Since selection would operate on favorable gene combinations only when specific genes of each locus happened to occur in the same zygotes, selection could be a force of only second or higher order in increasing the frequency of such genes. Thus any ultimate goal which could be achieved by more direct means, i.e., additive gene effects, would be controlled by genes which operated in that manner.

Four general conclusions appear clear with respect to these problems:

1. Genetic disruption and confusion do occur when crosses are sufficiently wide, leading to sterility, embryonic mortality, and impaired development of the hybrids.

2. Those traits which deteriorate most with inbreeding in the parental strains show most heterosis in crosses.

3. Heterosis is more marked in crosses of inbred strains from naturally cross-pollinated species than from crosses of naturally self-fertilized plants.

Physiological Mechanisms

The manifestations of heterosis usually observed and measured are associated with vitality, size, yield, etc. The metabolic processes which result in these end products are modified by constantly changing environmental influences. This concept leads to the suggestion that hybrids have greater environmental adaptability through having a greater number of metabolic pathways as a result of the greater number of unlike alleles. Conceivably, more kinds of substrates could be acted upon and more end products (in quantity or quality) could be produced to meet differing environmental stresses.

Heterosis appears to be most pronounced for vitality early in life and for other productive traits of the relatively young. Increased inbreeding also appears to have its most pronounced effects early in life. These observations indicate that heterotic mechanisms operate strongly only for a relatively short time, so that later in life, the early initial advantage is no more than maintained and is sometimes partially lost with approaching maturity. Yet heterosis is not present to any marked degree prior to birth in animals or prior to germination in plants.

The processes of growth and development in animals and plants are sufficiently different that quite different physiological mechanisms may be responsible for heterosis. For example, the important physiological adaptive mechanisms in the very young mammal when heterosis is most evident are temperature regulation and antibody production. Even a slightly earlier advantage in initiating these processes in the hybrid young could account for much of the observed heterosis.

REFERENCES

1. Anderson, Edgar, and William L. Brown. Origin of Corn Belt maize and its genetic significance. *Heterosis*, J. W. Gowen, Editor, p. 124. Iowa State College Press, Ames, Iowa, 1952.

2. Baker, A. L., and J. R. Quesenberry. Comparison of growth of Hereford and F_1 Hereford × Shorthorn heifers. *J. Animal Sci.*, 3, 322 (1944).

3. Craft, W. A. Results of swine breeding research. *U.S. Dept. Agr. Circ. No. 916*, 1953.

4. Crow, James F. Dominance and overdominance. *Heterosis*, J. W. Gowen, Editor, p. 282. Iowa State College Press, Ames, Iowa, 1952.

5. Davenport, C. B. Degeneration, albinism, and inbreeding. *Science*, 28, 454 (1908).

6. Dickerson, G. E., J. L. Lush, M. L. Baker, J. A. Whatley, Jr., and L. M. Winters. Performance of inbred lines and linecrosses in swine. *J. Animal Sci.*, 6, 447 (1947).

7. Gaines, J. A., and L. N. Hazel. Differences in litter size and growth rate among purebred and crossbred swine. *J. Animal Sci., 16,* 1066 (1957).

8. Lush, J. L., P. S. Shearer, and C. C. Culbertson. Crossbreeding hogs for pork production. *Iowa Agr. Expt. Sta. Bull. 380,* 1939.

9. Phillips, R. W., W. H. Black, Bradford Knapp, Jr., and R. T. Clark. Crossbreeding for beef production. *J. Animal Sci., 1,* 213 (1942).

10. Phillips, R. W., I. Tolstoy, and R. G. Johnson. Yaks and yak-cattle hybrids in Asia. *J. Heredity, 37,* 162 (1946).

11. Rhoad, A. O. Absorption and reflection of solar radiation in relation to coat color in cattle. *Proc. Am. Soc. Animal Production,* 290, 1940.

12. Shrode, R. R., and J. L. Lush. The genetics of cattle. *Advances in Genet., 1,* 209 (1952).

13. Winters, L. M., O. M. Kiser, P. S. Jordan, and W. H. Peters. A six-year study of crossbreeding swine. *Minnesota Agr. Expt. Sta. Bull. 320,* 1935.

Performance Testing in Livestock

N. D. Bayley, W. A. Craft, C. D. Gordon
G. M. Sidwell, and E. J. Warwick

*Agricultural Research Service, United States Department
of Agriculture, Beltsville, Maryland*

Selection of livestock on the basis of physical appearance preceded selection for performance by several centuries. Probably the earliest interest in performance records occurred in regard to race horses. Robert Bakewell who lived in the eighteenth century is credited with keeping records of performance while developing his Leicester sheep and Longhorn cattle. The Tompkines and the Galliers maintained some records of performance while laying the foundation for the Hereford breed. The Collings brothers and Thomas Bates kept careful records regarding beef and milk production in their Shorthorn cattle (18, 26).

Undoubtedly various private individuals in Europe and this country kept private performance records on their herds and flocks between the recorded period of Bakewell and the development of organized recording programs. It is safe to assume that most of these efforts, if not purely for advertising, were for the purpose of selecting individual animals. Denmark pioneered in progeny testing with swine, beginning in 1907. Since then progeny records, sib tests, and, very recently in poultry, the random sampling testing of specific stocks have received considerable attention.

Progeny testing in record of performance programs has varied with types of livestock as well as the traits for which selection was practiced. Lush (12) and others (3) have pointed out that the higher the heritability of a trait the less is the need for progeny testing. Also when the trait can be measured in both sexes, progeny testing is less needed than when performance can be measured in only one sex. Consequently, it is not surprising that we found only a moderate interest in progeny testing programs for feed-lot gain in beef cattle and body weight, fleece weight, and face covering in sheep. All these are traits having relatively high heritabilities and are measurable in both sexes. On the other hand, because of the sex-limited nature of milk production and the only moderate heritability of this trait, sire proving has been considered of value for improving dairy cattle (5, 17).

Swine producers particularly recognize still another factor affecting the value of progeny testing for their type of livestock. The use of all progeny tested sires would practically double the generation interval and as a result would actually slow rate of progress (2). Therefore, more emphasis on individual and litter testing (i.e., full sib testing) and use of progeny tests in a limited manner for retaining only a few of the really superior sows and sires seem justified. The effect of increased generation interval on rate of progress has influenced the attitude of beef, poultry, and sheep breeders toward the use of progeny tests. It is presently an unsettled matter of concern to artificial breeding organizations in the use of young dairy bulls versus the exclusive use of proved sires.

Raymond Pearl is given credit for bringing the importance of progeny testing to the attention of poultrymen (25), and practical breeders started to make use of these records in the 1920's. In recent years, the closed flock method of breeding has largely been replaced with strain and breed cross and other mating systems. Therefore, more and more interest has developed in performance testing of specific stocks in random sample tests as a means of providing unbiased information on the comparative genetic qualities of commercial poultry stocks. These tests were started in California in 1947. In 1959, egg production random sample tests were conducted in fifteen states. Four hundred and forty-one entries from twenty-six states and Canada were sent to the various stations for testing. There are also nine tests for measuring meat production in chickens and seven for measuring meat production in turkeys.

For nearly all the types of livestock, the early forms of performance testing were selective. Advanced Registry programs in dairy cattle permitted selection of the cow and the lactation of each cow which would be entered into the test. Ton litter contests in swine and similar contests in sheep and poultry allowed breeders a choice regarding nominations for entry. The early provisions of The National Poultry and Turkey Improvement Plans made it possible for breeders to select the birds tested. These programs served a purpose in stimulating interest in performance testing, but they did encourage undue emphasis on high individual records. Particularly in the dairy industry they provided an incentive for excessive individual care and uneconomical levels of feeding. In poultry, when complete families were tested, good results were usually achieved. For all livestock the genetic value of such tests is impaired because they usually represent the fortuitous sampling deviations from any one get.

Fortunately the history of all performance record plans shows a gradual change from selective to complete herd or flock forms of testing or to random sampling. Enrollment in Advanced Registry has declined markedly in the improvement programs of all dairy breeds and has been eliminated completely by one association. On-the-farm testing programs for dairy, beef cattle, sheep, swine, and poultry now give primary emphasis to testing all members of a herd or flock or utilizing random sampling with disinterested parties choosing the representatives to be tested. Samples, unaffected by selection for the performance traits to be evaluated, are needed for trials at central testing stations.

The growing use of central testing stations has raised the question regarding the extent to which they may replace or supplement on-the-farm performance testing. As mentioned previously, the poultry industry is characterized by a relatively small group of commercial breeders producing large volumes of breeding stock, and the cost of testing per individual is low enough to permit testing of most traits of commercial importance at reasonable expense at test stations. In this industry the comparison of specific stocks at central testing stations has grown in importance even though on-the-farm performance testing has been encouraged and has increased.

In the swine industry, the results of the Danish swine testing system (13) have contributed to the interest in establishing central testing stations. These stations not only provide records of rate of growth and feed conversion made under similar environmental conditions, but also permit carcass evaluations (1). In 1958, thirty-six swine testing stations were reported to be in operation in nineteen states. Eighteen new stations were being planned including locations in six additional states. The existing stations had an annual capacity of nearly 8000 hogs. These swine central testing stations do not evaluate the maternal traits but rather start with weanling pigs. Maternal traits as well as other characteristics are evaluated in on-the-farm swine testing programs which were reported by twenty-two states. In addition, the several breed associations have widespread on-the-farm programs.

Central testing stations for sheep are few in number. One is located in Texas for the purpose of individual and progeny testing of growth and wool producing ability. Texas, Utah, and Wisconsin have ram testing stations for comparing individual performance of rams. Ohio and Michigan are planning such stations. One reason for the slow development of these programs for sheep is that many breeders have not yet realized the need for such efforts. Further, in the Southwest and Rocky Mountain States, the industry is dominated by large commercial breeders who can provide their own facilities for making performance tests. Range sheep selection on the basis of performance records conducted by and within such large flocks is widespread in New Mexico and West Texas (21, 22). It is increasing rapidly in other western states.

Wisconsin (4, 9) pioneered in the production testing of farm sheep flocks, utilizing a selection index comprised of the pounds of wool produced and the pounds of lamb weaned, weighted by the relative economic importance of the two traits, their heritabilities, and genetic and environmental correlations. The weight of the lamb is adjusted for important measurable environmental factors. These factors include type of birth and rearing, age of the lamb, sex of the lamb, and age of the mother. Three other states have similar programs.

Beef cattle central testing stations of varying capacities have been established in at least ten states with the most interest in this approach to date being in the state of Texas, where there are currently nine locations at which bulls are being tested. To date most test stations have evaluated only rate of gain and conformation scores. Beef breeders have been reluctant to some extent to risk spread of disease by movement of animals to and from testing stations. Another important factor is that preweaning environment is known to influence postweaning performance to a considerable extent in beef cattle. This reduces the value of bringing cattle from several herds into a central station. Greatest public interest in performance testing of beef cattle has been associated with on-the-farm testing. In 1958 there were organized on-the-farm beef cattle testing programs in forty-two states, involving 3032 herds and 196,318 cows. This was nearly double the enrollment reported in 1957.

The lack of interest in central testing for dairy cattle is based on the high cost involved in such testing, the availability of records from the on-the-farm testing programs, and absence of evidence that the Danish system of testing stations for dairy cattle has advantages over the proper use of herd records (20, 24). In 1959, 66,000 herds and 2,232,268 cows were enrolled in production testing in the National Cooperative Dairy Herd Improvement Program. The various breed associations also conduct production testing on approximately 25,000 cows which are not tested in the National program as well as many which are also tested in Dairy Herd Improvement Associations.

One of the real benefits of on-the-farm performance records is the improved management which has resulted from increased interest in the herd or flock and added effort to make creditable records. This has long been recognized as one of the important causes of the 3700 pounds of milk per year difference between cows enrolled in Dairy Herd Improvement Associations and all cows in the United States. The importance of performance records for use in dairy management has been so generally accepted that opposition readily develops when it is suggested that more precise genetic measures be emphasized at the possible expense of some of the less accurate management evaluations. The importance of improved management resulting from on-the-farm programs has also been recognized in beef, sheep, and swine. The commercial farm flock programs for sheep which are being carried out in ten states were established to furnish records for management purposes.

Thus the advantages and disadvantages of central testing stations as compared to on-the-farm performance testing may be summarized as follows. Central stations are particularly suited for those types of livestock where the cost of testing per individual is low enough to permit the evaluation of most commercially important traits in a test station. They have real value for testing traits which cannot be tested easily in on-the-farm programs. They are useful for comparing genetic qualities of different stocks produced by commercial breeders. On the other hand, on-the-farm testing is particularly suited for the measurement of maternal traits and those traits which are affected by pretest environment. On-the-farm programs avoid some of the problems of disease spread which may occur in the movement of animals to and from central stations. Performance records obtained on the farm also have considerable value for evaluating herd or flock management and guiding management practices. Time and experience are still needed to ascertain the relative importance that these two methods of testing will eventually assume in the programs for most types of livestock. However, it appears that at least in the performance testing of poultry and swine, central testing stations can provide valuable information in addition to that obtainable on the farm.

As mentioned previously, improved management has contributed to the increased productivity of herds and flocks using records of performance. Therefore it is logical to ask, "What has been the genetic contribution to this increase?" The answer is not known. Except for a few studies (6-8) little effort has been made as yet to separate the genetic from the environmental contributions to improvement in large and diverse populations. Perhaps an enterprising mathematical statistician, armed with volumes of data from years of continuous testing, will some day devise a suitable analysis, submit his data and methods to the voracious capacity of modern electronic processing machinery, and emerge with an answer. However, today we do not know precisely what the genetic contribution to livestock improvement has been.

Estimates might be made of expected progress based on heritabilities of the traits involved and guesses regarding the percentage of the population which could be culled. However, all these estimates must be modified according to the number of traits for which selection occurs simultaneously, the weight given each trait, the extent to which non-performance characteristics influenced the breeders selection, etc. Robertson (19) estimated that improvement in milk yield of dairy cattle might be about 1.5% a year. In making this estimate he assumed a unit of 2000 cows, phenotypic variation of 20%, a heritability of 0.25, and the optimum use of progeny testing. He stated that this rate was more than twice the rate which could be expected in herds of conventional size and not using progeny testing. Robertson's calculations serve to illustrate the assumptions and qualifications necessary to make any estimate of genetic progress resulting from the use of performance records.

Despite the fact that realistic estimates cannot yet be made of genetic benefits obtained or obtainable from the practical use of records of performance, the outlook for expansion of the use of such records is good. Research has and is continuing to reveal misconceptions regarding traits which were thought to be of economic value or heritable. The inability of casual visual appraisal to yield precise estimates of performance has been made evident by studies with all types of livestock. Research information on the relative progress expected from selection for various traits is gradually being accepted by breeders and is giving them an improved basis for selecting the records of importance to them and discarding the rest. Finally, and most revealing, breeders have shown and continue to show an increased willingness to pay more for animals with performance information than for animals regarding which such records are not available.

In considering the future of performance testing, there is one characteristic of present-day programs which may be expected to gain in importance. This is the practice of comparing records in terms of their deviations from contemporary members of the herd or flock instead of comparing absolute records themselves (16). This practice is presently followed in some beef, sheep, and swine on-the-farm programs. Particularly in dairying, where the testing program has been prolonged and extensive, this will help to minimize misleading advertising and unwarranted emphasis on high records. It will simplify progeny evaluations by eliminating some of the need for guesswork regarding time trend effects inherent in the use of daughter-dam comparisons.

Also, in considering the future of performance records, it would be unwise to think exclusively in terms of numbers of animals tested and herds enrolled. In all types of livestock it is evident that the greatest opportunity for improvement will come through selection of superior sires (17, 23). Therefore, performance testing which emphasizes sire selection may overshadow female testing. Furthermore, the manual effort required in large commercial flocks of sheep and poultry encourage partial testing with appropriate sampling techniques. The advantage of central testing stations to the carcass evaluation of swine is an incentive to keep the tested samples to a minimum *size* in order that records may be obtained on the greatest *number* of samples. In this regard, some persons believe that the most efficient evaluation of dairy sires in artificial breeding would be accomplished through the use of progeny information from relatively few herds having high levels of production. Studies made on the Danish herds in Europe tend to confirm this belief (14). However, research efforts to evaluate such a practice in this country have produced no evidence in favor of its use (10, 11, 15).

In summary, the growth and development of performance testing of livestock have been characterized by the increased use of progeny records, sib tests, and tests of specific stocks. Selective testing has been largely replaced by the testing of complete herds or flocks or by random sampling tests. The extent to which central testing stations may replace or supplement on-the-farm testing is still to be determined by time and experience. However, it appears that central stations may have real value in the testing of swine and poultry. Breeders are accepting the research information pointing to the need for more accurate measurements of performance than visual appraisal provides. They are demonstrating this not only through increasing enrollments in performance testing programs for all types of livestock but also in their desire to have performance information on animals they are considering for purchase. This growth and development yields no evidence that there should be any relaxation of the efforts to expand testing programs. For all types of livestock the programs are still inadequate for providing the amount and kind of data needed.

References

1. Craft, W. A. Fifty years of progress in swine breeding. *J. Animal Sci.*, *17*, 960 (1958).

2. Dickerson, G. E., and L. N. Hazel. Selection for growth rate of pigs and productivity of sows. *J. Animal Sci.*, *3*, 201 (1944).

3. Dickerson, G. E., and L. N. Hazel. Effectiveness of selection on progeny performance as a supplement to earlier culling in livestock. *J. Agr. Research*, *69*, 459 (1944).

4. Felts, V. L. Construction of Ewe Selection Indexes for Use under Farm Flock Conditions. Ph.D. Thesis, University of Wisconsin, Madison, Wis., 1958.

5. Fohrman, M. H. Reminiscences on dairy cattle breeding. *J. Dairy Sci.*, *41*, 1465 (1958).

6. Henderson, C. R. Estimation of changes in herd environment. *J. Dairy Sci.*, *3*, 706 (1949).

7. Henderson, C. R. Estimates of environmental trends and biases resulting from errors in age factors and repeatability. *J. Dairy Sci.*, *41*, 747 (1958).

8. Henderson, C. R., O. Kempthorne, S. R. Searle, and C. M. Von Kvosigk. The estimation of environmental and genetic trends from records subject to culling. *Biometrics*, *15*, 192 (1959).

9. Karam, H. A., A. B. Chapman, and A. L. Pope. Selecting lambs under farm flock conditions. *J. Animal Sci.*, *12*, 148-164 (1953).

10. Legates, J. E. Heritability of fat yields in herds with different production levels. *J. Dairy Sci.*, *40*, 631 (1957).

11. Legates, J. E., F. J. Verlinden, and J. F. Kendrick. Sire by interaction in production traits in dairy cattle. *J. Dairy Sci.*, *39*, 1055 (1956).

12. Lush, J. L. Progeny test and individual performance as indicators of an animal's breeding value. *J. Dairy Sci.*, *18*, 1 (1935).

13. Lush, J. L. Genetic aspects of the Danish system of progeny testing swine. *Iowa Agr. Expt. Sta. Research Bull. 204*, 1936.

14. Mason, I. L. and A. Robertson. The progeny testing of dairy bulls at different levels of production. *J. Agr. Sci.* *47*, 367 (1956).

15. Mitchell, R. G., E. L. Corley, E. E. Heizer, and W. J. Tyler. Heritability and phenotypic and genetic correlations between type ratings and milk and butterfat production in Holstein-Friesian cattle. *J. Dairy Sci.*, *40*, 632 (1957).

16. Pirchner, F. and J. L. Lush. Genetic and environmental portions of the variations among herds in butterfat production. *J. Dairy Sci.*, *42*, 115 (1959).

17. Rendel, J. M., and Alan Robertson. Estimation of genetic gain in milk yield by selection in a closed herd of dairy cattle. *J. Genet.*, *50*, 1 (1950).

18. Rice, V. A., F. N. Andrews, E. J. Warwick, and J. E. Legates. *Breeding and Improvement of Farm Animals,* 5th edition. McGraw-Hill Book Company, New York, N. Y., 1957.

19. Robertson, Alan. Artificial insemination and livestock improvement. *Advances in Genet., 6,* 451 (1954).

20. Robertson, A. and I. L. Mason. The progeny testing of dairy bulls: A comparison of special station and field results. *J. Agr. Sci., 47,* 376 (1956).

21. Shelton, Maurice. Selection of fine-wool rams based on record of performance data. *J. Animal Sci., 18,* 925-930 (1959).

22. Stauder, J. R., and P. E. Neale. Selection as a method of improving sheep. *New Mex. Agr. Ext. Service Circ. 284,* 1958.

23. Terrill, C. E. Recent advances in sheep breeding. *Calif. Livestock News,* Oct. 14, 1958.

24. Touchberry, R. W., and K. Rottensten. A comparison of sire tests made at special Danish progeny testing stations with tests made in farmer herds. *J. Animal Sci., 17,* 1146 (1958).

25. Warren, D. C. A half century of advances in genetics and breeding improvement of poultry. *Poultry Sci., 37,* 3 (1958).

26. Winters, L. M., William Rempel, and J. N. Cummings. *Animal Breeding,* 5th edition. John Wiley and Sons, New York, N. Y., 1954.

IV. New Approaches in the Use of Plant and Animal Germ Plasm

Contributions of Laboratory Animals to Research in Livestock Improvement*

A. B. CHAPMAN

*Department of Genetics, University of Wisconsin,
Madison, Wisconsin*

We who are interested in gaining an understanding of the basis for the genetic improvement of livestock could, if given sufficient time and facilities, seek the solution to each specific animal breeding problem by doing our research exclusively with each class of livestock. This approach alone is inefficient if partial answers to our questions can be found by research effort in developing more precise deductions based on genetic theory and from research with cheaper, more rapidly reproducing organisms. Partial answers are available from these approaches because of the common base of genetic principle in different species and because of the statistics available for quantitative estimates of important biological parameters. The precision with which results are transferable between traits and between species will, of course, depend on the extent to which the truly common biological base is known and the extent to which its role in determining the results can be evaluated.

With these laboratory species we may check theoretical predictions against outcome for traits in which the genetic and environmental sources of variation have been evaluated statistically. If prediction and outcome are inconsistent in any of these tests the inquiry into the basis for inconsistency may well further the development of theory, biologically and statistically.

The values of laboratory animals in animal breeding research are not only as agents for checking theoretical prediction against outcome, providing basic results for further theory, and stimulation for development of research tools, but are also in the salutory effect that this research has on the research worker. The results which occur with large numbers of rapidly reproducing organisms

* Paper No. 821 from Department of Genetics, University of Wisconsin.

over many generations often point up, in rather dramatic form, the dangers of generalization from results based on small numbers, few generations, specific traits, and only partially defined experimental conditions. Recognition of this should leave the most cautious research worker with less dogmatism in interpreting results from livestock breeding experiments than he might have had if theory and livestock breeding alone were his experience.

What are the more specific contributions of laboratory animals to animal breeding research?

It is difficult to decide which of the laboratory animal breeding experiments to use in illustrating the potential contribution of this area of work to research in livestock improvement. Those chosen are some of the experiments which are impressive because they stand as rather clear biological examples of effects that we should bear in mind in thinking through the design, analysis, and interpretation of livestock breeding research. They do not necessarily lead to answers to which imagination and deduction would not lead, but they are soul-satisfying biological demonstrations of effects to which we can turn without having to worry about oversimplified assumptions in the model. The organisms or conditions may, of course, be oversimplifications of the species and conditions for which they are pilot experiments.

The early work on inbreeding with rats (12, 27, 36), mice (21, 22, 48), Drosophila (4, 25, 35, 49), and guinea pigs (51, 55) pointed to the pattern of results from inbreeding which formed a part of the bases for broad generalization as to the expected results from inbreeding in livestock.

The over-all reduction in vigor, size, and fertility, the variability in extent of decline for different traits from line to line, the apparent linear effect of inbreeding, and the general increase in vigor by crossing those lines which survived were the results which this work led us to expect in our livestock research.

Perhaps more importantly, a part of this work served as a stimulus for the development of some of the most valuable tools used extensively in research on livestock improvement as well as in other areas related to population genetics. This was Wright's (52) development of the coefficients of inbreeding and relationship, developed as quantitative base lines to which he could relate the inbreeding and crossbreeding results from his guinea pig research.

The intense interest of animal breeders in the effectiveness of different methods and intensities of selection in producing genetic improvement has led to a number of experiments with laboratory animals in which upward and downward selection, relaxed and reverse selection, crossing of selected lines, etc., have been practiced. The results are such that we must take them as part of our frame of reference for the concepts associated with heritability, and experimental work must be done to test hypotheses developed because of deviations from expectation in these experiments.

Most of the early experiments on laboratory animal selection did not provide statements or estimates of a number of important pieces of information for their interpretation. These will be listed in the hope that they may be helpful reminders to those undertaking selection experiments. They are (6):

1. The kind of selection practiced—the extent to which it was individual, pedigree and progeny selection.

2. The kind of mating system used—whether random mating, outbreeding, inbreeding, or assortive mating on somatic resemblance.

3. The selection pressure applied—the intensity and differential values.

4. The heritability of the characters in the foundation stock and in later generations. It would be preferable if measures of the relative genetic components—additive, dominance and epistatic deviations—were also available.

5. The amount of change in the environmental components of variation from time to time.

6. The averages and variations in each generation for the entire population, for the parents of the next generation and for their offspring.

7. The averages and variations in contemporaneous controls derived from the same foundation stock as the selected groups and maintained in an environment similar to that of the selected groups throughout the experiment.

8. The effects of back selection when it is begun after different numbers of generations of selection in the high and low lines.

9. The results of relaxation of selection after different numbers of generations of selection.

10. The extent of change in characters for which no conscious selection was practiced.

11. How much of the net selection practiced would have been ex-

pected to occur automatically and how much was artificially imposed.

12. The results of crossing divergent lines with each other and with tester stock.

13. The effects of selection on the regression of offspring on parent.

Generalization of the results of selection experiments could be made with even more assurance if they were also put in the context of any previous natural or artificial selection practiced on the trait, whether the organism has few or many chromosomes and any restriction on crossing over, and the types of environment in which the animals had been raised. The reasons for needing this kind of information in attempting to generalize are that:

1. Traits related in some way with fitness of the organism and hence on which natural selection has been imposed are presumably less likely to respond to artificial selection for the reason that most of the readily available (additive) genetic variance would have been exhausted. If any changes are produced by artificial selection, the expectation is that they have occurred by disrupting the harmonious genetic balance established in the organism by natural selection and hence will be largely nonadaptive. This may mean fixation of adaptively inferior genotypes or maintenance of sufficient genetic variability that, with relaxed or reverse selection, the population returns approximately to the original level for that trait. Traits not related to fitness and not previously selected artificially may have sufficient additive genetic variance to allow for many generations of effective selection and fixation at the resultant level.

2. The number of chromosomes and crossing-over restrictions should be considered because they determine the number of freely segregating units available for recombination in each generation (33).

3. The role of environment cannot be predicted on theoretical grounds, but its potential influence in conditioning the results should not be ignored in their interpretation.

The laboratory animal selection experiments reported since 1945 have included an increasing amount of the information needed for interpretation of the results (1, 5, 7-9, 15, 18, 28, 30-32, 40).

Typical, in a general but not a specific way, of the results found and of the conclusions reached in selection experiments are those of Falconer (16) from experiments on both upward and downward selection for body size, lactation, and litter size in mice. He found that these characters differed "in many features of their responses," a conclusion which must also be drawn from surveying the results of the many selection experiments in laboratory animals. Certain features predominate in the results of some experiments and not in others. The contribution of these selection experiments to our thinking in livestock breeding research is, in large measure, in making us aware of the important role certain factors may play in some cases, and the minor part they assume in others. In Falconer's work, for example, he points to the complications arising from maternal influence on body weight. This component of body weight did not increase in the line selected upward but did decrease in the downward selected line, thereby giving an asymmetrical response to selection in opposite directions. With lactation, the response in the two directions was also highly asymmetrical. Maternal effects seemed unimportant for this trait. Heritability remained high—about 50%—between the upper and lower limits, allowing large response in the direction away from the limit reached. Results from suspending selection suggest that natural selection was opposing change in both high and low lines.

Another example, also typical in a general way but not necessarily in specific detail, is reported by Robertson (38) on selection for body size in Drosophila in which he points out:

Among the more regular features we may note the immediate response to selection in either direction; the tendency to asymmetry with the greater response downward; the unstable equilibrium in large strains which can often be brought down to the original level by reversing selection; the eventual complete stability of small strains; the higher phenotypic variability which developed during selection for small size; the inverse relation between response and phenotypic variance in different large lines compared with the positive relation between them in small strains; the heterosis in crosses between large and also between small strains, in which it is more striking; the further increase in size caused by selection from crosses between large strains which have reached a limit; the initial failure to make progress in down selection from crosses between small strains; and finally the inference that these characteristic responses to selection are to be interpreted chiefly in terms of gene behaviour rather than correlated changes in fitness.

Another example of the use of laboratory animals to develop guideposts for our research in livestock breeding is to be found in the comparisons of different methods of selection such as those of Bell *et al.* (2). Comparisons have been made of individual and family selection within a closed population, early testing for combining ability, selection within and between inbred lines, reciprocal selection for specific combining ability, recurrent selection for specific combining ability with an inbred tester. In this work fecundity and egg size in Drosophila have been used, the former being a highly heterotic trait with low heritability, the latter with little or no heterotic effect in crosses and high heritability. They concluded from these studies, involving sixteen generations in one experiment and thirty-nine generations in another, that individual and family selection are superior for improving traits, like egg size, in which variation is determined largely by additive genes and that this type of selection is initially more effective than other methods for improvement of highly heterotic traits, like fecundity, in a newly formed population. Both reciprocal and recurrent cross selections were indicated to be superior to a closed population method for a highly heterotic trait. Based on the results of linecrossing they also postulate that selection should be combined with inbreeding in the reciprocal and recurrent segregating lines for maximizing heterosis in the cross populations.

Another pilot experiment directed toward determining "the relative value of different methods for predicting the outcome of specific crosses and for predicting the average (or general) combining value of lines for the quantitative character, 13-week individual body weight in the rat," was reported by Craig and Chapman (11). The relative performance for this trait (of relatively high heritability—40 to 50%) in cross progeny from specific crosses between inbred lines themselves and between inbred lines and outbred stock was found to be predictable from data on the parent groups. Also, the average or general combining value of lines used in a series of crosses was found to be predictable from a line's own performance and from results when lines were used on outbred or tester stock.

Because of the need for dealing with several traits at one time in improving livestock, any light which laboratory animal research can throw on the results to which genetic correlations lead are of interest. Many of the papers reporting the effects of selection on the traits consciously selected for have pointed to correlated responses in other traits. The patterns of response with the correlated traits seems to be similar to those occurring with the characters selected for directly.

Negative genetic correlations (between the trait in question and those of adaptive value) have been invoked to explain deviations from expectation in selection experiments, when expectation has been based on heritability of individual traits and without recognition of correlated variability in other traits. As Sokal and Hunter (44) point out, it is difficult to decide whether these correlations have arisen from: "(a) unwitting selection for a genetically independent trait, physiologically essential to successful establishment of the main selected character; (b) linkage of genes responsible for the correlated characters; (c) pleiotropic effects of a single group of genes." Sokal and Hunter feel that in their experiments on DDT resistance and peripheral pupation in *Drosophila* they have tended to eliminate unconscious selection and that studies now underway may provide a basis for distinguishing between partial linkage and pleiotropism.

Cochrem's (10) selection experiments with mice give a demonstration of "fairly rapid progress in selection for relationships between two traits different from those predictable from the expected correlated response" based on the genetic correlation between them.

Another area of interest to animal breeders and one neatly related to the concept of genetic correlation by Falconer (14) is that having to do with interaction of the effectiveness of selection within different environments. As Falconer pointed out, in explanation of his results when selecting mice under different feeding regimes, the results are fundamentally dependent on the genetic correlation between, and the heritabilities of, the "traits" which are expressed in the two environments. Here again, in explaining the results of a laboratory animal experiment, clarification of a point of view biologically and statistically occurred. It

became evident that the decision as to which environment provides the best background for effective selection does not have
to be a problem in semantics such as the generalization that
"optimum environment brings out the genetic differences."
Rather, this is a problem for research on particular traits of the
species in question and on each kind of environment. The extent
to which the size of the parameters vary from one set of conditions to another can be determined only by experimental test—it
may well be that the degree of generalization possible in terms
of deviations from an optimum is highly limited.

Another example of the function served by laboratory animals
in helping to clarify a livestock breeding problem is brought out
by the study of Dickerson and Gowen (13) on "Hereditary
obesity and efficient food utilization in mice." This research
stemmed directly from a question raised by a study of rate and
economy of gain and carcass composition in swine. The results of
the mouse experiment were both enlightening and thought-provoking. They demanded reappraisal of some of the thinking current in nutrition, physiology, and breeding of our livestock. It was
clear from the mouse results that a distinction needed to be made
between "the hereditary association of increased fat deposition
with lower feed requirements per unit gain in weight, and the
developmental association of increased fat deposition with higher
food requirements."

Grounds for pausing to reconsider some animal breeding concepts are given also by Grüneberg's (20) study of "Variation
within inbred strains of mice" and Robertson and Reeve's (41)
research on "Heterozygosity, environmental variation and heterosis." Grüneberg's studies on skeletal measurements in mice led
him to the conclusion that pure lines are "less homogeneous than
is widely believed" and that "the homozygous state tends to be
less stable developmentally than the heterozygous one." Robertson
and Reeve point to a reduction by about 50% in phenotypic
variance of body weight in a wild strain of Drosophila when
inbred under optimum conditions, suggesting that about "half the
variance of the original strain was due to the effects of uncontrol-
lable environmental variations within the culture." These highly
inbred lines, however, tended to have higher variance than the

crosses between them. Yoon (56), studying age at vaginal opening, and McLaren and Michie (34), studying duration of narcosis after injection of Nembutal in mice, report less variability in the F_1 than in the inbred parents.

Robertson and Reeve (41) show the beauty of Drosophila for probing deeper genetically than could be done with livestock. They have analyzed the relationships between heterozygosity and environmental variance with wing length by making up genotypes with specific combinations of the major chromosomes from certain inbred lines, as did Gowen and co-workers (19) in earlier work. Grouping the genotypes according to the numbers of heterozygous pairs of chromosomes Robertson and Reeve found that the average variance declined progressively with increased heterozygosity.

Have we hope of utilizing irradiation for furthering improvement in our livestock? In Drosophila, Scossiroli (42, 43), by x-ray treatment of selected lines which had reached a plateau, was able to make further progress with selection. This is a far cry from introducing directly or indirectly additional desirable genotypes into our livestock. It does, however, keep us alert to the possibilities of using tools which a few years ago were not even available.

What about the dependence of heterosis on environmental conditions? Vetukhiv and Beardmore (47) have shown that heterosis in fecundity and viability in the F_1 of geographic populations of *Drosophila pseudoobscura* expresses itself at certain temperatures, not at others.

Have we failed to hunt intensively enough in our livestock for superficial indicators of more profound effects? For example, in guinea pigs Wright (54) found that the genotype for silver-white causes high postnatal mortality, complete male and partial female sterility, and lowered hemoglobin concentration in the blood. Wolfe and Weir (50) reported correlated differences between lines of mice in pH of the blood, sex ratio, and order in which the mice are caught when different lines and crosses are caged together. The possibility of differences in thyroid activity is being investigated. Hollander and Gowen (24) give evidence of a single-gene ("hair-loss") antagonism between mother and fetus in the mouse. "Normal hair" progeny of "hair-loss" mothers are ordinarily born alive but suffer excessive mortality, associated with inadequate lung inflation, inferior growth, and fragile bones, during the first two weeks, even when fostered by normal mothers.

The influence of the male on the size of litters which he sires is usually considered not to be important but should not be ignored. Tyler and Chapman (45) reported a case of partial sterility in rats characterized by uterine resorption of approximately 60% of the progeny of partially sterile sires or dams who transmitted the trait to about 50% of their progeny. This condition was thought to be due to a chromosomal translocation.

Another use to which laboratory animals have been put is to check on the value of different kinds of controls for animal breeding experiments. Lasley (29), for example, using Tribolium, compared a replicate family type of control with random-bred controls and concluded that replicate family controls were more efficient than random-bred if equal numbers of full sib families were considered.

Robertson (39) points to a need for "synthesis between the concepts of population and developmental genetics" and sets the stage for this by his studies on the relationship of cell size and cell number with wing size in Drosophila. He shows that high temperature during larval growth results in smaller wing size due to smaller cell area, but that inadequate nutrition reduced wing size primarily by reduction in cell number, which is also true for the major differences in wing size between different wild populations —different patterns of development leading to the same end result. Selecting for one of these patterns and not the other may give more rapid progress than selecting for the end point itself.

There are many other breeding areas into which the laboratory animal research worker has probed or may probe (37) and set the stage for a better understanding of the possibilities available for livestock breeding research and improvement. Many of the questions raised at this symposium on how best to utilize the germ plasm of exotic breeds urges one to think in terms of conducting experiments on selection and mating systems following wide crosses in laboratory animals (3, 17, 23, 26, 46, 53) as a basis for a first approximation to some of the answers.

It is hoped that the above survey illustrates the value of laboratory animal research for checking outcome against prediction, providing basic results for further development of theory, urging the development of research tools, stimulating the imagination in livestock improvement research, and setting broad limits within which it is likely that results with livestock will fall.

REFERENCES

1. Bell, A. E., C. H. Moore, and D. C. Warren. A biological evaluation with *Drosophila melanogaster* of four methods of selection for the improvement of quantitative characteristics. *Proc. 9th Intern. Genet. Congr. Caryologia, 6, Supp.*, 851-853 (1953).

2. Bell, A. E., C. H. Moore, and D. C. Warren. The evaluation of new methods for the improvement of quantitative characteristics. *Cold Spring Harbor Symposia Quant. Biol.*, 20, 197-212 (1955).

3. Castle, W. E. A further study of size inheritance in rabbits, with special reference to the existence of genes for size characters. *J. Exptl. Zool.*, 53, 421-454 (1929).

4. Castle, W. E., F. W. Carpenter, A. H. Clark, S. O. Mast, and W. M. Barrows. The effects of inbreeding, cross-breeding, and selection upon the fertility and variability of Drosophila. *Proc. Am. Acad. Arts and Sci.*, 41, 731-786 (1906).

5. Chapman, A. B. Genetic and nongenetic sources of variation in the weight response of the rat ovary to a gonadotrophic hormone. *Genetics*, 31, 494-507 (1946).

6. Chapman, A. B. Effectiveness of selection in laboratory animals. *J. Animal Sci.*, 10, 3-8 (1951).

7. Chung, C. S., and A. B. Chapman. Comparisons of the predicted and actual gains from selection of parents of inbred progeny of rats. *Genetics*, 43, 594-600 (1958).

8. Clayton, G. A., J. A. Morris, and A. Robertson. An experimental check on quantitative genetical theory. I. Short term response to selection. *J. Genetics*, 55, 131-151 (1957).

9. Clayton, G. A., and A. Robertson. An experimental check on quantitative genetical theory. II. The long-term effects of selection. *J. Genetics*, 55, 152-170 (1957).

10. Cochrem, F. Selection for relationships opposite to those predicted by the genetic correlation between two traits in the house mouse (*Mus musculus*). *Nature*, 183, 342-343 (1959).

11. Craig, J. V., and A. B. Chapman. Experimental test of predictions of inbred line performance in crosses. *J. Animal. Sci.*, 12, 124-139 (1953).

12. Crampe, H. Zuchtversuche mit zahmen Wanderratten. *Landwirtsch. Jahrb.*, 13, 389-458 (1883).

13. Dickerson, G. E., and J. W. Gowen. Hereditary obesity and efficient food utilization in mice. *Science, 105,* 496-498 (1947).

14. Falconer, D. S. The problem of environment and selection. *Am. Naturalist, 86,* 293-298 (1952).

15. Falconer, D. S. Selection for large and small size in mice. *J. Genet., 51,* 470-501 (1953).

16. Falconer, D. S. Patterns of response in selection experiments with mice. *Cold Spring Harbor Symposia Quant. Biol., 20,* 178-196 (1955).

17. Falconer, D. S., and J. W. B. King. A study of selection limits in the mouse. *J. Genet., 51,* 561-581 (1953).

18. Falconer, D. S., and A. Robertson. Selection for environmental variability of body size in mice. *Z. Induktive Abstammungs u. Vererbungslehre, 87,* 385-391 (1956).

19. Gowen, J. W. Hybrid vigor in Drosophila. *Heterosis,* Chap. 29. Iowa State College Press, Ames, Iowa, 1952.

20. Grüneberg, H. Variation within inbred strains of mice. *Nature, 173,* 674-676 (1954).

21. Guiata, G. von. Versuche mit Kreuzungen von verschiedenen Rassen der Hausmaus. *Ber. naturforsch. Ges. Freiburg, 10,* 317-332 (1898).

22. Guiata, G. von. Zweite Mittheilung über Versuche mit Kreuzungen von verschiedenen Hausmausrassen. *Ber. naturforsch. Ges. Freiburg, 11,* 131-143 (1900).

23. Hammond, J. The inheritance of fertility in the rabbit. *Harper Adams Utility Poultry J.,* 19, 1934.

24. Hollander, W. F., and J. W. Gowen. A single-gene antagonism between mother and fetus in the mouse. *Proc. Soc. Exptl. Biol. Med., 101,* 425-428 (1959).

25. Hyde, R. H. Fertility and sterility in *Drosophila ampelophila. J. Exptl. Zool. 17,* 141-171, 173-212 (1914).

26. Johansson, I., and O. Venge. A study of the variation in weight during growth and in some skeletal characteristics of adult rabbits. *Kgl. Lantbrukögskol. Ann., 19,* 161-195 (1953).

27. King, H. D. Studies on inbreeding. *J. Exptl. Zool., 26,* 1-54; *26,* 55-98; 27, 1-36; *29,* 71-112 (1918, 1919).

28. Kyle, W. H., and A. B. Chapman. Experimental check of the effectiveness of selection for a quantitative character. *Genetics, 38,* 421-443 (1953).

29. Lasley, E. L. The problem of genetic control. *Proc. 51st Ann. Nat. Meeting of Am. Soc. Animal Production,* 1959. (Mimeo.)

30. Lewis, W. L., and E. J. Warwick. Effectiveness of selection for body weight in mice. *J. Heredity, 44,* 233-238 (1953).

31. MacArthur, J. W. Selection for small and large body size in the house mouse. *Genetics, 34,* 194-209 (1949).

32. Mather, K. *Biometrical Genetics*. Dover Publications, Inc., New York, N. Y., 1949.

33. Mather, K., and B. J. Harrison. The manifold effect of selection. *Heredity, 3*, 1-52, 131-162 (1949).

34. McLaren, A., and D. Michie. Are inbred strains suitable for bioassay? *Nature, 173*, 686-687 (1954).

35. Moenkhaus, W. J. The effects of inbreeding and selection on fertility, vigor, and sex-ratio of *Drosophila ampelophila. J. Morphol.* 22, 123-154 (1911)).

36. Ritzema-Bos, J. Untersuchungen über die Folgen der Zucht in engster Blutverwandtschaft. *Biol. Cent., 14*, 75-81 (1894).

37. Robertson, A. Laboratory breeding experiments and animal improvement. *Proc. 10th Intern. Congr. Genet., 1*, 199-205 (1959).

38. Robertson, F. W. Selection response and the properties of genetic variation. *Cold Spring Harbor Symposia Quant. Biol., 20*, 166-177 (1955).

39. Robertson, F. W. Studies in quantitative inheritance. XII. Cell size and number in relation to genetic and environmental variation of body size in Drosophila. *Genetics, 44*, 869-896 (1959).

40. Robertson, F. W., and E. C. R. Reeve. Studies in quantitative inheritance. I. The effects of selection of wing and thorax length in *Drosophila melanogaster, J. Genet., 50*, 414-448 (1952).

41. Robertson, F. W., and E. C. R. Reeve. Heterozygosity, environmental variation and heterosis. *Nature, 170*, 296-298 (1952).

42. Scossiroli, R. E. Effectiveness of artificial selection under irradiation of plateaued populations of *Drosophila melanogaster. Symposium on Genetics of Population Structure, U.I.B.S. Publ.* Series B, No. 15, Pavia, Italy, pp. 42-66, 1954.

43. Scossiroli, R. E., and S. Scossiroli. On the relative role of mutation and recombination in responses to selection for polygenic traits in irradiated populations of *D. melanogaster. Intern. J. Rad. Biol., 1*, 61-69 (1959).

44. Sokal, R. R., and P. E. Hunter. Reciprocal selection for correlated quantitative characters in Drosophila. *Science, 119*, 649-651 (1954).

45. Tyler, W. J., and A. B. Chapman. Genetically reduced prolificacy in rats. *Genetics, 33*, 565-576 (1948).

46. Venge, O. Studies of the maternal influence on the birth weight in rabbits. *Acta Zool., 31*, 1-148 (1950).

47. Vetukhiv, M. O., and J. A. Beardmore. Effect of environment upon the manifestation of heterosis and homeostasis in *Drosophila pseudoobscura. Genetics, 44*, 759-768 (1959).

48. Weismann, A. *The Evolution Theory*. (Translated by J. A. and M. R. Thompson.) London, 1904.

49. Wentworth, E. N. The segregation of fecundity factors in Drosophila. *J. Genet.*, *3*, 113-120 (1913).

50. Wolfe, H. G., and J. A. Weir. Correlated responses to selection for blood-pH in the mouse. *Genetics*, *44*, 544-545 (Abs.) (1959).

51. Wright, S. The effects of inbreeding and crossbreeding on guinea pigs. *U. S. Dept. Agr. Bull. 1090 and 1121*, 1922.

52. Wright, S. Coefficients of inbreeding and relationship. *Am. Naturalist*, *56*, 330-338 (1922).

53. Wright, S. General, group and special size factors. *Genetics*, *17*, 603-619 (1932).

54. Wright, S. Silvering (si) and diminution (dm) of coat color of the guinea pig, and male sterility of the white or near-white combination of these. *Genetics*, *44*, 563-590 (1959).

55. Wright, S., and O. N. Eaton. The persistence of differentiation among inbred families of guinea pigs. *U. S. Dept. Agr. Bull. 103*, 1929.

56. Yoon, C. H. A decrease in variability in hybrid generations of the time of vaginal opening. *Genetics*, *38*, 704 (Abs.) (1953).

Immunogenetics and Its Application to Livestock Improvement[*]

M. R. Irwin and W. H. Stone

Department of Genetics, University of Wisconsin,
Madison, Wisconsin

The term "immunogenetics," implying a combination of the techniques and principles of both genetics and immunology, was patterned after the term "immunochemistry" which had already achieved a position of respectability in scientific circles at the time the newer term was proposed. In essence, it represents another example of the hybridization of previously separate fields of knowledge in attempts to analyze biological processes. This discussion will be concerned primarily with the subject of blood groups which at present is the largest single topic among those in the field of immunogenetics. However, such topics as tissue transplantation, tumor immunity, disease resistance, and antigens of serum and of tissues other than blood cells are reputable members of immunogenetics and are rapidly growing in scope and importance.

Only one comment will be made with respect to the historical development of events in these two separate scientific disciplines preceding their joint usage. The year 1900 represents a landmark in both genetics and immunology because of the appearance of the three papers announcing the rediscovery of the basic findings of Mendel [(49); see also (53)] and of the appearance of the first of two papers by Landsteiner (71, 72) describing three of the four constituents of the ABO system of blood groups in man.

[*] Paper No. 818 from the Department of Genetics, Agricultural Experiment Station, University of Wisconsin. The experimental results from this department cited in this paper were supported in part by the Research Committee of the Graduate School from funds supplied by the Wisconsin Alumni Research Foundation and by a research grant (E-1643) from the Department of Health, Education and Welfare of the National Institutes of Health, Public Health Service.

239

Landsteiner's discovery (71, 72) of individual differences in the blood of man, and the recognition by von Dungern and Hirschfeld (127) that these differences were inherited, gave the impetus for the investigations of blood groups in a variety of animal species. Even though the early studies on animal blood groups (41, 45, 86, 98, 128) did not yield results which permitted the establishment of well-defined groups, a few reports demonstrated that the antigens of the red blood cells were an index to individuality. As Todd and White (126) pointed out in their studies on cattle blood, "The red blood corpuscles of any individual are thus characterized by a definite individuality of their own, and can be distinguished from those of any other individual." This view, presented at a time when it was generally believed that there were relatively few genes producing cellular antigens, has been amply supported.

CHEMICAL BASIS OF SPECIFICITY

It was assumed at the time of the early studies on cellular antigens that proteins were primarily responsible for antigenic specificity. In fact, in his classic book, Landsteiner (73) argued against the possibility that polysaccharides play a significant role in the specificity of proteins, but he recognized their serological significance. The findings by Heidelberger and Avery (61, 62) that the serological differentiation of the various types of pneumococci depended on the polysaccharides of the capsular material opened new vistas in the field of immunology.

It is universally accepted that the respective cellular antigens which allow the demonstration of the individuality within a species must have their own individuality in chemical terms. An understanding of the chemical basis for the specificities of the cellular antigens is only recently beginning to emerge, even though the information is based on studies of *soluble* blood group substances and not on substances obtained from the red blood cells. The A and B substances of humans appear to be mucopolysaccharides, i.e., macromolecules containing carbohydrate chains and peptide units bound together (67). Morgan and Watkins (80) summarize the evidence which indicates that the specificity of the

A and B soluble substances resides in the carbohydrate portion of the mucopolysaccharide molecules. Different, yet closely related carbohydrate structures appear to be responsible for the differences in the specificities of the A and B substances. It is interesting to note that the full serological activity of the mucopolysaccharide molecules requires the peptide moiety. Some work on the nature of blood group substances of species other than humans has been done. The J substance of cattle (11, 58) appears to be a mucopolysaccharide closely related in terms of its constituents to the ABO blood group substances of humans. In addition, the R substance in sheep (57), as well as the A substance of pigs (110) are antigenically and undoubtedly chemically related to the human A blood groups substance [see Kabat (67) for extensive references] and presumably also to each other. The chemical basis for the cross reactions noted among these various blood group substances is not completely known, but undoubtedly will be forthcoming as further studies on the chemical nature of each of these antigenic characters are made. A wide open field for investigations is awaiting the development of techniques which can break through the difficulties accompanying the use of blood cells as experimental material.

Extensive findings in the field of immunochemistry allow the general conclusion that antibodies to a particular antigen may be reactive with a wide range of related chemical substances. For example, Avery and Goebel (8) found that derivations of two simple monosaccharides, glucose and galactose, which differ only in the spatial configuration at the fourth carbon atom, exhibited complete immunological specificity when combined with chemically distinct proteins derived from widely separated species. In contrast, the antibodies against the α and β azophenol glucosides of glucose (when combined with distinct proteins) were cross-reactive (9). These glucosides differed in spatial configuration at the terminal carbon atom. Similar cross reactivities of antisera to relatively simple chemical substances that are antigenic by virtue of attachment to proteins are well known (73).

The cross reactivity demonstrable with antisera to relatively simple chemical substances which are antigenic (i.e., capable of antibody production) only after attachment to a protein is an example (a) of the high degree of specificity characteristic of antibodies as well as (*b*) of the formation of divers antibodies against even a simple chemical substance. Whether the cross reactivities that may be noted among related naturally occurring antigens, like those of cellular antigens within a blood group system (as the ABO system in man), are due to similar variations in the chemical structure of relatively simple chemical substances is an open question. It appears to the authors, however, that the chemical relations among naturally occurring antigens may be more appropriately illustrated by those which are the basis of the cross reactivities that exist among the pneumococci. Owen (89a) discusses other possible explanations of the chemical relations among naturally occurring antigens.

Types III and VIII of the pneumococci have long been known to be immunologically cross-reactive. The specific capsular substance of Type III is a polycellobiuronic acid, meaning that it is composed of glucose and glucuronic acid in definite linkage. The capsular substance of Type VIII has the same cellobiuronic acid units as part of its molecule, but it also has additional glucose and galactose. The reason for the reciprocal cross reactivity of the antibodies to these two types is the occurrence of multiple cellobiuronic acid units in both capsular substances, although the linkages of the glucose and glucuronic acid units are different. However, mere possession of the same basic units need not result in cross reactivity, as exemplified by the presence of L-rhamnose and D-glucose in both Types II and XVIII, but no cross reactivity has been noted of these two types. [For references, see Heidelberger (60).]

A dramatic example of a practical outcome of theoretical expectations of cross reactivity of substances with cellobiuronic acid units has been described by Heidelberger (60). Cotton is a common example of an insoluble cellulose with long chains of glucose. After oxidation, the oxidized cotton contains multiple cellobiuronic acid units, and these react with Type III and Type VIII antipneumococcus sera. Oxidized cotton is used in the United States as a packing for wounds, without harmful effects. The surgeons can be told the very day that the last bit of oxidized cotton leaves the body because the immunological cross reaction of the oxidized cotton with the two kinds of sera is detectable at a dilution of about one in a million.

These examples of cross reactivity by virtue of "antigenic groupings" would be pertinent if the cross reactivity of antigens of the erythrocytes were due to carbohydrates—a condition for which there is only scanty evidence. Perhaps the only justifiable conclusion to be drawn at present is that cross reactivity indicates a chemical similarity of the antigens, but a chemical similarity may exist without cross reactivity.

DETECTION OF BLOOD GROUPS

The techniques of detection of the blood groups (cellular antigens or antigenic characters) have been described elsewhere (43, 64, 86, 98, 124) and will not be considered here. These entail the interaction of antigens of the erythrocytes and antibodies of the antiserum as measured by agglutination or lysis of the blood cells. More specialized techniques are required for the demonstration of soluble blood group substances (67, 116) and of antigens of tissues other than blood (32). More recently, techniques have become available for the demonstration of individual differences in serum proteins, but these require highly specialized equipment (112, 113).

The objective in the laboratory is to prepare antisera from which typing fluids can be obtained. The antisera usually contain a multiplicity of antibodies and as such are not useful in demonstrating individual differences of the blood cells. Thus, these antisera must be absorbed with blood cells of an appropriate type so that their reactions will be specific for a single antigenic factor. Such absorbed antisera are called *reagents* or *typing fluids*. The antibodies may occur naturally without apparent immunization or may be obtained from antisera following immunization of an individual with cells of another of the same species (isoimmunization) or by immunization with cells from one species into another (heteroimmunization). At present, isoimmunization appears to have produced antibodies with a greater capacity of detecting individual differences *within* a species than antibodies produced by heteroimmunization. However, both kinds of antisera are useful for a complete immunogenetic analysis of the red cell antigens.

Each antigenic substance of the blood cells is studied to determine if it conforms to orthodox genetic expectation. In general, the cellular antigens (factors, groupings, or specificities), although they themselves may act as if composed of multiple antigenic groupings (complexes or phenogroups), behave as expected of Mendelian characters. In fact, with few exceptions, the blood groups behave as simple Mendelian dominant characters. The blood type of an individual can be determined by virtue of the reactions of the cells with a full complement or battery of reagents. The antigenic characters which are determined by genes that behave as though they were at one locus are designated as members of a blood group system. For example, the ABO antigenic characters of man constitute one system and the Rh antigenic characters another.

BLOOD GROUP SYSTEMS OF VARIOUS SPECIES

There are about 59 antigenic characters identified on the red blood cells of man (94, 95). About 49 of these fall into 11 independent blood group systems. In the future, some of the remaining ten, known as "private" and "public" factors, will doubtless be found to belong to systems already established or will represent new systems. Several million combinations of these antigenic factors are theoretically possible in constituting the blood type for each individual. However, Race and Sanger (94) point out that the vast majority will be so rare that they are not likely to be found.

Similarly, in cattle, the only other species which has been so extensively studied, there are 11 blood group systems (64, 123). There are at least 60 antigenic characters detectable within these 11 systems and an additional 15 or more factors which may belong to one of these systems or to new systems. Stormont (123) estimates that many billions of combinations of the cellular antigens in cattle are theoretically possible. From five to nine presumably independent blood group systems are presently recognized in each of the following species: horses (47, 92, 93), sheep (96, 97, 99,

132), pigs (2, 3, 66, 107), chickens (18, 19, 22, 52, 109), and rabbits (31, 65), as listed in Table I. One would anticipate that parallel findings from various laboratories may be made in any species of animal, on the basic assumption that genes on many chromo-

TABLE I.   Blood group systems of various species of animals

Species	Number of Chromosome Pairs[a]	Number of Blood Group Systems Described	Approximate Number of Antigenic Factors Detectable	Hemolytic Disease Reported[b]	Erythrocyte Mosaicism Reported
Human	23	11	59	Yes	Yes
Cattle	30	11	75	No	Yes
Horses	33	5-7	9-10	Yes	No
Sheep	27	7	34	No	Yes
Pigs	20	9	12-14	Yes	No
Chickens	39	6-8	20 ± 3	Yes	No
Rabbits	22	5	7	Yes	No
Dogs	39	?	7	Yes	No

[a] Data obtained from *Handbook of Biological Data,* W. S. Spector, Editor, W. B. Saunders Co., Philadelphia, Pa., 1956.
[b] Either naturally occurring or induced.

somes of a species affect antigens on the red blood cells. Many more antigens are theoretically possible in and on the cells than are demonstrable with presently available techniques, but since the immunological reactions are primarily surface reactions, the number detectable will undoubtedly be less than the theoretical maximum.

BLOOD GROUPS AS AN INDEX TO INDIVIDUALITY

In a species such as cattle in which almost complete individuality of the blood type is possible, except in closely related and inbred individuals, the individuality of the blood types is akin to finger printing in man but with the definite advantage that the inheritance of each of the components of the blood type is understood. Consequently, it is obvious that the blood type can be very useful in identifying an animal in studies where identification by gross physical appearances may not be dependable or feasible.

A very important use of the blood test is in solving cases of disputed parentage. The principle involved is that an individual will possess a cellular antigen only if one or both parents possess it. A very few exceptions to this general rule are known, and the genetic basis for these exceptions strengthens rather than weakens one's confidence in the use of the blood test in disputed parentage. As research on the blood groups of each animal species proceeds, new antigenic characters are certain to be found, and their relationships to presently known blood group systems will be determined. The efficiency of the blood test in cases of disputed parentage increases with increasing knowledge of the antigenic characters, particularly if the genotype as well as the phenotype of an individual can be determined directly from the results of the blood test.

The growing importance of the use of identical twins in experimental procedures means that a reliable test to differentiate identical from fraternal twins would be valuable. In those species whose blood groups have been studied profitably, the blood test is an indispensable part of the diagnosis of zygosity among twins. Here again, the efficiency of the test is directly related to the accuracy with which one individual can be differentiated from another. In other words, the blood test becomes more of an index to individuality as more antigenic factors become known and more information about their inheritance becomes available.

Until recently, the majority of workers in animal blood groups would have stated emphatically that an individual would possess an antigenic character on his erythrocytes only if one or both parents possessed it. However, an observation made on the cells of sheep indicated that the dominant R substance of sheep cells, and probably also the recessive r substance (also called O by various authors) may be inhibited by independent genes (99, 102). Consequently, it is possible to obtain R-positive offspring from R-negative parents. The R and r substances are both normal constituents of the plasma which are taken up by the blood cells, rather than being gene products on the blood cells, and the influence of another pair of genes on the appearance of either R or r in the plasma might not be considered an unusual event. However, similar explanations of a block in the formation of the A character (129) and of the B character (77) of man have been invoked. The question may well be asked whether other antigenic characters may be similarly blocked.

Another situation in which a calf can possess cellular antigens which need not be detected on the cells of either parent in a routine test may occur if one parent is a twin. If the blood of the parent which is a twin happens to contain erythrocytes of the type of the cotwin in greater proportion than its own blood cells (see explanation below), the true blood type of the parent may not be recognized without additional tests. A few cases of this kind have been observed in various laboratories, of which that described by Stone and Palm (117) is an example. Further, Stormont (121a) has observed erythrocyte mosaicism in a heifer recorded as a single birth. (Presumably only one of the twin embryos survived *in utero*.) All workers dealing with blood typing in cattle are aware of the necessity for extra precautions in testing the offspring of twins.

Another source of discrepancies of blood typing between parent and offspring is mutation. Unfortunately there is no information available at present on the rate of mutation of genes affecting cellular antigens. Several examples are known in various laboratories of discrepancies in which mutations *might* be the explanation, and a few of these possible mutations have been recorded (38, 101, 121, 122).

Erythrocyte Mosaicism

Ordinarily one expects that all the red blood cells within an individual are of the same phenotype, that is, have the same blood type. However, there are examples of individuals whose red cells are of two types. This condition is known as erythrocyte mosaicism, and it has turned out to be a very interesting and informative phenomenon.

During the early years of studies of blood groups in cattle, it was tacitly assumed (as has been shown for humans), that identical twins would have the same blood types, but those of fraternal twins would be no more alike than if they had been born singly. It was noted, however, that the blood of twins often reacted peculiarly. Tests on the bloods from twins arising from a case of superfecundation disclosed an unusual and unexpected phenomenon (89). The bloods of these twins gave parallel reactions in the laboratory tests, as would have been expected only if they had been identical twins, and this finding became understandable when it was demonstrated that the blood of each twin carried *not one*, but two kinds of blood cells. Parallel results were noted of the bloods of about 90% of other twin pairs.

Briefly, in the majority of twins in cattle the anastomosis of embryonic membranes *in utero* provides a bridge for the reciprocal migration of embryonic cells ancestral to the hematopoietic tissues, so that each twin carries the two kinds of hematopoietic tissue. Each twin then possesses erythrocytes formed by its own hematopoietic tissues as well as those formed by the tissues derived (transplanted) from the cotwin, and thus exhibits erythrocyte mosaicism. It is readily understandable now why fraternal twins of cattle usually possess identical blood types. It is further apparent that to distinguish between identical and fraternal twins with identical blood types requires the detection of erythrocyte mosaicism. Twins without erythrocyte mosaicism *could* be identical but *need* not be, whereas twins with erythrocyte mosaicism cannot be identical. Despite the frequent occurrence of erythrocyte mosaicism in cattle twins, the blood test is probably the best means at present of distinguishing between identical and fraternal twins because mosaicism can usually be detected (100, 120).

As often happens in basic research, the findings turn out to be of some practical significance. One aspect of the studies on cattle twins of unlike sex is particularly pertinent. A female born twin to a bull and possessing erythrocyte mosaicism will be a freemartin or non-breeder, by virtue of the anastomosis of blood vessels with the male cotwin *in utero*, but a female twin to a bull with a different blood type from the cotwin will be as fertile as if born singly (118).

It appears that there may be a migration in cattle twins of embryonal cells other than those ancestral to the hematopoietic tissues, because the extremely sensitive biological test of tissue transplantation has failed to differentiate between fraternal and identical twins (1); that is, twins judged to be fraternal by morphological criteria accepted grafts of each other's skin, but would not accept grafts from a sib or other individuals. These results are readily understandable on the basis that antigens or antigen-like substances from each of the twins have created a state of "immunological tolerance" in each twin toward antigenic substances belonging to the cotwin.

The erythrocyte mosaicism resulting from anastomosis of embryonic membranes *in utero* may appear in other species of animals. It has been noted in sheep (125), and the ewe was reported to be a freemartin. Three cases have been reported in man [for references, see Race and Sanger (94)], but no effect on fertility has been noted. It will be of considerable biological importance and interest to determine whether anastomosis of fetal membranes and erythrocyte mosaicism occur in other species, particularly in species in which multiparous births are the rule.

There is at least one other way by which mosaicism of the erythrocytes can result. Somatic mutations, or phenocopy production (6), occurring in the blood-forming tissues could provide blood exhibiting mosaicism. Cotterman (34, 35) reported two human families involving four individuals, not twins, who showed erythrocyte mosaicism presumably as the result of somatic mutations of the genes responsible for the ABO blood groups. Recently, Furuhata *et al.* (48) reported the apparent transmission of erythrocyte mosaicism of the AO groups from a mosaic father to four of his seven children. (One son exhibited mosaicism in factors other than A and O.) Atwood and Scheinberg (7) found a frequency of about 1:1000 mutant cells in several individuals studied. Presumably they were measuring normal rates of somatic mutation in tissues forming the red blood cells. These "mutational" mosaics also involved the ABO blood group system. Thus, it appears that mosaicism of the erythrocytes resulting from some kind of genetic change in the somatic tissues promises to provide the geneticist with a new tool for studying differences *within* an individual (35). The domestic animals should be excellent material for such studies.

Hemolytic Disease of the Newborn

The dramatic findings in man that incompatibility of the blood groups between mother and fetus may result in hemolytic disease (erythroblastosis fetalis) of the newborn (74-76) provided the explanation for a similar affliction of foals (26, 28, 33). One difference in the appearance of the hemolytic disease in foals, called neonatal isoerythrolysis (24, 55), is that the antibodies formed by the mother against the cells of the developing fetus are passed on to the foal only through the milk (25), whereas in humans the antibodies traverse the placental membranes and therefore are present in the serum of the infant at birth. Thus, in species whose placentae are essentially impermeable to antibodies, hemolytic disease of the newborn may be expected only if the newborn ingests milk (colostrum) containing antibodies within the first few days after birth. Nursing on foster mothers is an effective control measure (36), and this is actually a rediscovery and slight variation of the control measure prescribed for mule foals by Chicoli (29) [cited by Roberts (103)] in 1861.

Hemolytic disease of the newborn has been reported also in pigs (23, 27, 39) and in dogs (130, 131). However, in these animals the antibodies are usually induced by direct immunization of the mother with blood from the father or with other blood containing some of the cellular antigens of the father, rather than by transplacental immunization as in humans and horses. The antibodies reach the newborn through the mother's milk, since the placentae are apparently not permeable to antibodies. The observation by Briles (16), that hemolytic disease may be induced in chickens by passage through the egg yolk of antibodies induced in the hen suggests that hemolytic disease of the newborn is possible in any animal species provided that the antibodies of the mother reach the red cells of the offspring irrespective of the route. However, there are reliable reports that antibodies from the mother may be demonstrable in the circulation of the newborn in both humans (54) and rabbits (59, 68) without harmful effects being detectable. The mechanism which protects the cells of the newborn from destruction by these antibodies is unknown and presents a challenge for further research.

Attempts to induce hemolytic disease in cattle (14, 69) and sheep (99) have been unsuccessful. In cattle, it appears that the newborn calf is protected by the neutralization of the antibodies during their passage through the alimentary canal after the ingestion of the mother's milk. Thus, antibodies that could react with the calf's cells fail to enter the circulation (69).

GENE FREQUENCIES AS AN INDEX TO BREED STRUCTURE

Differences in the frequency of genes account for the differences between species as well as for the differences among various populations, varieties, or breeds within a species. Thus, soon after it was discovered that the human blood groups were genetically controlled, it was noted (63) that their frequencies were different in different populations. At present, the physical anthropologists depend primarily upon blood groups in describing the relationships and origins of populations (13, 83).

A knowledge of the frequency, within and between various populations, of genes which produce cellular antigens would add materially to our understanding of the evolution of the various breeds of livestock and the relationships among them. However, only a few such studies have been made, primarily in cattle. The most extensive ones have been made by Neimann-Sørensen (85) on three breeds of Danish cattle, by Rendel (101) on three Swedish breeds, by Bouw (12) on two Dutch breeds, and by Braend (15) on Norwegian breeds. Earlier studies by Owen et al. (90) reported differential frequencies of 25 of 30 antigenic factors in American Holstein-Friesian and Guernsey cattle, and Stormont (119) studied the gene frequencies at two of the blood group loci in these breeds. Preliminary data on the gene frequencies in five American breeds have been presented recently by Stormont (123), and of cellular antigens in pigs by Joysey et al. (66). The frequencies of the antigenic factors and of the causative genes in three European and two African breeds of cattle in South Africa are being studied by Osterhoff (87).

As the knowledge of the blood groups of various species increases, it is to be expected that additional studies of this kind will be made. Comparisons of the subpopulations of breeds which are scattered in various parts of the world and of breeds indigenous to widely separated areas, as in Europe, Asia, Africa, and the Americas, offer a fertile field for investigation.

BLOOD GROUPS AND FITNESS

For many years it was assumed that the genes controlling blood groups in man were selectively neutral; that is, the fitness of an individual was not affected by the presence or absence of any of the blood group genes, and consequently the gene frequencies were not altered by natural selection. Recent evidence from a variety of sources strongly suggests that this view is incorrect. Now that it is generally accepted that the blood group genes may not be selectively neutral it is not necessary to adhere to the unlikely assumption that mutation and perhaps genetic drift are the only factors responsible for maintaining this polymorphism. Selection could easily account for the high degree of diversity or polymorphism noted among the blood groups.

The first and most striking example of selection acting on the human blood groups is the incompatibility between mother and fetus with respect to the Rh groups. Also, hemolytic disease, fetal death, stillbirths, miscarriages, sex ratio, and general fertility effects have been ascribed to incompatibilities between fetus and mother with respect to the ABO blood groups. [See Race and Sanger (94) for literature citations.] At present there is only suggestive evidence that fetal-maternal incompatibility operates in livestock. Morton *et al.* (82) reported preliminary findings in cattle of a 10% deficiency of calves from incompatible matings. Recently, Plum (91) suggested that there was an apparent increase in survival in cattle as the number of antigenic factors by which the mates differed increased. He proposed that the dissimilarities in antigens might be used as an index to hybrid vigor. The significance of these findings is questionable because Plum used the blood factors rather than the "genes" for his calculations and seemingly did not distinguish between compatible and incompatible matings. The preliminary findings of Ashton (5) suggest that there may be a differential advantage in cattle for embryo survival in which either the β globulins of the dam, or a particular β globulin from either parent, provided an advantage.

The examples cited represent selection operating sometime between fertilization and early postnatal life. But selection may operate also in later life. Recent reports of the association between certain of the ABO blood groups in man and the incidence of adult diseases are further evidence that the genes controlling the blood groups are not selectively neutral (30, 104, 105). The associations between blood group O and duodenal ulcer and blood group A and gastric carcinoma are particularly striking. However, in these instances the net genetic effect is not likely to be as great as it might be if the effect occurred early in life before the reproductive period.

Fisher (46) stated that a "stable" polymorphism could be maintained in a population if the heterozygote were at a selective advantage over either homozygote. The best data available relative to this question come from Briles (17, 18, 20, 21), Shultz and Briles (111), and Gilmour (50-52) in their studies on blood groups in chickens. These data indicate that artificial selection favored the heterozygote in at least two of the blood group loci. These observations of Briles and co-workers also indicate that the heterozygotes for at least one of the blood group systems of chickens maintained an advantage over the homozygotes in such characters as hatchability of fertile eggs, body weight at nine weeks of age, and egg production. Seemingly, heterozygosity at one of the loci has a major influence on a fundamental physiological process, and there was some indication that this effect might vary in different genetic combinations.

Only preliminary data on the possible heterotic effect of blood group genes are available in cattle. Morton, Stone and Irwin (unpublished observations) noted more cattle heterozygous at the Z locus than would have been expected from the inbreeding coefficient of the sample. These data are now being extended. Recently, Laben and Stormont (70) reported suggestive evidence that in an inbred Jersey herd a few individuals which were heterozygous at the B locus produced more fat-corrected milk than homozygotes, and in another group the heterozygotes were slightly more efficient in reproduction than the homozygotes. Rendel (personal communication) advised that animals heterozygous at the B locus seemingly had a significantly higher fat percentage than those homozygous. The whole field of the possible heterotic effects of blood group genes in livestock awaits exploration with better than average chances of finding useful information.

In man, various workers have recorded an excess of MN children from MN × MN matings. [See Morton and Chung (81) for references.] This excess of heterozygotes has been attributed to errors of technique by Wiener (128), although this explanation was disputed by Haldane (56). A recent analysis of the data indicates that the excess of MN offspring may be an example of an advantage of the heterozygotes, apparently limited to MN mothers (81).

An obvious question in the minds of livestock breeders is whether or not the blood groups are correlated with any morphological or physiological characteristics of economic importance. Correlations might result if the genes controlling the blood groups had pleiotropic effects, that is, having effects on both the blood groups and other characteristics, or if the blood group genes were closely linked to genes controlling other characteristics.

It seems unlikely that genetic linkage between genes for blood groups and those for quantitative characters will be a useful tool in animal improvement, because of the expectation of crossing over. But if the genes for blood groups have some pleiotropic effect other than on the surface of the erythrocyte, it is conceivable that such an effect might influence the expression of a morphological or physiological character. Various ramifications of this topic, with arguments pro and con, have been considered by Robertson (106).

A few reports in the literature deal with attempts to find such correlations in cattle. McClure (78) observed no correlation between the presence of the factor A and variations of the butterfat test in Holstein-Friesians. Mitscherlich et al. (79) found a significant relation between the blood factor M and first lactation yield. Animals carrying M yielded *much less* milk than those not carrying this factor. Dunlop (42) reported only a doubtful correlation between certain of the blood factors and three of the "type scores" on 13 morphological characters. Nair *et al.* (84) noted some evidence of an association of cellular antigens and the frequency of certain defects.

Two additional studies on the association between blood groups and production characters in cattle have been made, but the results are not as yet published. Rendel (1959, personal communication) found a significant relationship between blood group alleles at the B locus and fat percentage of the milk. Cows carrying the allele $B^{BO_1Y_2D'}$ produced 0.16 more unit of fat than those lacking the allele. Rendel also found a depressing effect of the blood factor L on fat percentage. A similar study by Neimann-Sørensen (1959, personal communication) also revealed a statistically significant influence of certain B alleles on fat percentage and milk yield. However, with the present evidence, it is doubtful that the blood groups have prognostic value for a practical breeding program.

In order to be certain that a blood group gene exerted a significant influence upon a complex character, such as milk production, at least a thousand animals in each of two groups would be required if the difference in the standard deviations of the two groups were 10%, and more than 6000 animals in each group if the difference were 5%. Needless to say, data of this magnitude will take time to obtain, and may well require the joint efforts of different laboratories. (We are indebted to our colleague, Dr. Newton Morton, for the estimates of the numbers required in the groups.)

Genetic Effects on Proteins

Many attempts have been made to demonstrate individual differences in the serum (proteins) within a species, but until recently these attempts have generally been unsuccessful. [For references, see Landsteiner (73).] An indication that individual differences existed in the serum, presumably of the proteins, of humans was implied in the report of Cumley and Irwin (37), but no information was then available on the inheritance of these differences. Recent studies of Smithies and Walker (114, 115) have verified that genetic differences exist in the serum proteins of man. Further, Smithies and Hickman (113) have demonstrated five distinct types of proteins in cattle serum. These were β globulins, and their inheritance could be explained by the assumption of a triple allelic series of genes. Ashton (4, 5) has recognized the sixth type of β globulin. Different types of hemoglobin have been reported in cattle (10, 108), and in sheep (44). The techniques used have been either paper or starch gel electrophoresis.

Attempts to demonstrate individual differences in the serum proteins by isoimmunization have generally been unsuccessful (73). In contrast, reports by Oudin (88) and Dray and Young (40) indicate that antibodies were produced in rabbits against serum antigens (of rabbits), with electrophoretic mobilities corresponding to α, β, and γ globulins in the experiments of Dray and Young.

Thus it appears certain that the more refined methods now available for the study of slight differences in (related) proteins, as migration in a starch gel or antigen-antibody reactions in a gel, will allow individual differences in proteins to be added to the arsenal of the immunogeneticist.

GENERAL STATEMENT

It is our belief that all research findings which contribute to a better understanding of the biological processes of any species will become an integral part of the steps toward improvement. On this basis, one may apply to the present situation of immunogenetics as a new approach in the study of animals the words of one of the great statesmen of the world: "This is not the end, nor is it the beginning. It is, perhaps, the end of the beginning."

REFERENCES

1. Anderson, D., R. E. Billingham, G. H. Lampkin, and P. B. Medawar. The use of skin grafting to distinguish between monozygotic and dizygotic twins in cattle. *Heredity*, 5, 379-397 (1951).

2. Andresen, E. Investigations on bloodgroups in pigs. *Nord. Veterinärmed.*, *9*, 274-284 (1957).

3. Andresen, E., and M. R. Irwin. The E blood group system of the pig. *Nord. Veterinärmed.*, *11*, 540-547 (1959).

4. Ashton, G. C. Genetics of beta-globulin polymorphism in British cattle. *Nature*, *182*, 370-372 (1958).

5. Ashton, G. C. β-Globulin polymorphism and early foetal mortality in cattle. *Nature*, *183*, 404-405 (1959).

6. Atwood, K. C., and D. Megill. Erythrocyte automosaicism in polycythemics treated with phosphorus-32. *Science*, *130*, 1411-1412 (1959).

7. Atwood, K. C., and S. L. Scheinberg. Some variation in human erythrocyte antigens. *J. Cellular Comp. Physiol.*, *52* (*Suppl. 1*), 97-125 (1958).

8. Avery, O. T., and W. F. Goebel. Chemo-immunological studies on conjugated carbohydrate-proteins. II. Immunological specificity of synthetic sugar-protein antigens. *J. Exptl. Med.*, *50*, 533-550 (1929).

9. Avery, O. T., W. F. Goebel, and F. H. Babers. Chemo-immunological studies on conjugated carbohydrate-proteins. VII. Immunological specificity of antigens prepared by combining α- and β-glucosides of glucose with proteins. *J. Exptl. Med.*, *55*, 769-780 (1932).

10. Bangham, A. D. Distribution of electrophoretically different hemoglobins among cattle breeds in Great Britain. *Nature*, *179*, 467 (1957).

11. Bednekoff, A. G., W. H. Stone, M. R. Irwin, and K. P. Link. Chemical studies on the J substance of cattle serum. *Proc. X Intern. Congr. Genet. 2*, 19. University of Toronto Press, Toronto, Canada, 1958.

12. Bouw, J. Blood group studies in Dutch cattle breeds. H. Veenam & Sons, Wageningen, Holland, 1958.

13. Boyd, W. C. Genetics and the races of man. Little, Brown and Co., Boston, Mass., 1950.

14. Braend, M. Some results from cattle blood group work in Norway. *Proc. VII Intern. Congr. Animal Husbandry, Madrid, Subj. 2*, 53-63 (1956).

15. Braend, M. Blood groups of cattle in Norway. Serological and genetical studies. *Skandinavisk Bladforlag*, 1959.

16. Briles, W. E. Induced hemolytic disease in chicks. *Genetics*, *33*, 96-97 (1948).

17. Briles, W. E. Evidence for overdominance of the B blood group alleles in the chicken. *Genetics*, *39*, 961-962 (1954).

18. Briles, W. E. The relationship between B blood group phenotype and adult performance in two White Leghorn inbred lines. *Poultry Sci.*, *35*, 1134-1135 (1956).

19. Briles, W. E. A new blood group system, E, closely linked with the A system in chickens. *Poultry Sci.*, *37*, 1189 (1958).

20. Briles, W. E., C. P. Allen, and T. W. Millen. The B blood group system of chickens. I. Heterozygosity in closed populations. *Genetics*, *42*, 631-648 (1957).

21. Briles, W. E., and W. F. Krueger. The effect of parental B blood group genotypes or hatchability and livability in Leghorn inbred lines. *Poultry Sci.*, *34*, 1182 (1955).

22. Briles, W. E., W. H. McGibbon, and M. R. Irwin. On multiple alleles effecting cellular antigens in the chicken. *Genetics*, *35*, 633-652 (1950).

23. Bruner, D. W., R. G. Brown, F. E. Hull, and A. S. Kinkaid. Blood factors and baby pig anemia. *J. Am. Vet. Med. Assoc.*, *115*, 94-96 (1949).

24. Bruner, D. W., and E. R. Doll. Blood groups in horses (Indian System): Their value in transfusions and neonatal isoerythrolysis. *Cornell Vet.*, *43*, 217-222 (1953).

25. Bruner, D. W., E. R. Doll, F. E. Hull, and A. S. Kinkaid. Further studies on hemolytic icterus in foals. *Am. J. Vet. Research*, *11*, 22-25 (1950).

26. Bruner, D. W., F. E. Hull, P. R. Edwards, and E. R. Doll. Icteric foals. *J. Am. Vet. Med. Assoc.*, *112*, 440-441 (1948).

27. Buxton, J. C., and N. H. Brooksbank. Haemolytic disease of new-born pigs caused by iso-immunization of pregnancy. *Nature*, *172*, 355 (1953).

28. Caroli, J., and M. Bessi. Sur la cause et le traitement de l'ictère grave des muletons nouveau-nés. *Compt. rend.*, *224*, 969-971 (1947).

29. Chicoli, N. *G. Med. Vet. Prat.*, *10*, 84 (1861).

30. Clarke, C. A. Correlations of ABO blood groups with peptic ulcer, cancer, and other diseases. *Am. J. Human Genet.*, *11* (2), 400-404 (1959).

31. Cohen, C. Blood group factors in the rabbit. II. The inheritance of six factors. *Genetics*, *40*, 770-780 (1955).

32. Coombs, R. R. A., D. Bedford, and L. M. Rouillard. A and B blood-group antigens on human epidermal cells demonstrated by mixed agglutination. *Lancet*, *1*, 461-463 (1956).

33. Coombs, R. R. A., R. C. Crowhurst, F. T. Day, D. H. Heard, I. T. Hinde, J Hoogstraten, and H. B. Parry. Haemolytic disease of new-born foals due to iso-immunization of pregnancy. *J. Hyg.*, *46*, 403-418 (1948).

34. Cotterman, C. W. Mosaicism in two families. Unpublished paper read at the 8th Annual Meeting American Society of Human Genetics, East Lansing, Mich., 1952.

35. Cotterman, C. W. Erythrocyte antigen mosaicism. *J. Cellular Comp. Physiol.*, *52* (*Suppl. 1*), 69-96 (1958).

36. Cronin, M. T. I. Haemolytic disease of newborn foals. *Vet. Record*, *67*, 479-495 (1955).

37. Cumley, R. W., and M. R. Irwin. Individual specificity of human serum. *J. Immunol.*, *46*, 63-70 (1943).

38. Datta, S. P., W. H. Stone, W. J. Tyler, and M. R. Irwin. A possible heritable exception in cattle blood groups. *Records Genet. Soc. Am. 28* (abs.), 1959.

39. Doll, E. R., and R. G. Brown. Isohemolytic disease of newborn pigs. *Cornell Vet.*, *44*, 86-93 (1954).

40. Dray, S., and G. O. Young. Differences in the antigenic components of sera of individual rabbits as shown by induced isoprecipitins. *J. Immunol.*, *81*, 142-149 (1958).

41. Dujarric de la Rivière, R., and A. Eyquem. *Les Groupes Sanguin Chez les Animaux*, 1st edition. Flammarion, Paris, 1953.

42. Dunlop, A. A. Type differences and blood antigens in a Guernsey herd. *J. Dairy Sci.*, *34*, 154-166 (1951).

43. Dunsford, I., and C. C. Bowley. *Techniques in Blood Grouping*. Oliver & Boyd, London, 1955.

44. Evans, J. V., J. W. B. King, B. L. Cohen, H. Harris, and F. L. Warren. Genetics of hemoglobin and blood potassium differences in sheep. *Nature*, *178*, 849 (1956).

45. Ferguson, L. C. The blood groups of animals. *Advances in Vet. Sci.*, *2*, 106-137 (1955).

46. Fisher, R. A. *The Genetical Theory of Natural Selection*. Oxford University Press, London, 1930.

47. Franks, D. The red cell antigens of the horse. II. Antigens defined by immune isoantibodies. *J. Comp. Pathol.*, *69*, 353-366 (1959).

48. Furuhata, T., M. Kitahama, and N. Nozawa. A family study of the so-called blood group chimera. *Proc. Japan Acad.*, *35*, 55-57 (1959).

49. *Genetics*, Editors of. The birth of genetics. Supplement to *Genetics*, *35* (5, p. 2), 30-47 (1950).

50. Gilmour, D. G. Selective advantage of heterozygosis for blood group genes among inbred chickens. *Heredity*, *8*, 291 (1954).

51. Gilmour, D. G. Maintenance of segregation of blood group genes during inbreeding in chickens. *Heredity*, *12*, 141-142 (1958).

52. Gilmour, D. G. Segregation of genes determining red cell antigens at high levels of inbreeding in chickens. *Genetics*, *44*, 14-33 (1959).

53. Glass, B. The long neglect of a scientific discovery: Mendel's Laws of Inheritance. *Studies in Intellectual History, History of Ideas Club*, pp. 148-159. Johns Hopkins Press, Baltimore, Md., 1953.

54. Haberman, S., and E. E. Aguilar. The specificity of the elution and direct Coomb's tests for the detection of erythroblastosis. *Papers in Dedication of 60th Birthday of P. H. Andresen*, pp. 51-64. Munksgaard, Copenhagen, Denmark, 1957.

55. Hagan, W. A., and D. W. Bruner. *The Infectious Diseases of Domestic Animals*, 2nd edition, pp. 86-87. Comstock Publishing Co., Ithaca, N. Y., 1951.

56. Haldane, J. B. S. The formal genetics of man. *Proc. Roy. Soc. (London), B135*, 147-170 (1948).

57. Hayashi, J. A., A. G. Bednekoff, and W. H. Stone. Unpublished observations, 1959.

58. Hayashi, J. A., W. H. Stone, K. P. Link, and M. R. Irwin. The J substance of cattle. V. Immunochemical studies of the J substance from bovine gastric mucosa. *J. Immunol., 81*, 82-90 (1958).

59. Heard, D. H., I. T. Hinde, and L. S. Mynors. An experimental study of haemolytic disease of the newborn due to isoimmunization of pregnancy. I. An attempt to produce the syndrome in the rabbit. *J. Hyg., 47*, 119-131 (1949).

60. Heidelberger, M. *Lectures in Immunochemistry*. Academic Press, New York, N. Y., 1956.

61. Heidelberger, M., and O. T. Avery. The soluble specific substance of pneumococcus. *J. Exptl. Med., 38*, 73-79 (1923).

62. Heidelberger, M., and O. T. Avery. The soluble specific substance of pneumococcus. Second paper. *J. Exptl. Med., 40*, 301-316 (1924).

63. Hirschfeld, L., and H. Hirschfeld. Serological differences between the blood of different races. The results of researches on the Macedonian front. *Lancet, 197* (II), 675-679 (1919).

64. Irwin, M. R. Blood grouping and its utilization in animal breeding. *VII Intern. Congr. Animal Husbandry Subj., 2*, 7-32 (1956).

65. Joysey, V. C. The serology, inheritance and distribution of some red cell antigens in the rabbit. Ph.D. Thesis, University of Cambridge, England, 1956.

66. Joysey, V. C., R. F. W. Goodwin, and R. R. A. Coombs. The blood groups of the pig. VII. The distribution of twelve red cell antigens in seven breeds. *J. Comp. Pathol., 69*, 292-299 (1959).

67. Kabat, E. A. *Blood Group Substances*. Academic Press, New York, N. Y., 1956.

68. Kellner, A., and E. F. Hedal. 1953. Experimental erythroblastosis fetalis in rabbits. II. The passage of blood group antigens and their specific isoantibodies across the placenta. *J. Exptl. Med., 97*, 50-60 (1953).

69. Kiddy, C. A., W. H. Stone, W. J. Tyler, and L. E. Casida. Immunological studies on fertility and sterility. I. An attempt to produce hemolytic disease in cattle by isoimmunization. *Acta Haematol., 20*, 236-245 (1958).

70. Laben, R. C., and C. Stormont. Genetic analysis of the B, F-V and Z blood group loci in an inbred Jersey herd. *J. Animal Sci., 17*, 1139-1140 (abs.) (1958),

71. Landsteiner, K. Zur Kenntis der antifermentativen, lytischen und agglutinierenden WirKungen des Blutserums und der Lymphe. *Zentr. Bakteriol.*, 27, 357-362 (1900).

72. Landsteiner, K. Ueber Agglutinations-erscheinungen normalen menschlichen Blutes. *Wien. klin. Wochschr.*, 14, 1132-1134 (1901).

73. Landsteiner, K. *The Specificity of Serological Reactions.* Harvard University Press, Cambridge, Mass., 1945.

74. Levine, P., L. Burnham, E. M. Katzin, and P. Vogel. The role of isoimunization in the pathogenesis of erythroblastosis fetalis. *Am. J. Obstet. Gynecol.*, 42, 925-937 (1941).

75. Levine, P., and E. M. Katzin. Isoimmunization in pregnancy and the varieties of isoagglutinins observed. *Proc. Soc. Exptl. Biol. Med.*, 45, 343-346 (1940).

76. Levine, P., and R. E. Stetson. An unusual case of intragroup agglutination. *J. Am. Med. Assoc.*, 113, 126-127 (1939).

77. Levine, P., E. Robinson, M. Celano, O. Briggs, and L. Falkinburg. Gene interaction resulting in suppression of blood group substance B. *Blood*, 10, 1100-1108 (1955).

78. McClure, T. J. Correlation study of bovine erythrocyte antigen A and butterfat test. *Nature*, 170, 327 (1952).

79. Mitscherlich, Von E., A. Tolle, and E. Walter. Untersuchungen über das Bestehen von Besiehungen zwischen Blutgruppenfactoren und Milchleistung des Rindes. *Z. Tierzücht. Züchtungsbiol.*, 72, 289-301 (1959).

80. Morgan, W. T. J., and W. M. Watkins. Some aspects of the biochemistry of the human blood-group substances. *Brit. Med. Bull.*, 15, 109-113 (1959).

81. Morton, N. E., and C. S. Chung. Are the MN blood groups maintained by selection? *Am. J. Human Genet.*, 2, 237- 251 (1959).

82. Morton, N. E., W. H. Stone, and M. R. Irwin. Linkage and fitness of cattle blood factors (abs.). *Genetics*, 41, 655 (1956).

83. Mourant, A. E. Blood groups and anthropology. *Brit. Med. Bull.*, 15, 140-144 (1959).

84. Nair, P. G., T. M. Ludwick, E. J. Lazear, and L. C. Ferguson. Preliminary report comparing cellular antigens with type defects in dairy cattle. *J. Dairy Sci.*, 38, 615-616 (1955).

85. Neimann-Sørensen, A. Blood groups and breed structure as exemplified by three Danish breeds. *Acta Agr. Scand.*, 6, 115-137 (1956).

86. Neimann-Sørensen, A. *Blood Groups of Cattle.* A/S Carl Fr. Mortensen, Copenhagen, Denmark, 1958.

87. Osterhoff, D. R. Personal communication, 1959.

88. Oudin, J. L' "allotypie," de certains antigenes protéediques du serum. *Compt. rend.*, 242, 2606-2608 (1956).

89. Owen, R. D. Immunogenetic consequences of vascular anastomoses between bovine twins. *Science, 102,* 400-401 (1945).

89a. Owen, R. D. Immunogenetics. *Proc. 10th Intern. Congr. Genet., 1,* 364-374 (1959).

90. Owen, R. D., C. Stormont, and M. R. Irwin. An immunogenetic analysis of racial differences in two breeds of dairy cattle. *Genetics, 32,* 64-74 (1947).

91. Plum, M. Hetero blood types and breeding performance. *Science, 129,* 781-782 (1959).

92. Podliachouk, L. Les antigenes de group sanguins des équides et leur transmission héréditaire. Ph.D. Thesis, Faculty of Science, University of Paris, 1957.

93. Podliachouk, L. Les groupes sanguins des équides (cheval, mulet, âne). *Ann. inst. Pasteur., 95,* 7-22 (1958).

94. Race, R. R., and Ruth Sanger. *Blood Groups in Man,* 3rd edition. Blackwell Scientific Publications, Oxford, England, 1958.

95. Race, R. R., and Ruth Sanger. The inheritance of blood groups. *Brit. Med. Bull., 15,* 99-108 (1959).

96. Rasmusen, B. A. Blood groups in sheep. Ph.D. Thesis, University of California, Davis, Calif., 1958.

97. Rasmusen, B. A. Blood groups in sheep. I. The X-Z system. *Genetics, 43,* 814-821 (1958).

98. Rendel, J. Blood groups of farm animals. *Animal Breeding Abstracts, 25,* 223-238 (1957).

99. Rendel, J. Further studies on some antigenic characters of sheep blood determined by epistatic action of genes. *Acta Agr. Scand., 7,* 224-259 (1957).

100. Rendel, J. Studies of cattle blood groups. III. Blood grouping as a method of diagnosing the zygosity of twins. *Acta Agr. Scand., 8,* 162-190 (1958).

101. Rendel, J. Studies of cattle blood groups. IV. The frequency of blood group genes in Swedish cattle breeds, with special reference to breed structure. *Acta Agr. Scand., 8,* 191-215 (1958).

102. Rendel, J., A. Neimann-Sørensen, and M. R. Irwin. Evidence for epistatic action of genes for antigenic substances in sheep. *Genetics, 39,* 396-408 (1954).

103. Roberts, F. Hemolytic disease of the newborn. *Brit. Med. Bull., 15,* 119-122 (1959).

104. Roberts, J. A. Fraser. Some association between blood groups and disease. *Brit. Med. J., 15,* 129-133 (1959).

105. Roberts, J. A. Fraser. Some further observations on associations between blood groups and disease. *Proc. 10th Intern. Congr. Genet., 1,* 120-125 (1959).

106. Robertson, A. Blood-grouping in dairy cattle improvement. *Proc. 7th Intern. Congr. Animal Husbandry Subj., 2,* 79-84 (1956).

107. Saison, R. Report of a blood group system in swine. *J. Immunol.*, *80*, 463-467 (1958).

108. Salisbury, G. W., and D. C. Shreffler. Hemoglobin variants in dairy cattle. *J. Dairy Sci.*, *40*, 1198-1199 (1957).

109. Scheinberg, S. L. Genetic studies of cellular antigens in the chicken. *Genetics*, *41*, 834-844 (1956).

110. Schermer, S., W. Kayser, and A. Kaempffer. Vergleichende Untersuchungen über die Isoagglutinine in Blute des Menschen und des Schweines. *Z. Immunitätsforsch.*, *68*, 437-449 (1930).

111. Shultz, F. T., and W. E. Briles. The adaptive value of blood group genes in chickens. *Genetics*, *38*, 34-50 (1953).

112. Smithies, O. Zone electrophoresis in starch gels and its application to studies of serum proteins. *Advances in Protein Chem.*, *14*, 65-113 (1959).

113. Smithies, O., and C. G. Hickman. Inherited variations in the serum proteins of cattle. *Genetics*, *43*, 374-385 (1958).

114. Smithies, O., and W. F. Walker. Genetic control of some serum proteins in normal humans. *Nature*, *176*, 1265-1266 (1955).

115. Smithies, O., and W. F. Walker. Notation for serum-protein groups and the genes controlling their inheritance. *Nature*, *178*, 694-695 (1956).

116. Stone, W. H., and M. R. Irwin. The J substance of cattle. I. Developmental and immunogenetic studies. *J. Immunol.*, *73*, 397-406 (1954).

117. Stone, W. H., and J. E. Palm. A disputed parentage case in cattle involving mosaicism of the erythrocytes. *Genetics*, *37*, 630 (1952).

118. Stone, W. H., C. Stormont, and M. R. Irwin. Blood typing as a means of differentiating the potentially fertile from non-fertile heifer born twin with a bull. *J. Animal Sci.*, *11*, 744 (1952).

119. Stormont, C. The F-V and Z systems of bovine blood groups. *Genetics*, *37*, 39-48 (1952).

120. Stormont, C. Research with cattle twins. In *Statistics and Mathematics in Biology*, O. Kempthorne, T. A. Bancroft, J. W. Gowen, and J. L. Lush, Editors, pp. 407-418. Iowa State College Press, Ames, Iowa, 1954.

121. Stormont, C. On the genetics and serology of the B system of bovine blood groups. *Proc. 9th Intern. Congr. Genet.*, *2*, 1205-1206 (1954).

121a. Stormont, C. Erythrocyte mosaicism in a heifer recorded as single-born. *J. Animal Sci.*, *13*, 94-98 (1954).

122. Stormont, C. Linked genes, pseudoalleles and blood groups. *Am. Naturalist*, *89*, 105-116 (1955).

123. Stormont, C. On the applications of blood groups in animal breeding. *Proc. 10th Intern. Congr. Genet.*, *1*, 206-224 (1959).

124. Stormont, C., and R. W. Cumley. Cellular antigens in cattle blood. *J. Heredity, 34*, 34-41 (1943).

125. Stormont C., W. C. Weir, and L. L. Lane. Erythrocyte mosaicism in a pair of sheep twins. *Science, 118*, 695-696 (1953).

126. Todd, C., and R. G. White. On the haemolytic immune isolysins of the ox and their relation to the question of individuality and blood relationship. *J. Hyg., 10*, 185-195 (1910).

127. von Dungern, E., and L. H. Hirschfeld. Ueber Nachweis und Vererbung biochemischer Strukturen. *Z. Immunitätsforsch., 4*, 531-546 (1910).

128. Wiener, A. S. *Blood Groups and Transfusion*. C. C Thomas, Springfield, Ill., 1943.

129. Weiner, W., H. B. M. Lewis, P. Moores, R. Sanger, and R. R. Race. A gene, y, modifying the blood group antigen A. *Vox Sanguinis, 2*, 25-37 (1957).

130. Young, L. E., R. M. Christian, D. M. Ervin, R. W. Davis, W. A. O'Brien, S. N. Swisher, and C. L. Yuile. Hemolytic disease in newborn dogs. *Blood, 6*, 291-313 (1951).

131. Young, L. E., D. M. Ervin, and C. L. Yuile. Haemolytic reactions produced in dogs by transfusion of incompatible dog blood and plasma. *Blood, 4*, 6-73 (1949).

132. Ycas, Mary K. W. Studies of the development of a normal antibody and of cellular antigens in the blood of sheep. *J. Immunol., 61*, 327-347 (1949).

Using Germ Plasm for New Products

QUENTIN JONES

Agricultural Research Service,
United States Department of Agriculture, Beltsville, Maryland

and
IVAN A. WOLFF

Agricultural Research Service,
United States Department of Agriculture, Peoria, Illinois

The minuscule use being made of the great variety of germ plasm known to botanists is emphasized by the small number of species used for our economic crops which represents less than 1% of the total. What about the 99% known to science but not to agriculture? Herein lies an opportunity! However, to use the world's germ plasm in higher plants for a greater variety of products, it is axiomatic that we have to know more about that germ plasm. We have to know which units of it produce sufficiently valuable constituents that anyone would want to go to the trouble of growing them, where they can be grown, how they grow, and if they are amenable to modern agronomic practices. Throughout the ages man has discovered plants that have been either beneficial or detrimental to his welfare. There are plants that are suitable for food for him and his animals—those that are poisonous and those that have medicinal value or utility for fiber—and those seemingly useless ones that merely invade his land as weeds and need to be removed. In our specialized and complex industrial civilization, we can no longer resort to the trial and error methods of our ancestors for evaluating natural plant products. If we do so, more research-minded technologists in other fields such as petrochemicals will continue to forge ahead and new plant materials, germ plasm for new products, will not attain as large a proportion of new use areas as might be possible. On the other hand, a well-planned, coordinated research effort to collect and learn more about the chemical composition of plants cannot fail to uncover interesting information of eventual utility. This is one major purpose of new crops research in the United States Department of Agriculture.

IDENTIFYING NEEDS

Agricultural

The present forceful impetus for new crops research stems from a desire to find workable solutions to the knotty problems brought on by mounting surpluses in certain major farm commodities. Alternative crops are needed which will be economically attractive to some of the farmers who are now growing corn, wheat, and cotton. For example, a new crop for wheat lands which would utilize as many acres as are now growing soybeans, a relatively new crop, could eliminate expected future increments of surplus of wheat. Or, a number of smaller new crops could accomplish the same results.

Another, and in the long run more cogent, reason for discovering and developing new crops is based on the benefits to be gained through agricultural diversification. The hazards attendant upon a one-crop agriculture over large areas are well known. Insect and disease outbreaks can quickly reach disastrous proportions. Adverse weather conditions will be reflected throughout large areas in lowered production and consequent widespread economic depression. Agricultural areas with a high degree of, or potentials for crop diversification can, on the other hand, attain and maintain greater economic stability through flexibility in meeting market demands, through reducing the potential impact of the ravages of insects, disease, and weather, and through permitting desirable land conservation practices. Over large areas of the country increased crop diversification can come only through the successful introduction of new crops. Satisfactory alternative crops are not now available.

Industrial

It has been said (15), "The human stomach is not elastic." This truism can be paraphrased for our purposes by saying that we cannot eat our way out of our surpluses into a better agricultural economy. Even if entirely new food crops could be discovered and developed, and this is highly doubtful, market opportunities would have to be developed largely at the expense of present food products. Consequently, searching for new food crops would not appear to be a promising undertaking where the objectives are alternative crops which can profitably utilize large acreages.

The development of modern science and technology in the last hundred years has produced and is continuing to produce an ever increasing pressure for new and different raw materials to keep pace with changing industrial needs. Materials of mineral or petrochemical origins have captured major markets based on many of these industrial needs. Agricultural raw materials, owing to a number of reasons such as instability of supply and inherent inadequacies in available plant products, have lost sizable markets they once held.

It appears obvious that if new, large outlets are to be found for agricultural commodities, industrial (including feed) rather than food markets should receive our attention. It also appears evident that we should concentrate on those industrial needs for which plant products have an inherent competitive advantage over materials of non-agricultural origin. This means that our efforts should be centered on those plant constituents, such as seed oils, proteins, gums and fibrous cellulose, which are present in major amounts, and that within these categories we should search for new and unusual characteristics and properties which can be adapted to special uses.

Plants synthesize many complex glycosides, pigments, steroids, alkaloids, tannins, enzymes, and other classes of substances having complicated structures, perhaps of considerable value. Yet most of these are materials that are present in relatively minor amount. Important as they may possibly be, the major lipid, carbohydrate, and protein constituents are so little known and studied that the job should begin with them, because a discovery there would be the most significant in terms of economics and acres utilized.

This screening study of major constituents has been initiated. Search has been directed toward new industrial seed oils, to seeds that can yield rich sources of protein in themselves or as a by-product meal after oil extraction, to especially nutritious seed proteins, to seed mucilages desired by industry, and to new agricultural sources of paper pulp. Significant results have already been achieved after only about three years of operating the screening program. Several facets of this success will be referred to in succeeding sections, which will include mention of contributions to a more theoretical understanding of plant relationships, and then a short discussion of some of the practical implications.

Identifying Promising Sources

Botanochemical Relationships

Implicit in the plan to screen and use plant germ plasm for new products is the tenet that chemical compositions of plant materials are phenotypic expressions of the complex of interactions between genetic and environmental factors. As with morphological phenotypes, qualitative makeup appears to be largely controlled by genetic factors whereas environmental factors are mostly reflected in quantitative differences such as *relative proportions* of constituents. Thus certain species, grown in cooler regions where maturity is attained less rapidly, produce seed oils having increased proportions of unsaturated fatty acids (7). Fertilization level also can influence the percentage of selected constituents in plant materials. More pertinent, however, are the distinct chemical similarities and differences which can often be demonstrated among and between families, genera, and species. Taxonomists have long used morphological characteristics in developing remarkably good schemes for orderly grouping of members of the plant kingdom. The more occult chemical composition is harder to determine and far less well known. Yet with improved laboratory tools, an aroused interest in naturally occurring compounds, and the conviction that chemical diversity will parallel the vast differences we note outwardly among plants, more extensive research into the chemical aspects should be most fruitful. Rewards should include both improved understanding of interrelationships and evolutionary development in the plant kingdom and practical knowledge of new raw materials available to man, with information on best plant sources for obtaining them economically. Acquisition of this type of information requires close cooperation between botanists who procure, identify, and evaluate the crop potential of new species, and chemists who analyze, characterize, modify, and appraise the utilization potential of the constituents (16).

Several examples, using data from our own recent screening and from published sources, will serve to illustrate types of correlation that can be made between chemical composition and systematic botanical classification of plants.

Total Oil and Protein Content of Seeds. In seeking new crops we want species with unique and useful constituents, different from those readily available in present raw materials. Yet unless a new source is sufficiently rich in a desired constituent, its use may be uneconomic despite attractive chemical structure and characteristics. Hence, the first step in our seed screening program has been to assay for presence and amount of selected major constituents before choosing species for more detailed chemical work on type and structure of these components. In this research about 1500 samples have been screened chemically. Among this group 392 species were found to have more than 20% oil, 85 species more than 40% protein, 189 more than 60% oil plus protein (reference percentages selected on basis of soybean composition), and 186 with no starch and low oil plus protein content (possible seed mucilage sources). As one guide to further screening, we have attempted to deduce from our results which plant groups are most likely to be good sources of particular constituents. We present our tentative conclusions with the full realization that these will undoubtedly be modified as the extent of our sampling of the plant kingdom increases.

Relatively few families contain species with high (> 40%) protein in their seeds. Of 112 families investigated only 16 are in this category and 62% of the samples containing high protein were legumes. However, legumes account for more than one-third of the total samples available in our early investigations, and this needs to be considered in interpreting results. Other plant families having, on the average, seeds of highest protein content are the cucurbits (Cucurbitaceae), milkweeds (Asclepiadaceae), the mustards (Cruciferae), the mallows (Malvaceae), and the composites (Compositae). This, however, does not preclude exceptionally high or low individual samples within a family which differ markedly from the average. Thus the grass *Fingerhuthia sesleriaeformis* with 33.1% seed protein is far above the family average of 14.0%.

Seed samples with high oil content are more widely distributed in the plant world; 75 families have representatives in this class (> 20% oil). The well-known legume (Leguminosae) and grass (Gramineae) families are near the lowest in average seed oil content. Among the families with seeds of high average oil content are cucurbits, poppies (Papaveraceae), crucifers, mints (Labiatae), spurges (Euphorbiaceae), capers (Capparidaceae), and composites.

Two-thirds to three-fourths of all seeds analyzed were found to contain no starch. This is of timely significance at present when we have such surpluses of starch-bearing commodities, the cereal grains.

In acquiring additional samples cognizance will be taken of sources already found to be rich in desired constituents. Screening of botanical relatives should prove more fruitful than random screening alone.

Fatty Acids of Seed Oils. Oleic, palmitic, and closely related 18- and 16-carbon acids occur most frequently of all long-chain acids in seed oils and, in fact, in all plant and animal sources. In contrast, a few seed oils contain long-chain compounds with twenty or more carbon atoms. These occur in specific botanical groups. In the order SAPINDALES (4) *Simmondsia californica* (Buxaceae) seed contain an unusual liquid mixture of long-chain acids and alcohols, predominantly twenty and twenty-two carbon compounds, and usually is referred to as a liquid wax. *Cardiospermum halicacabum* (Sapindaceae) of the same order has recently (2) been shown to contain a 20-carbon acid (11-eicosenoic) as a major component (42% of the total acids). Knowing this, even though other oilseeds in the order contain quite the usual sorts of oils, it was not completely surprising when in our screening program *Limnanthes douglasii* (Limnanthaceae) seed oil, which had never been examined before, was found to be most unusual in that it contained less than 5% of the normally found 18-carbon acids and over 60% of 20-carbon acids, the remainder being largely of still longer chain length. Additional chemical work is presently in progress to identify more definitely the structures of the major component acids of the *L. douglasii* oil.

Erucic acid, a 22-carbon monounsaturated compound, is the most frequently found natural fatty acid having a carbon chain length of greater than eighteen. It is of interest that its occurrence is almost exclusive to two plant families and is especially prominent in the large family Cruciferae, in seed oils of which it is often present to the extent of 50% or more.

Interesting interrelationships among structures of fatty acids in Compositae seed oils have been encountered in our work. Linoleic acid is widely occurring and comprises the principal acid of sunflower and safflower seed oil. In *Vernonia anthelmintica* oil carbon atoms 12 and 13, which carry a double bond in linoleic acid, now appear as part of an epoxide ring (5). In fact, this naturally occurring acid with a reactive epoxy group was correctly characterized only in 1954. We examined for the first time the seed oil of *Chrysanthemum coronarium* and demonstrated that it, too, contained an epoxy acid. Upon detailed structural characterization in the laboratory this was found (12) to be not vernolic acid but an isomer, also related to linoleic acid, in which the 9 and 10 positions in linoleic acid have become epoxidized with the 12-13 double bond intact. The same biosynthetic precursor appears probable for these epoxy acids, but one can only speculate and await the necessary research in plant physiology for further clarification. With the natural occurrence of epoxy acids demonstrated and suitable analytical methodology in use, we are finding them to be more generally distributed than hitherto realized, and to occur in a number of plant families. Other investigators (6) have just found an epoxy acid which bears the same relationship to linolenic acid as vernolic and coronaric do to linoleic.

Recently the United States Department of Agriculture's new crops team discovered and elucidated the structure of another new acid from a composite, *Dimorphotheca aurantiaca* (14). The

reactive acid is an 18-carbon compound containing two conjugated double bonds and a hydroxyl group; we named it dimorphecolic acid. Again, one interest was to examine related species
and genera for presence of this same substance both to get leads
on species possessing the best crop potential and to demonstrate
any structural chemical relationship that might be found in
closely related botanical groups. All species of the genus examined contained the same acid in their seed oil. This included
D. ecklonis which has a larger and heavier seed than the others
tested and which some taxonomists consider to be in a separate
but closely related genus, *Osteospermum*. This now provides considerable incentive for screening in the genus *Osteospermum*. Another relative of *Dimorphotheca*, *Calendula* (*C. officinalis*), on
the other hand, did not contain dimorphecolic acid but a fatty
acid having no hydroxyl group and three conjugated double
bonds. Although we have not proved its structure unequivocally,
it is probably the position isomer that is closely related to dimorphecolic acid, with one the biochemical precursor of the other
in the plant through loss or addition of water.

Many additional examples could be given of chemical similarities among seed oils of botanically related groups but we should
emphasize that there are also many exceptions. Thus among numerous species of *Vernonia* seed analyzed, only *V. anthelmintica*
has so far been found in our laboratory to contain a very large
percentage (65%) of vernolic acid in its oil. Others examined
in our work contain none or only traces although Chisholm and
Hopkins (1) report one additional species to have a "high content."

Although most crucifer seeds, as stated, contain erucic acid
oils, at least two species, *Hesperis matronalis* and *Matthiola
bicornis*, have been found which have oils more like linseed, with
no erucic acid. Perhaps as we acquire more knowledge, we should
be better able to explain such similarities and differences.

Amino Acids in Seeds. Seed protein composition has not been
as extensively studied as has the fatty acid content of seed oils.
In fact, an extensive literature search on our part has revealed
(13) that there are only some 100 or so species for which re-

liable amino acid data are available and about half of these are among the much studied grasses and legumes. Yet some interesting relationships are evident. Canavanine, an amino acid related in structure to arginine, has been found to exist in free form in seeds of numerous legume genera, all in the subfamily Papilionoideae. In other subfamilies of legumes, all other plant families investigated (3), and even in some genera of Papilionoideae, the canavanine is absent. Canavanine is known to have biological activity as an antimetabolite, but its specific function, if any, in this closely related group of plants has not been clarified.

As regards feeding values of seeds and seed meals, there is considerable interest in the nutritionally essential amino acids and especially lysine and methionine. Among our common feedstuffs, products of the legume family such as soybean oil meal are usually good lysine sources but deficient in methionine. The grass family, including all our most frequently used cereal grains, present the reverse pattern; they are richer in methionine but poor lysine sources. In our new crops program, seeds from selected other families appear to be better balanced nutritionally than either legume or grass seeds. Similar claims are in the literature (9-11) for certain species of *Amaranthaceae, Polygonaceae,* and *Chenopodiaceae.* Considerably more data must be acquired to substantiate and expand generalizations relating protein composition to botanical source.

Stalk Fiber Cells. Cellular dimensions of more than 200 samples of plant stalks have been measured after mild maceration procedures. This is one facet of evaluation of species as sources of new nonwoody pulping raw materials. Again our sampling is limited, but generalizations are becoming apparent. The length-to-diameter (L/D) ratios of *Gramineae* and other monocotyledons are generally high, and in the range of those for soft woods. For whole stems of dicotyledons or just their core the L/D ratio is low, overlapping corresponding values for North American hardwoods but on the low side of that range. Bast fiber cells of dicotyledons generally have high L/D ratios, with considerable variation dependent upon botanical type. Thus, bast fibers of legumes and mallows appear to have greater L/D ratios than composite bast fibers. These findings are valuable supplements to chemical and other technical data in appraisal of species for value as pulp sources.

Other Constituents. Many other classes of chemical compounds, such as specific types of alkaloids and polysaccharides having certain monomer units, may also be related to their origin in particular segments of the plant kingdom. However, the examples given will suffice to illustrate some of the types of relationships that can be developed.

Utilization Significance of Leads

We have described briefly the direction of our screening program and some of the implications in systematic botany which are valuable both theoretically and in providing practical guidance for continued screening. We also know that research chemists and technologists have found many ways to modify agricultural commodities and have derived products for a multitude of industrial uses. *New* raw materials from presently unused germ plasm may open whole new horizons for further development. Now it may be appropriate to present selected examples of laboratory progress, since initiation of our program, in selecting promising germ plasm for new products.

Dimorphotheca. We mentioned earlier the new fatty acid we identified in the seed oil of *Dimorphotheca* species. This finding has many favorable aspects which lead us to believe that the foundation for a new crop may be in the making. The genus is largely herbaceous, and many of the species are already used as ornamentals. The seeds have acceptably high oil content, and the unique acid in the oil is a *major* component, present to the extent of about 60%. Because of high chemical functionality, excellent use potential may be predicted if problems attendant to economical production can be solved. At the *trans, trans* unsaturation many types of well-known addition and polymerization reactions are possible. Because of presence of a hydroxyl group, properties of these products should be quite different from presently available ones. Numerous reactions at the hydroxyl and carboxyl groups will yield other series of new products, with various combinations of derivatives also possible. The Department of Agriculture's Western Division at Albany, California, has been designated to study this interesting new oil to acquire further data on its utilization potential.

Other Potential New Oilseeds. Glyceride oils and derived products are now chemically epoxidized industrially for use as plasticizers for vinyl resins or components of plastics. Apparent current epoxy fatty acid plasticizer usage is at a level of about 35 million pounds a year. Since a chemical processing step with its attendant cost is involved here, it would appear that a ready market exists for a seed oil that naturally contains considerable epoxy content as obtained by extraction. The presence of such oils has, as mentioned, been demonstrated in the laboratory. Perhaps the plant originally found to contain such novel constituents is not the best agronomically. Then other sources must be sought through joint effort of chemists and botanists until a suitable crop is at hand. But the occurrence of a natural plant product suitable for a specific use has been demonstrated and the plant is worth further attention.

Rapeseed, a major world oil source, is used almost entirely for edible purposes. A few specialized industrial uses in fields such as lubricants, specialty rubber compounding, and plasticizers have been found (17). Yet there has been no major chemical effort to find uses peculiar to oils such as rape containing erucic and other especially long-chain fatty acids. Maximum use of available germ plasm for new products warrants considerable additional investigations into this group of plants with well-demonstrated crop potential which are produced in negligibly small acreage now in the United States. Other natural sources of related long-chain compounds have been said to be promising for preparation of a variety of end products (8).

Almost 200 million pounds of coconut oil is imported annually into the United States. This is mostly used in soaps and detergents because of its high content of fatty acids of intermediate (mostly lauric: C-12) chain length. Our recent indications by gas chromatography of a seed oil (*Cuphea llavea*) having quite preponderant amounts of C-10 acids provide a good lead to existent germ plasm which could be utilized to supply intermediate-chain-length acids for use by industry, perhaps in a species with good crop potential for the United States.

Still other oilseeds, such as the *Calendula* previously referred to or the umbellifers as a group, contain oils previously unused industrially, but having latent, undeveloped possibilities. The former may have use in protective coatings, the latter as sources of petroselinic acid to be used as a base for chemicals for making nylon and detergents. Undoubtedly sources of many other types of new seed oils having good commercial possibilities will be found.

Kenaf. With very few exceptions (straw and flax shives) wood is the source of paper pulp in the United States. However, this need not necessarily be so. In our screening of plant materials other sources are being encountered which merit consideration. For example, kenaf (*Hibiscus cannabinus*) is a productive annual of rather wide temperate zone adaptability which has chemical composition and fiber dimensions in a usable range. Trial plantings and laboratory pulping investigations are in progress to assess its suitability for conversion to some of the variety of paper products, consumption of which totals over 32 million tons annually in the United States. Kenaf is but one of the better species under consideration for conversion to pulp products.

Other Uses for Plant Products. What about new insecticides? Antitumor agents or other pharmaceuticals? Alkaloids? Yes, there are many, many possibilities for using plant germ plasm in addition to ways that we now do. Their discovery just awaits the persevering efforts of scientific groups with the spirit and resources to search the plant kingdom and not rest until their positive findings are reduced to practical utilization.

REFERENCES

1. Chisholm, Mary J., and C. Y. Hopkins. An oxygenated fatty acid from the seed oil of *Hibiscus esculentus*. *Can. J. Chem.*, 35, 358-364 (1957).

2. Chisholm, Mary J., and C. Y. Hopkins. Fatty acids of the seed oil of *Cardiospermum halicacabum*. *Can. J. Chem.*, 36 (11), 1537-1540 (1958).

3. Fearon, W. R., and E. A. Bell. Canavanine: Detection and occurrence in *Colutea arborescens*. *Biochem J.*, *59*, 221-224 (1955).

4. Fernald, M. L. *Gray's Manual of Botany*, 8th edition. American Book Co., New York, N. Y., 1950.

5. Gunstone, F. D. Fatty acids. II. The nature of the oxygenated acid present in *Vernonia anthelmintica* (Willd.) seed oil. *Chem. Soc. J.*, *1954*, 1611-1616.

6. Gunstone, F. D., and L. J. Morris. Fatty acids. VI. The oxygenated acid present in *Camelina sativa* (Crantz.) seed oil. *Chem. Soc. J.*, *1959*, 2127-2132.

7. Hilditch, T. P. *The Chemical Constitution of Natural Fats*, 3rd edition. John Wiley and Sons, New York, N. Y. 1956.

8. Jones, Maria A., and Nestor B. Knoepfler. Wax uses of desert shrub, jojoba, subject of promising study. *Chemurg. Dig.*, *16* (1), 5-6, 11 (1957).

9. Kimura, S. Studies on Japanese foods. XXIV. The amino-acid compositions of cereal and soya-bean proteins by column chromatographic analysis. *J. Sci. of Food Agr.*, *8* (9), ii-111 (1957).

10. Quiros-Perez, Felipe, and Conrad Arnold Elvehjem. Quality of plant proteins: nutritive value of Quinoa proteins. *J. Agr. Food Chem.*, *5* (7), 538-541 (1957).

11. Ramachandran, M., and S. V. Phansalkar. Essential amino acid composition of certain vegetable foodstuffs. *Indian J. Med. Research*, *44*, 501-509 (1956).

12. Smith, C. R., Jr., Kay F. Koch, and I. A. Wolff. Evidence for a new oxygenated fatty acid in the seed oil of *Chrysanthemum coronarium*. *Chem. & Ind.*, *1959* (8), 259-260.

13. Smith, C. R., Jr., M. C. Shekleton, I. A. Wolff, and Quentin Jones. Seed protein sources—amino acid composition and total protein content of various plant seeds. *Econ. Botany*, *13* (2), 132-150 (1959).

14. Smith, C. R., Jr., T. L. Wilson, E. H. Melvin, and I. A. Wolff. Dimorphecolic acid, a unique hydroxydienoid fatty acid. *J. Am. Chem. Soc.*, *82*, 1417-1421 (1960).

15. Stobbe, L. H. O. May we use wisdom and be thritfy. *Chemurgic Dig.*, *18* (1), 4 (1959).

16. Wolff, Ivan A., and Quentin Jones. Cooperative new crops research—what the program has to involve. *Chemurgic Dig.*, *17* (9), 4-8 (1958).

17. Zuckerman, A., and N. H. Grace. Utilization of erucic acid oils. *Can. Chem. Process Indus.*, *33*, 588-593, 607 (1949).

Irradiation and Plant Improvement[*]

RICHARD S. CALDECOTT[†]

Department of Agronomy and Plant Genetics,
University of Minnesota, St. Paul, Minnesota

Since 1930, but particularly since World War II, ionizing radiations have been used by plant geneticists in efforts to induce heritable changes of economic significance. By and large these studies have involved attempts to induce so-called point mutations. The organisms most commonly studied have been the small-grains, peanuts and corn (5, 6, 10). Sufficient data have been obtained and published to indicate the essential worth of the approach, when used by careful investigators, so that in a symposium such as this one, no useful purpose can be served by rehashing what, scientifically speaking, is now ancient history. Accordingly, the intent of the present report is, insofar as is possible, to accept the mandate of the symposium organizers and discuss "new" approaches to plant improvement using ionizing radiations. For the most part these new approaches involve the application of theoretical considerations that have likely been discussed many times by radiation geneticists. Certainly, because they are presented in this report largely without literature citations, because few exist, it should not be construed as meaning that they originated with the writer.

In using ionizing radiations in plant improvement one must take into consideration the degree of ploidy and the breeding behavior or mode of reproduction of the species with which he intends to work. In addition, one must be cognizant of the fact that ionizing radiations not only induce point mutations but also all manner

[*] This work was conducted under Contract At(11-1)-332 between the University of Minnesota and the United States Atomic Energy Commission.

[†] Contribution from the United States Department of Agriculture, Field Crops Research Branch, Agricultural Research Service, and the University of Minnesota, Paper No. 4226, Scientific Journal Series, Minnesota Agricultural Experiment Station.

of structural chromosomal anomalies, such as reciprocal translocations, inversions, duplications, and deletions. Furthermore, he
must be aware that the frequency with which these types of
events are produced, and their ease of detection, will depend upon
the species being studied and the ontogenetic stage of the plant to
which the irradiation is given.

To reduce this complex of variables in the present report,
unless otherwise stated, we shall consider only what may possibly
be achieved through seed irradiation of the naturally self-fertilized
cereals which occur in nature as diploids, tetraploids, and hexa-
ploids.

MUTATIONS FROM A SINGLE DOSE OF RADIATION

On a priori grounds, in the X_2 from populations receiving one
dose of radiation, it would be expected that plants expressing
mutant phenotypes for qualitative characters would occur commonly in diploid species, less frequently in tetraploid species and
only rarely in hexaploid species. The reason for this is simply
that most radiation-induced mutations are recessives, and the
simultaneous mutation of genes that influence the expression of
the same character, but are located on homeologous chromosomes,
would be a relatively rare event, even under optimal conditions of
treatment. The essential validity of this consideration has been
borne out by chlorophyll mutation studies on tetraploid and hexaploid oats and wheat (11).

In addition to the above consideration, there is another important factor which makes it difficult to recover a large number
of mutant phenotypes after administration of a single dose of
radiation to an organism. This is because ionizing radiations induce chromosomal aberrations as well as mutations. Such aberrations are often responsible for cell depth, and it is apparently a
simple matter of chance whether a mutational event, a chromosomal anomaly, or both are induced in a cell after the absorption
of photons or ionizing particles. Accordingly, as the dose to
which the population is subjected is increased, the number of cells
in the population that contain both aberrations and mutations also
increases. Because one or, at most, a very few aberrations can

result in cell death, it is apparent that the probability is very low of inducing mutations at more than a few loci before a lethal aberration is induced.

From these considerations, it should be apparent that similar complications prevail when attempting to obtain mutations for quantitative traits. Since many of the most important characters with which the breeder works are under polygenic control, the desirability of using ionizing radiations in other than a "one-shot" approach in mutation breeding should be obvious.

MUTATIONS FROM A DOSE ADMINISTERED TO A SEQUENCE OF GENERATIONS

In Diploids

It seems obvious that any method that would increase the relative frequency of mutations to lethal or semilethal aberrations in a population, before it is subjected to the expensive process of screening for economic mutations, would be of distinct value to the geneticist. At this time there appears to be only one simple way in which this can be achieved. That is to irradiate successive seed generations of the material under test, always selecting for re-irradiation seed from spikes or panicles that do not evidence structural chromosomal anomalies. This is a particularly simple procedure in diploid species, such as barley, because all cells that are cytologically deficient in their chromosome complement are incapable of competing with more normal cells during the development of the plant from irradiated seed. The end result is that, effectively, only reciprocal interchanges and inversions are detected in the analysis of sporocytes arising from irradiated diploid seed. Reciprocal interchanges invariably induce 25 to 50% sterility. Thus, when selecting seed for re-irradiation one can select it only from fertile heads. Because mutations and chromosomal aberrations tend to be induced independently (4), seed from fertile heads will carry as many mutations as seed from semisterile heads. While seed selected in this way may incidentally carry an inversion, providing the inverted segment did not involve a mutant gene of significance, it would likely be of little consequence to the breeder and could easily be eliminated if the need was indicated.

In suggesting the use of recurrent irradiation in diploid species for inducing maximum genetic variability for both quantitative and qualitative traits, it is recognized that gene mutations of both a deleterious and beneficial nature will be induced in the same cells and that the method does not provide for their separation between generations. From this it follows that the immediate products from recurrent irradiation of a diploid could not likely be used as commercial varieties. However, after screening for mutants of agronomic value in a population that had been subjected to recurrent irradiation, it would be easy to produce hybrids between the original progenitor and the irradiated material to place the character, or characters, of value in what was an otherwise desirable genetic background. Insofar as the author is aware, this particular approach has received little consideration by plant breeders.

In Polyploids

When attempting the induction of detectable mutations in the self-fertilizing polyploids among the small grains, a special set of circumstances confronts the geneticist. For every pair of genes that influence the expression of a character in the diploid, both quantitative and qualitative, there presumably usually exist two and three times as many genes in the tetraploid and hexaploid, respectively.

If considering mutation only for qualitative characters, theoretical assumptions suggest that continued re-irradiation of the seed generation of the polyploids, in which the genes governing the same order of biochemical function are in the homozygous dominant condition on homeologous chromosomes, will ultimately result in the appearance of a high frequency of chlorophyll mutations in the population. When such mutations appear, F_2 segregation for the mutant trait in crosses with the original parental type should be 15:1 in the case of the tetraploid and 63:1 in the case of the hexaploid. Some of the normal F_2 phenotypes from these crosses should include genotypes in which the normal gene is in the homozygous dominant condition on one pair of homologs and in a homozygous recessive condition on the other pair or pairs of homeologous chromosomes. In plants of this genetic constitution crosses with the recessive phenotype should give a 3:1 segregation for the mutant character. In effect then, it can be said that the polyploid has been "diploidized." It follows that the recurrent re-irradiation of any polyploid that shows bivalent pairing should eventually result in the material used in such studies being indistinguishable, by simple Mendelian tests, from naturally occurring diploids.

It might well be asked if there exist any factual data to support these considerations. The answer is simply that the incidence of chlorophyll mutations in hexaploid oats has increased each generation through six successive generations of re-irradiation. Mutant types have been perpetuated but crosses with the parental type have not been made.

In addition to the hexaploid oat work, which will be mentioned again in the next section, recurrent irradiation studies are also underway at the University of Minnesota with diploid and tetraploid oats and tetraploid and hexaploid wheat. The incidence of chlorophyll mutations in the wheat material after irradiation of two successive seed generations supports the general considerations.

It seems pertinent to ask the following question. If diploidization of a polyploid is indeed possible, is it likely that it will have any practical significance? The answer, based on theory and existing recurrently irradiated plant material, is yes. To give substance to this assertion it is again necessary to resort to theoretical considerations and the findings of other workers. Heterosis in corn is commonly attributed to differences in alleles which govern expression of the same characters, i.e., heterozygosity at several loci. Similarly, it has been demonstrated by Wallace and Vetukhiv (12) in *Drosophila* that genes that are recessive and deleterious when in the homozygous condition may benefit the survival and growth of a fly in which they are in the heterozygous state.

What has this to do with diploidization of a self-fertilizing polyploid; specifically for ease of presentation, hexaploid wheat? As has been indicated, in the hexaploid often there are presumably six genes, one on each of three pairs of homeologous chromosomes, which influence the expression of a given character. Furthermore, apparently these genes are often in the homozygous dominant condition on more than one pair of the homeologous chromosomes. Now, if in diploids a heterotic effect is obtained when differences exist between alleles on a pair of homologs, it seems possible that, in a polyploid, differences between genes that govern the expression of the same character, but are on homeologous chromosomes, may also confer increased vigor to plants in which the condition exists. If such is the case, the self-fertilizing polyploid would have an advantage over the diploid in that the "heterozygous" state (between genes of homeologous chromosomes) could be perpetuated by selfing and thus provide permanent heterosis by merely maintaining the alleles on one pair of homologous chromosomes in the homozygous dominant condition.

In regard to the possible usefulness of this approach in plant breeding, it seems relevant to mention a promising study that is in progress using recurrent irradiation on hexaploid oats. In this program the following procedure has been used. Seed from a single plant from three oat varieties, Park, Missouri 0-205, and Clintland, was increased and irradiated. In the X_1, 1000 fertile panicles were chosen from different plants in each of the three varieties. The seed from these panicles was re-irradiated and planted in panicle rows. From these panicle rows one fertile panicle was chosen from one agronomically suitable looking plant to form the seed source for the next cycle of radiation. This procedure has been continued through six cycles.

Some interesting general observations on this material are worth reporting, although at this time there are no grounds for assuming that a state of permanent heterosis exists in any of the material. First, and most significant, is the fact that variability in the material for height, panicle type, and maturity date was not evident until after the second cycle of radiation. Subsequent to this there has been a continued increase in variability for these characters. At the end of the fifth cycle of radiation the variability was so extreme in all the material that a considerable number of types with characteristics of agronomic interest were selected for critical study. These selections were increased in 1959, and the promising ones were turned over to plant breeders for yield tests in comparison with the parental types. It is important to emphasize that most of the material derived from this long series of recurrent irradiation is agronomically undesirable despite the selection for desirable plant types in each generation. This is particularly true of the material derived from Clintland.

Another point that warrants consideration is the fact that no attempt was made to isolate the irradiated material from possible outcrossing. However, as indicated, each year seed for re-irradiation was taken only from completely fertile panicles. Accordingly, there should have been no more outcrossing in the material than the breeder usually finds in his nursery plots. Since the incidence of outcrossing in fertile oats should be very low, it seems unlikely that outcrossing can account for the extreme variability that has been observed, or for the apparently desirable types that have been selected for further study. However, this possibility cannot be ignored and studies to resolve this question are presently under way with polyploid series in oats and wheat.

Use of Intraspecific Chromosome Structural Changes

Duplications

Among the complex types of chromosomal aberrations induced by ionizing radiations is a class known as the "duplication." As the name implies, material governing specific gene functions is duplicated in the chromosome complement. Duplications may arise in two simple ways that do not simultaneously result in a loss of genetic material in the cell. The first involves translocations between corresponding arms of homologous chromosomes that were broken at dissimilar points. The second involves breakage and reunion of sister chromatids in which the break points were not at corresponding loci.

From previous discussion, it should be evident that polyploids have a built-in system of duplications of what can amount to whole sets of genes in the case of a true autopolyploid. It would appear, then, that radiation-induced duplications would likely be of greatest practical use in diploid species. Accordingly, the discussion will center around their possible use in self-fertilizing diploids.

The previously mentioned work of Wallace and Vetukhiv (12) with Drosophila has demonstrated that flies heterozygous for one or a few loci may be better adapted to their environment than when they are either homozygous dominant or recessive for those loci. This information could be of import to the plant breeder using diploid species if he could devise some method of obtaining lines that would breed true for the heterozygous condition. There seems to be only one possible method for achieving this in a diploid. That is to obtain a duplication involving a translocation of the first type mentioned above so that the normal and mutant alleles are located on the same chromosome. This would necessitate irradiating F_1 seed that were heterozygous for the allele under consideration.

One might well ask three questions concerning the feasibility of using the method. (a) What is the probability of obtaining a translocation at dissimilar points on homologous chromosomes? (b) What is the probability that the duplicated segment of the interchange will involve the gene in question? (c) What is the likelihood of recognizing the duplication once it was produced?

The answer to the first question is that translocations between opposite arms of homologous chromosomes occur with a frequency that is apparently due to chance (7). It can be assumed, therefore, that translocations between corresponding arms would occur with the same frequency. From this it follows that the lower the number of chromosomes in the species under study the more readily will such interchanges arise. Actually, cytogenetic studies have shown that translocations between opposite arms of homologous chromosomes are a relatively common occurrence in diploid barley and maize (1, 2, 8).

The second question cannot be answered except to point out that, based on purely physical assumptions, a gene in the median position of an arm should be involved in duplications more commonly than one close to the centromere or on the distal end of an arm.

The answer to the third question is simply that it depends on whether or not the heterozygous state produces a recognizable phenotype. If it does, plants carrying a duplication involving a dominant and recessive allele should be readily detected because they will either not segregate for the character in question or give aberrant segregation ratios.

Duplications arising in the second mentioned manner, viz., by joining of sister chromatids that were broken at dissimilar points, are exceedingly common, as based on cytological observations. However, they may be extremely difficult to detect phenotypically and would appear to have little practical value except in cases in which additive gene action prevailed in the production of a particular trait, such as disease resistance and pigmentation.

Production of Fertile Tetraploids

Since the discovery that colchicine was an effective polyploidizing agent, plant breeders have doubled the chromosome complement of numerous species. In only a few instances have the induced polyploids been useful economically. One immediate reason for this is that meiosis in an autopolyploid is disturbed by multivalent formation which, along with some undetermined physiological imbalance, apparently results in sterility. In addition aneuploid types often arise in the progenies. If these problems could be overcome, adequate tests of polyploids, originating from common genetic backgrounds, could be undertaken and the genetic diversity within a species could be increased accordingly.

One possible method of overcoming multivalent associations would be to structurally reorganize the chromosomes of a species to the point that very little or no homology remained between the structurally modified lines and the progenitor. At this stage F_1's between the modified lines and the progenitor could be doubled to produce a fertile tetraploid that would be similar to artificially and naturally occurring amphidiploids.

An attempt is being made to produce such structural modification in barley by using ionizing radiations to induce translocations, inversions, duplications, and deficiencies. For the past six generations, the procedure has been to use irradiation to induce at least one interchange per generation in each of four lines

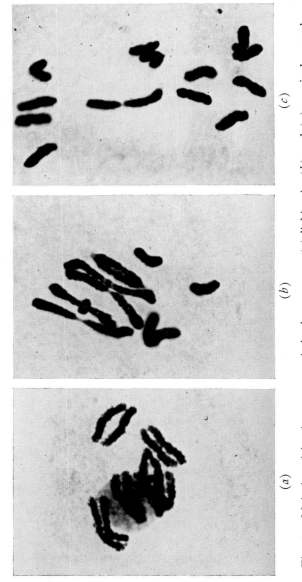

Fig. 1. Meiotic pairing in an asynaptic barley mutant: (*a*)diakinesis; (*b*) and (*c*), typical metaphase cells.

originally selected from four different varieties. Incidental to the addition of the interchanges, but equally effective in inducing structural differentiation, are the addition of the other anomalies mentioned.

Hybrids between some of the material, in which structural differentiation of the chromosomes is being attempted, and the parental genotype have just been achieved. They will be examined cytologically in the spring of 1960 and it is to be hoped that some of the F_1's will show the kind of reduced pairing that is common in species crosses or in two of the asynaptic mutants that have arisen from the material (Fig. 1).

Use of Interspecific and Intergeneric Chromosome Interchanges

With few exceptions, cereal breeders are limited in their improvement programs to using the phenotypes they can obtain by recombining the genes that exist in the species with which they are working. The reason for this is simply that when wide crosses can be effected there frequently is little homology between the chromosomes from the two parents and correspondingly little recombination takes place. The consequence is that there is often either the divergence toward parental types that is indicated in Fig. 2, or the progenies from such crosses contain additions of whole chromosomes to the basic complement. The lines in which whole chromosomes have been added to a basic complement invariably have proved too inferior for commercial usage.

In most instances, what the breeder is seeking from intergeneric and interspecific crosses is one or a few characters, such as disease or insect resistance, that can be incorporated in a commercial strain without impairment to that strain. Recently ionizing radiations have been effectively used to achieve this where conventional methods failed. In this regard, Sears (9) reported the successful translocation of a segment of chromosome carrying a gene for leaf rust resistance from *Aegilops umbellulata* to *Triticum vulgare*, and Elliott (3) had comparable success in transposing a piece of chromosome carrying a gene for stem rust resistance from *Agropyron elongatum* to *T. vulgare*. The general principle is illustrated in Fig. 3.

Because of these successes, there would appear to be considerable merit to the suggestion that ionizing radiations should be used extensively, in hybrids involving *Triticum, Avena* and

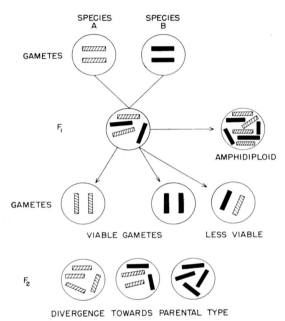

Fig. 2. Tendency for progeny from interspecific hybrids to diverge toward parental types.

their related genera, to obtain recombinant types that cannot be obtained by conventional methods. An initial approach to this procedure in the case of hexaploid wheat is illustrated in Fig. 4. By using the method outlined, it should be possible to derive lines that contain all the 42 chromosomes of *T. vulgare* plus one pair from a related genus. Theoretically, where there is no homology between chromosomes from the two genera, it should be possible to derive distinct strains, each containing a different pair of chromosomes from the related genus. By screening the derived strains, it could be determined whether any particular added pair of chromosomes carried a factor or factors of economic significance. In strains in which some economic worth was apparent, irradiation could be undertaken to translocate a region of the chromosome carrying the gene or genes of significance into the *T. vulgare* background of chromosomes. Once this had been

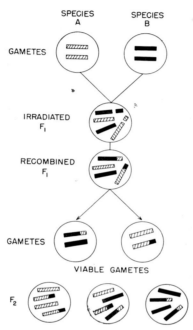

Fig. 3. Use of radiation for transposing chromatin from one genome to another in an interspecific hybrid.

achieved it would be a simple matter to eliminate the extra pair of chromosomes from the related genus by backcrossing to *T. vulgare* and selecting only those progenies with a complement of 42 chromosomes.

Concluding Remarks

In recent years a great deal of attention has been given to the use of one acute dose of ionizing radiation for inducing mutations of a beneficial nature. At the same time, relatively little consideration has been directed to other possible approaches involving both mutations and chromosome structural modifications, which would appear to have great potential promise. The present report is an attempt to emphasize proven and theoretical considerations which suggest that, if effectively utilized, ionizing radiations should become of increasing significance to the applied geneticist.

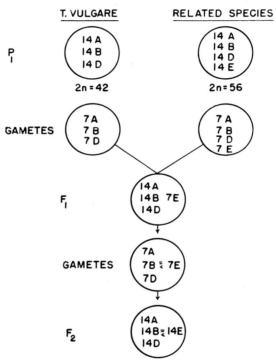

Fig. 4. One possible step in the introduction of chromosomes from one species into a related species.

References

1. Caldecott, R. S. The effects of x-rays, 2-Mev electrons, thermal neutrons, and fast neutrons on dormant seeds of barley. *Ann. N. Y. Acad. Sci.*, 59, 514-535 (1955).

2. Caldecott, R. S., and Smith, L. A study of x-ray induced chromosomal aberrations in barley. *Cytologia*, 17, 224-242 (1952).

3. Elliott, F. C. X-ray induced translocation of *Agropyron* stem rust resistance to common wheat. *J. Heredity, 48*, 77-81 (1957).

4. Gaul, H. Present aspects of induced mutations in plant breeding. *Euphytica, 7*, 275-289 (1958).

5. Gregory, W. C. Induction of useful mutations in the peanut. *Brookhaven Symposia in Biol., 9*, 177-190 (1956).

6. Konzak, C. F. Induction of mutations for disease resistance in cereals. *Brookhaven Symposia in Biol., 9*, 157-176 (1956).

7. Koo, F. K. S. Expectations on random occurrence of structural interchanges between homologous and between non-homologous chromosomes. *Am. Naturalist, 43*, 193-199 (1959).

8. Morris, R. Induced reciprocal translocations involving homologous chromosomes in maize. *Am. J. Botany, 42*, 546-550 (1955).

9. Sears, E. R. The transfer of leaf-rust resistance from *Aegilops umbellulata* to wheat. *Brookhaven Symposia in Biol., 9*, 1-22 (1956).

10. Smith, H. H. Radiation in the production of useful mutations. *Botan. Rev., 24*, 1-24 (1958).

11. Stadler, L. J. Chromosome number and the mutation rate in *Avena* and *Triticum. Proc. Natl. Acad. Sci. U. S., 15*, 876-881 (1929).

12. Wallace, B., and Vetukhiv, M. Adaptive organization of the gene pools of Drosophila populations. *Cold Spring Harbor Symposia Quant. Biol., 20*, 303-310 (1955).

Possibilities for Genetic Improvement
of Beneficial Insects

Reece I. Sailer

*Agricultural Research Service, United States Department
of Agriculture, Beltsville, Maryland*

Left to their own devices few people are likely to concern themselves with prospects for genetic improvement of beneficial insects. This is scarcely surprising, for even the entomologist
ordinarily thinks first of insects as injurious. They are creatures
that voraciously attack the rose and vegetable gardens, the dog,
cat, and dad's winter suit. They are the uninvited guests at all
picnics and the bane of all campers. Furthermore, some of man's
great empires have been toppled by insect-borne diseases. So, we
may expect that few people outside the field of entomology are
aware of the importance of insects to man's welfare.

Not only do insects provide us with useful commodities such
as honey, beeswax, silk, shellac, and dye materials, but they also
pollinate about fifty seed and fruit crops. Insect-pollinated
legumes increase production of meat and milk while adding
fertility to our soils. However, of equal or greater importance are
the numerous parasites and predaceous species that hold in check
a great many actual or potential crop and animal pests. Without
their help we would be plagued with higher production costs and
additional pesticide residue problems. It is my intention to
emphasize the urgent need to find sources of insect germ plasm
that will provide more effective counterpests for control of
insect enemies of our crops.

Such counterpests can be obtained in two ways: (*a*) by exploration, introduction, and colonization or (*b*) by means of
breeding programs. The first method has been in use for seventy-
five years and the second has yet to be tried. According to Clausen
(2), about 485 species of beneficial insects have been introduced
into the United States, but less than 100 became established, and

most of these provide only partial control of their hosts. Since the work has been largely empirical, reasons for the success or failure of an introduction are seldom known. In many cases the potential counterpest was not suited to the climate or biotic environment of the area where it was needed. When an effective counterpest cannot be found through exploration, a breeding program should be undertaken designed to tailor-make a parasite or predator suited to the environment where it is needed.

Reports from Pennsylvania, Ohio, and Iowa during 1958 show that 30% of the European corn borers were parasitized by *Lydella grisescens* (R.D.). In that same year total losses attributable to the borer in corn-producing states were estimated to amount to $98,500,000. Now what would it mean if the efficiency of the *Lydella* fly could be increased to 50%? Various factors make it difficult to translate such a difference into dollar value, but we can be reasonably sure that more bushels of corn would be raised, and if this is regarded as objectionable in light of our current surplus, why concern ourselves with crop improvement or plant protection?

I have indicated that little has been done to improve useful insects. In 1940 Clausen (1) included no reference to such work in a bibliography of more than 1000 titles. In 1958, when DeBach (4) summarized the results of research in this field, he was able to cite five significant contributions published after 1941. In these papers the authors report significant modifications in laboratory strains of several insects in such characteristics as temperature preference, sex ratios, host preference, and host-finding ability, and one paper, by Pielou and Glasser (9), reports a several-fold increase in the tolerance of a laboratory strain of *Macrocentrus ancylivorous* Rohwer to DDT. This important parasite of the oriental fruit moth had been exposed to DDT for nine months, and selection had progressed through about the same number of generations.

DeBach concluded that races or strains of parasites differing from one another in important respects are fairly commonplace in nature, and that this fact offers encouragement for similar developments in the laboratory through selective breeding. He also expressed the view that laboratory manipulation can duplicate and greatly speed up events that occur rarely in the field. Thus there is no reason to believe that breeding techniques so successfully used to improve crop plants and livestock would not also have application in the field of pest control.

The best source of information pointing to both the possibilities and pitfalls of breeding programs designed to improve parasitic or predaceous insects can be found in literature pertaining to the lac insect, the honey bee, and the silkworm, all insects that man has reared or in some degree cultured for many centuries. The lac insect (*Laccifer lacca*) is still not really domesticated, for though 40 to 90 million pounds of lac are harvested each year in India and other oriental countries, it lives wild on native forest trees, and man simply disperses it from tree to tree. More progress has been made toward domestication of the honey bee (*Apis mellifera* L.), but though this insect has been kept for its honey and beeswax for at least 5000 years, it is still essentially wild. The various races bred and maintained today are the subspecies of *mellifera* that originated as geographically isolated wild populations. For reasons mentioned later, breeding techniques that so successfully modified other organisms failed when applied to the honey bee.

Only the silkworm (*Bombyx mori* L.) has been domesticated to a degree approaching that of wheat or cattle. At the present time the silkworm is not known to exist outside the domesticated state, and there are a great number of races or strains, each restricted to a particular area. The different races are often distinguished by number of broods and physiological characteristics of value for adaptation to climatic conditions of different localities. Many are so distinctive that some taxonomists have treated them as different species. Nonetheless they will interbreed and respond to selection.

For more than fifty years the Japanese have conducted sustained and productive research on silkworm genetics. This has been intensified since World War II in an effort to reduce the cost of production and permit silk to compete with synthetic fibers for the market it once dominated. Much progress has been made. The phenomenon of hybrid vigor was recognized early, and most of the silk produced in Japan since 1949 has originated from F_1 hybrid worms. Sex-linked mutations affecting the color of eggs and small larvae have been found, thus making it possible to sex stock at an early age and concentrate on the more productive females. Present genetic research on the silkworm is slanted toward factors concerned with nutrition (6). It is hoped that a strain can be developed that will feed on an artificial medium suitable for industrialized production of the silkworm. According to Tanaka (13), 1241 papers have been published on silkworm genetics. Ninety per cent of this literature is in Japanese and has received slight attention from western geneticists.

As mentioned earlier, the history of breed improvement in the honey bee is different. Centuries of selection and, during recent years, intense genetic study have resulted in little real progress (10). This has not been for lack of genetic variety from which to select and breed. Existing strains of bees show great variation in characteristics of importance to the beekeeper and to agriculture (11), which involve honey-producing ability, wintering ability, resistance to disease, and differences in size, color, length of proboscis, and temper.

As a result of recent research in genetics of the honey bee and other species of Hymenoptera, the reason for the lack of progress is now clear. It has been known for many years that males of this order are normally haploid, and for this reason the Hymenoptera present a situation different from that encountered in other plant and animal breeding programs. At first sight breeding problems would seem to be simplified since the less complex genotype of the male would make his contribution to a zygote more readily predicted. In practice efforts to improve bees by simple selection techniques used by animal and plant breeders ended in the production of weak, unproductive colonies.

Whiting's research (14, 15) on the sex-determining mechanism of *Bracon* (=*Habrobracon*) suggested an explanation. He found that in this parasitic wasp sex determination involved at least nine alleles. Any homozygous combination of alleles at the sex loci led to male differentiation if the individual was viable. A haploid, being hemizygous at the sex locus, would develop into a normal male.

Mackensen (7) was able to demonstrate by brood-viability

studies that a similar series of sex alleles are present in the honey bee. The practical significance of this sex-determining mechanism is obvious, for a queen mating with a drone having an allele different from either of hers will produce all viable eggs; if the drone's allele is the same as one of hers, half her eggs will be inviable. Here then is the reason for the failure of simple selection in the production of superior bees.

Inbreeding inevitably results in sex-allele homozygosity and consequent reduction in fertility. Since the colony is the standard performance unit for the honey bee, a reduced population will more than cancel out the benefits of successful selection for other characters of value to the beekeeper. Under natural mating inbreeding is unlikely to occur, since the queen normally mates with six to fifteen drones which may come from any colony within a radius of at least 6 miles.

One of the most practical ways of ensuring the production of queens invariably capable of producing highly viable brood is through hybridization of inbred lines having known constitution. Through this understanding of the nature and implications of the sex-determining mechanism, apiculturists are now able to plan inbreeding programs and subsequent crosses that will result in gradual improvement of honey bees. At the same time beekeepers can be provided not only with hybrid queens that produce highly viable brood but with colonies that exhibit other characteristics of hybrid vigor.

Although the discussion so far summarizes the results of the most significant work involving efforts to breed improved strains of insects, no mention has been made of the vast amount of work done in the collateral field of pure genetics. Aside from *Drosophila*, which for years was the principal experimental animal of genetics research, various other insects have been used in experimental studies. Another source of information about the possibilities for genetic modification of insect populations is found in the rapid adaptation of many insect pests to insecticides. This phenomenon and the research that it has stimulated are having far-reaching repercussions in such fields as physiology, ecology, and evolution (3, 5).

In the face of so much evidence that the genetic constitution of insects can be changed, why has so little progress been made in the improvement of beneficial species? Much of the explanation rests with the small size of most insects and with the problem of rearing them in sufficient quantity to allow proper testing, selection, and breeding work. Much less patience and acuity of observation are needed to count the eggs a hen may lay in her lifetime than to count those laid by a female parasite in its insect host.

Substantial progress toward breeding strains of insects having superior tolerance to adverse climatic factors, higher fecundity, and improved host-finding ability almost certainly can be made if entomologists will avail themselves of the techniques used by animal and plant breeders. But they will have to adapt these techniques to the insects with which they work. Once a species has been selected for genetic improvement, rearing techniques must be devised that will permit populations to be evaluated and superior individuals to be discovered and propagated. The gene pool of the species must be known. Through interspecific hybridization it will often be possible and desirable to tap the gene pools of related species for characters not available intraspecifically. This is routine in plants, and virtually every study involving attempted crosses between closely related insect species has demonstrated the possibility of some degree of gene exchange.

Figures 1 and 2 show an example of interspecific gene exchange. In this case the gene involved mutated to form a semilethal dominant allele, which was transferred from the species where it first appeared to a related but different species. The insects involved are two stink bugs, *Euschistus servus* (Say) and *variolarius* (P. de B.). These are sympatric species found over much of temperate North America. They are readily separable in both sexes, and the male of *variolarius* invariably bears a black spot on the venter of the genital segment (see middle specimen in Fig. 2). Crossbreeding experiments have resulted in the production of highly viable hybrid strains (12).

Figure 1 shows mutant (left) and normal (right) siblings belonging to the species *Euschistus servus*. The specimen in the middle is mutant, and turned ventral side upward to show that

Fig. 1. *Euschistus servus.* Left specimen shows absence of numerous shallow pits on dorsal surface (subimpunctate) in contrast with normal specimen on right. Middle specimen shows uniformly colored apical abdominal segment characteristic of *servus*.

Fig. 2. *Euschistus variolarius.* Left specimen exhibits the sub-impunctate mutation identical to that shown by left specimen in Fig. 1. Right specimen is a normal sibling and middle specimen shows the black spot on the venter of the apical abdominal segment characteristic of *variolarius*. The mutation was transferred from *servus* to *variolarius* through introgressive hybridization.

there is no black spot on the venter of the apical segment of the abdomen. All specimens are male. Mutant specimens are characterized by the near absence of the small dark pits that normally cover the dorsal surface of all species of *Euschistus*. The specimen to the left is identical in all respects, save sex, to the type of *Euschistus subimpunctatus* Malloch (8). This specimen was collected in 1883 and was the only known example of its kind until the same character appeared in a laboratory colony specimen in 1955. Unquestionably, Malloch's specimen is an example of *servus*, for it is identical with that species in all other respects.

Figure 2 shows the same mutation built into the related species *Euschistus variolarius*. This was accomplished by crossbreeding mutant *servus* to normal *variolarius* followed by six backcrosses to *variolarius*. The resulting laboratory strain of *variolarius* produce normal specimens that in no way differ from wild *variolarius* but in each generation an expected portion are mutants.

As indicated in the figures, the laboratory colonies of these two species include mutant and normal individuals, clearly illustrating a case of parallel polymorphism that is known to have arisen through introgressive hybridization. If this kind of character can be moved across species boundaries, there is no reason why a wide variety of useful characters cannot be similarly moved from one species to another and combined to form strains of insect parasites or plant pollinators that are superiorly adapted to the environments where they are needed.

At our present state of knowledge in the field of biocontrol, it is evident that wild species of parasites and predators and their intraspecific components are still far from fully exploited. Not only must we find and identify the species of possible value to us, but we also must explore the distributional ranges of at least the more promising kinds in order to fully utilize the naturally occurring intraspecific variation in useful characteristics. Inevitably we shall, in time, approach the limits of finding preadapted, highly efficient natural enemies of our pests and have to give increasing attention to improving the species already known to be of some value.

The sooner we can apply ourselves to a systematic worldwide search for additional counterpests and to the task of learning how to improve the performance of those we find or now have available, the more likely will America continue to enjoy the good fortune of being able to worry about a surplus food problem.

References

1. Clausen, C. P. *Entomophagous Insects*. McGraw-Hill Book Co., New York, N. Y., 1940.

2. Clausen, C. P. The biological control of insect pests in the Continental United States. *Proc. 10th Intern. Congr. Entomol.*, 4, 443-447 (1958).

3. Crow, J. F. Genetics of insect resistance to chemicals. *Ann. Rev. Entomol.*, 2, 227, 246 (1957).

4. DeBach, Paul. Selective breeding to improve adaptations of parasitic insects. *Proc. 10th Intern. Congr. Entomol.*, 4, 759-768 (1958).

5. Dobzhansky, T. *Genetics and the Origin of Species*, 3rd edition, Columbia University Press, New York, N. Y. 1951.

6. Legay, J. M. Recent advances in silkworm nutrition. *Ann. Rev. Entomol.*, 3, 75-86 (1958).

7. Mackensen, O. Viability and sex determination in the honey bee (*Apis mellifera* L.). *Genetics*, 36, 500-509 (1951).

8. Malloch, J. R. Additions and descriptions of new species. In C. A. Hart, The Pentatomoidea of Illinois with keys to the Nearctic genera. *Bull. Illinois State Nat. Hist. Surv.*, 13, 157-223 (1919).

9. Pielou, D. P., and R. F. Glasser. Selection for DDT resistance in a beneficial insect. *Science*, 115, 117-118 (1952).

10. Roberts, W. C., and Otto Mackensen. Breeding improved honey bees. *Am. Bee J.*, 91, 292-294, 328-330, 382-384, 418-421, 473-475 (1951).

11. Rothenbuhler, W. C. Genetics and breeding of the honey bee. *Ann. Rev. Entomol.*, 3, 161-180 (1958).

12. Sailer, R. I. Interspecific hybridization among insects with a report on crossbreeding experiments with stink bugs. *J. Econ. Entomol.*, 47, 377-383 (1954).

13. Tanaka, Y. *Genetics of Bombyx*. Shokabo, Tokyo, Japan, 1952.

14. Whiting, P. W. Multiple alleles in sex determination of *Habrobracon*. *J. Morphol.*, 66, 323-355 (1940).

15. Whiting, P. W. Multiple alleles in complementary sex determination of *Habrobracon*. *Genetics*, 28, 365-382 (1943).

Discussion of New Approaches in the Use of Plant and Animal Germ Plasm

W. V. Lambert

College of Agriculture, University of Nebraska,
Lincoln, Nebraska

In the face of the present large surpluses of grains and other agricultural products in the United States, I am sure that many people may question why agricultural scientists should be giving attention in this symposium to new approaches to plant and animal improvement. Such a viewpoint, of course, is extremely shortsighted. With the population in the United States expanding at the rate of 3 to 4 million a year, there will probably be from 225 to 240 million people in the nation by 1975, 350 million by the year 2000, and a century hence, 600 million or more. In addition to the greatly expanded demand for food, agricultural products will be required in ever increasing amounts to replace products now made from our rapidly diminishing mineral resources. Today we are producing annually in the United States only about 7% in excess of our yearly requirements.

In the long run it would appear that America is not immune to the problem of hunger so prevalent in some parts of the world today. As a nation, we must take heed of this possibility if we are to be prepared to meet the food and industrial needs of tomorrow. Since many of the principles used in agricultural practice in the years 1975 to 2000 will come largely from theoretical problems under study today, scientists must continue to explore vigorously all problems that will ensure an adequate food supply in the decades ahead.

Over many centuries selective breeding was the principal tool that man used for the improvement of plants and animals. While great progress was made in many species, no real scientific basis for this progress was established until the rediscovery of Mendel's law in 1900. The latter discovery, the research leading to the establishment of the physical basis for inheritance, and studies of the effects of inbreeding and crossbreeding on plant and animal populations by East, Jones, Wright, and others, laid the scientific foundation for the methods being used for the improvement of plants and animals today.

The first major practical breakthrough as a result of these developments was hybrid corn. This outstanding achievement set off a chain reaction which has resulted in extending these principles to the improvement of many different plants and animals. In the intervening years new discoveries have been made, and many techniques from related sciences have been used in probing further into the unknown problems of heredity, and in using this knowledge for improving plants and animals.

Time does not permit more than a brief mention of these developments, all of which are bringing a better understanding of the genetics and physiology of plants and animals, and of the manner in which these principles may be used in effecting inherent improvement in these species. One of the important developments has involved the use of mathematical and statistical tools for interpreting the results of breeding experiments, a broad and active field of endeavor that now is known generally as population genetics. Another step was the discovery that chromosome structure could be modified by the use of chemical and physical agents, notably by certain types of irradiation. More recently immunological principles have been used to acquire an understanding of the genetics of the elusive qualities of the blood, a science that we now call immunogenetics. These developments and other studies concerned with the biochemical and physiological aspects of genetics have opened entirely new approaches to the improvement of plants and animals.

CONTRIBUTION OF LABORATORY ANIMALS TO RESEARCH IN LIVESTOCK IMPROVEMENT

Dr. Chapman has pointed out that if ample time and facilities were provided, it would be possible to seek the solution to each animal breeding problem by doing the necessary research with each class of livestock. Such a procedure, however, is very inefficient when small, rapidly reproducing animals can be used for the elucidation of many of the problems that are common to the smaller, as well as the larger, species. As one example, laboratory animals can be used very effectively in studying problems concerned with the effects of inbreeding and crossbreeding in a population. They can be used effectively in evaluating the effect of different methods and intensities of selection and in testing many of the concepts of heritability that need to be redefined in the light of previous work, and of new concepts in genetics. They furnish excellent material for studies in population genetics, in physiological genetics, and in the physiology of reproduction.

The early work with laboratory animals furnished the basis for many of the broad generalizations that have been used in developing our current concepts of animal breeding. They should be used extensively for this purpose in the future. Many of the theoretical problems of animal breeding can be explored much more effectively with laboratory animals than with larger species. These species should be used more extensively to point the way for genetic and physiological studies in livestock.

Laboratory animals offer other possibilities that cannot be achieved equally well with larger species. They afford much greater opportunity for adequate replication of experiments. Environmental conditions can be controlled more carefully, thus affording a better opportunity for getting at the difficult problems of genetic-environmental-physiological interactions. Also, because of the number of animals that can be used, experiments with small animals can be so designed that the results lend themselves better to the use of the statistical tools that are so essential in ferreting out the complex problems involved in the genetic improvement of livestock.

As Dr. Chapman has so well indicated, much of the early work with laboratory animals did not provide answers to many of the questions needed to guide animal breeding programs with the larger species. Animal breeders are becoming increasingly aware of these gaps in our knowledge and of the important part that small animals may play in establishing the theoretical bases for the applied programs. Within the current year a new regional program on population genetics has been approved by the Directors of the North Central Experiment Stations. The scope and importance of this type of research are emphasized by the objectives of this program, which are: (*a*) to determine the optimum properties of control populations; (*b*) to evaluate various methods of determining genetic parameters; (*c*) to compare the effectiveness of different methods of selection; (*d*) to investigate the causes of the failure of observed gain from selection to agree with that expected; and (*e*) to determine the genetic effects of radiation and other mutagenic agents.

New research projects with small animals already have been initiated under this project in several of the experiment stations, and one regional laboratory has been established. This resurgence of interest in the use of small animals as a tool in livestock improvement should help to discover many of the facts needed to guide the further improvement of our livestock and poultry and to put this work on a more solid scientific basis.

Dr. Chapman did not mention the excellent work that is being done on the genetics and physiology of various types of neoplasms in the Roscoe B. Jackson and other laboratories. This work is contributing much to our understanding of these complex genetic and physiologic problems, some of which have a bearing on problems of livestock breeding. Because of the large number of inbred lines and the short life cycle, the mouse has proved to be an excellent species for such studies.

IMMUNOGENETICS AND ITS APPLICATION TO LIVESTOCK IMPROVEMENT

Dr. Irwin has pointed out that the red blood cells of any individual are characterized by a definite individuality of their own and that they can be distinguished from those of any other individual. He also has told us how some of these techniques can be used in a livestock improvement program even though there are still many gaps in our understanding of these processes. He indicated that eleven blood group systems are presently known in man, that eleven blood group systems have been demonstrated in cattle and a number in various other species. With the system of blood groups now in cattle, Dr. Irwin has indicated that many million combinations of cellular antigens are theoretically possible. This knowledge is already being put to practical use in solving cases of disputed parentage in man and in identifying questionable pedigrees in cattle. For livestock this technique might be considered akin to finger printing in man.

The use of immunogenetics opens up wide possibilities for animal improvement. One of the possibilities is in the association of antigenic characteristics with other characteristics of the organism. As an example of such possible relationships, research in chickens suggests that some of the genes in the B system of cellular antigens influence significantly one or more of the fundamental physiological processes of the fowl. Birds heterozygous for genes affecting this system of antigens showed advantages in hatchability and in body weight at nine weeks of age. Although the evidence to date is only suggestive, it indicates that the blood antigens may prove useful in studying the genetics of important characters which are difficult to measure with other available techniques.

Dr. Irwin has pointed out other ways in which a knowledge of the genetics of blood antigens can contribute to genetic science. For instance, studies relating to the gene frequency of the factors affecting blood antigens in a population undergoing inbreeding would provide an index of residual heterozygosity in successive generations. Such studies might also be useful in following through on gene frequencies of these antigens in populations where different mating systems are being used.

The blood antigens have proved useful in studying certain problems in reproductive physiology, particularly in the case of the freemartin. The pattern of distribution of the blood genes in related populations, species, and genera may contribute to our understanding of what has happened in the course of evolution to these forms. Such studies eventually should throw much light on problems of cellular specificity and of the mechanisms involved in the success or failure of tissue transplants.

Immunogenetics is still a very young science. The techniques and methods are still not well understood and are cumbersome.

This science offers great opportunities for investigation of techniques which can be used to break through some of the difficulties now accompanying the use of blood cells as experimental materials. When these breakthroughs come, studies on blood antigens should make significant contributions to genetics.

Possibilities for Genetic Improvement of Useful Insects

Considering their widespread distribution, their economic importance, and their important role in the history of civilization, insects have probably received less scientific attention aimed at their improvement for the use of man than any other great class in the animal kingdom. Much of the research that has been done has been concerned with such studies as morphology, taxonomy, physiology, and the role of insects as vectors of diseases and parasites. Dr. Sailer has pointed out that of the many thousands of species of insects (over 650,000 species are known in the class Insecta), only the honey bee, the silkworm, and the lac have been cultured by man for the products they produce. Of these three, only the silkworm has been domesticated to a degree approaching that of most of our crop plants and livestock.

This situation is somewhat difficult to comprehend in view of the importance of such commodities as honey, shellac, silk, dye materials and beeswax, and of the importance of insects in the pollination of some fifty of our most important seed and fruit crops. Why is it that so little progress has occurred in putting insects to use in the service of man? Dr. Sailer attributes much of it to the small size of insects. This is probably an important factor, but perhaps a major reason lies in the lack of interest of professional entomologists in the applied aspect of improving insects. Only a relatively few entomologists have given attention to the applied problems of improvement of beneficial insects. Perhaps the science of entomology would gain much in stature and importance if more workers would give attention to these phases.

The opportunities for use of insects in the interests of man are great indeed. Little has been done to survey the insect kingdom for species that produce products useful to man, and to improve the few species that have been found useful. Among the many thousands of species there must be many that produce useful products, including chemicals, drugs, and even food.

Dr. Sailer has enumerated many of the ways in which the techniques of plant and animal breeders can be used in improving insect populations if the applied entomologists will but undertake these tasks. One of the great opportunities would appear to be in developing strains of predators that would be effective in controlling harmful insects. Control by this method might be much less costly than the development and marketing of insecticides. This method of control, where successful, also presents less hazards to beneficial insects, wildlife, and man. It certainly would appear to offer a much greater means to supplement control by chemicals than has been developed to date.

Studies with Drosophila, the silkworm, the honey bee, and the wasp, *Habrobracon*, have contributed greatly to the development of the science of genetics. It is unfortunate that these studies have not been extended to many other species. As Dr. Sailer has aptly pointed out, there is no real obstacle to the genetic improvement of useful insects if time, money, and ingenuity are devoted to this task. In view of the seemingly great opportunities, these efforts should not be delayed longer.

Using Germ Plasm for New Products

Dr. Jones and Dr. Wolff have called attention to the small number of plant species known to botanists that are used for economic crops. In the report of the Commission on Increased Industrial Use of Agricultural Products* it is reported that, of some 250,000 species of plants which have been identified, only about 150 are used in producing most of the world's cultivated crops. A few hundred additional species have been used but in only a limited way. Surely this great reservoir of germ plasm should be explored vigorously for sources of new crops that could contribute to the national welfare. In addition to the possibility of finding new crops of great value for food, medicinal and industrial uses, many of these species might be the source of new characters of great im-

* Senate Document 45, 85th Congress, 1st Session, p. 61, June 15, 1957.

portance that could be incorporated into existing commercial species by hybridization and the use of other genetic techniques.

It would seem that time is long past due when a large and vigorous program should be undertaken to tap this potential reservoir of material. The recent step taken by the United States Department of Agriculture to augment such exploration is in the right direction, but it is too limited. As a nation, we must anticipate the day when products from plants and animals will be needed on a large scale to replace materials now obtained from non-renewable resources that are rapidly being utilized by the nation's great industries.

Finding new germ plasm resources is a long-range program, for in addition to discovering which of the many species produce valuable products, Dr. Jones and Dr. Wolff have pointed out that information will be needed on where they can be grown, how to grow them, and whether they are amenable to modern agronomic practices. Then there is the very important economic problem of whether the market demands will make them competitive with other crops.

The real need for alternative crops to replace those now in surplus is well known. While surpluses will likely disappear in the next forty to fifty years, due to the needs of our rapidly expanding population, the effort expended in finding such crops would be justified because a greater number of economic crops would permit greater diversification of production. Such diversification is important to the farmer as a hedge against drought, insect attacks, and similar problems. Hand in hand with the efforts to find new crops there must be research aimed at finding new industrial outlets for the products produced by these crops. This screening must start with the major lipids, carbohydrates, and proteins since these are the major constituents of all plants. They need to include, however, the less important constituents for possible use as drugs, food additives, fibers, pulp, fungicides, insecticides, and the many other uses to which plants are put. In the limited screening (only about 1500 samples) which has been done to date by Dr. Jones and Dr. Wolff and their co-workers, some valuable new oils and other products have been found. Other plants have been found that offer promise as sources of pulp for paper. To supply our needs for paper over 32 million tons of pulp are required annually. This large and growing demand for pulp may offer one of the most promising outlets for replacement crops.

IRRADIATION AND PLANT IMPROVEMENT

Dr. Caldecott has outlined the efforts that are being made by plant geneticists in using various forms of irradiation to induce heritable changes in crop plants. He has also discussed the factors that must be considered in using irradiation in plant improvement, such as the degree of ploidy, the nature of the changes produced, the mode of reproduction of the species with which one is working, the ontogenetic stage of the plant to be irradiated, the desirability of using ionizing irradiation in more than a one-shot approach in mutation breeding, as well as some of the breeding techniques that can be used in sorting out and evaluating the changes produced; and in incorporating those of value in a desirable genetic complex.

Although the results of such studies are so far mostly theoretical, the facts obtained would indicate that this is one of the promising tools for plant improvement. Many practical and difficult theoretical problems remain to be answered in applying these techniques in plant improvement. Their successful use undoubtedly will require close collaboration between physicists, geneticists, and cytologists. Only a handful of scientists are working on these problems and there is need for increasing such efforts. Eventually breakthroughs will come which will be of great theoretical as well as practical importance. One of the major theoretical results should be in providing a better understanding of the mechanisms of evolution of plants and animals.

GENERAL CONSIDERATIONS

The many problems raised by the panelists in this symposium emphasize the need for basic research in the sciences underlying the genetic improvement of plants and animals as well as the need for discovery of new sources of germ plasm useful for food, fiber, and chemicals. In view of the complexity of the problems and the need for close collaboration of the specialists with different training, it seems to me that there is need for the establishment of special centers for research in various of these fields. The establishment of a center for screening of new plants by the United States Department of Agriculture is an important step in this direction, but this alone is not adequate for the job. Similar centers for the screening of insects and their products might well pay large dividends. Other centers for immunogenetics and for irradiation genetics would speed the job of developing new techniques for application in the improvement of our germ plasm resources. Such centers would provide for a concentration of top scientific manpower and they would provide for most economic use of the expensive facilities needed for such research. If centers of this type are to be established they should be in locations where they can also become centers for the training of young scientists. This should be one of their very important functions.

Other steps such as the organization of cooperative regional programs of animal breeding and population genetics are helping to bring about more effective use of the manpower and facilities available for genetic research with our economic plants and animals. These events bode well for the discoveries that will be needed if scientists are to make it possible to produce the food and fiber that will be needed for the world's rapidly expanding population.

V. Perpetuation and Protection of Breeding Stocks

Perpetuation and Protection
of Germ Plasm as Seed

Edwin James

*Agricultural Research Service, United States Department
of Agriculture, Fort Collins, Colorado*

In tracing the history of the crops now grown in the United States we find that, with two or three exceptions, they originated outside of our continental boundaries. This applies even to our most important crop, corn. It is not the purpose of this paper to discuss crop history, but since the earliest colonial times agriculturists depended on foreign sources of germ plasm as a means of crop improvement. The history of this activity and some of the results were covered thoroughly in Part I.

Unfortunately, many important sources of germ plasm are now closed to explorers as a result of Iron Curtain policies. When explorers had access to areas behind the Iron Curtain, restrictions were not anticipated and, consequently, no provision was made for preserving thousands of early collections. Mute evidence to this fact is the loss of 70% of our soybean collections, 98% of the clovers introduced since 1898, and 66% of the world collection of oats. No one can estimate the value of these losses.

The tragedy of genetic losses is not confined to introductions alone. Many varieties of agricultural crops grown fifty years ago no longer exist. The question may be raised as to why we should be concerned about them when today we have so many new superior varieties. We should bear in mind that while breeders are developing new varieties of crops, nature is also developing new races and strains of pathogens. We recognize the fact that old varieties are replaced by new ones because of their superior agricultural qualities or higher degree of resistance to diseases or insects, but we cannot assume that the old varieties will not be resistant to newly developed pathogens. A forcible reminder of this possibility is the fact that resistance to yellow dwarf mosaic of oats is found in two old varieties, Fulghum, dating back to 1900, and Albion, released as a variety in 1906. It is likely that many other instances of this kind can be found. If old varieties are preserved, the breeder will be able to capitalize on the efforts of his predecessors and begin his program with lines previously accepted as having superior characteristics. Even though there is no assurance that positive results will be obtained, we do have proof of the value of preserving obsolete varieties which involved much effort on the part of earlier plant breeders.

The importance of old varieties is recognized by modern breeders. For many years it was practically impossible to buy seed of Tennessee 76 lespedeza, but this variety is now offered by seed growers. In the corn belt hybrid corn has practically eliminated open-pollinated varieties. The fact that the hybrids arose from inbred lines developed from the old standard varieties prompted corn breeders to collect the latter and place them in storage for future use if needed. At present a similar collection of obsolete vegetable varieties is being made by the American Seed Trade Association for storage in the National Seed Storage Laboratory.

Seed perpetuation may be accomplished in two ways. First, we may simulate nature's program of regeneration. Regeneration has been followed with the world collection of grains wherein a portion has been regrown every five years. This obviously expensive procedure has been commonplace, also, at our experiment stations. Elements of risk are inherent in this method. Insect or disease infestation may eliminate a planting in any one year. Repeated failures may exhaust seed reserves and eliminate the line.

The other method is preservation of seed under favorable storage conditions. To store seed for prolonged periods of time certain requirements must be met. Seed must have a high initial viability. In the process of deterioration decline in viability is at first gradual until a certain point in degeneration is reached. Then the viability drops at a very rapid rate. Longevity has only a slight relation to initial germination of fresh seed, but a dangerously low point in viability is reached sooner with seed of low viability than with that of high when the rate of degeneration is the same. When the break in the curve occurs, regeneration rather than favorable storage conditions is necessary.

Seed must be dry to store well. It is common knowledge that seed high in moisture cannot endure high temperatures without injury. Even the most backward agricultural peoples recognize the necessity of drying seed and use primitive means to dry them to the extent that their atmospheric conditions permit. Sun-drying, and storing in straw containers which permit aeration are typical examples. Their purpose in drying seed was not to provide for posterity, but to preserve planting stock for the next year's crop. Seed drying is one of the difficult problems facing some of our agricultural missions in the humid tropics. In temperate zones the problem is not so acute, but moisture limits are present above which seed cannot be successfully stored.

We are fortunate that research men in advanced countries during the past fifty to seventy years have determined the hygroscopicity of practically all our crop seeds and the moisture-temperature relationships for satisfactory seed storage. Requirements vary somewhat among the genera, but in general, if percentage humidity and degrees Fahrenheit total 100, conditions are considered favorable for seed longevity. In brief, seed with very low moisture will withstand high temperatures, while seeds with high moisture contents must be kept cold. These combinations do not imply that seed kept at 10% R.H. and 90°F will keep as long as those stored at 40% R.H. and 60°F. Changes in seed not encountered at lower temperatures take place at higher temperatures. Seed subjected to temperatures as low as −200° and −250°C have survived (2), but information as to how long they will withstand subfreezing temperatures is limited. It has been found, however, that sugar beet seed can be held at temperatures of 10° to −10°F for twenty-two years with only a 10% loss in viability (2). Regal lily seed has been stored fifteen years at −5°C with only a moderate drop in viability (5). Seeds of a number of pine species have been stored successfully for five to seven years at −5° and −15°C (4, 16), and little loss of viability of delphinium seed resulted from storage at −15°C for five years (3).

Seed may also be preserved at room temperatures after being dried and sealed in air alone, under vacuum, or with the air replaced by gases such as nitrogen or carbon dioxide. Many commercial seed concerns are now marketing seed in sealed containers.

At present little definite information is available as to the longevity of seed stored under hermetic conditions beyond five to six years. At the laboratory we have initiated a project to determine the longevity of hermetically stored seed.

How long will seed remain viable? There is sufficient evidence from testing of seed obtained from herbarium specimens that many species will germinate after 200 years. Ewart (10) reports in his classic tabulation that seed germinated after being interred in Roman tombs for 1000 to 2000 years. According to Groves (11) calculations on the rate of coagulation of seed proteins, under certain conditions, Turkey wheat should have a life expectancy of 2800 years! No one I have contacted, however, lends credence to the reports of the viability of Egyptian mummy wheat.

Regardless of storage conditions seeds do deteriorate, but no agreement has been reached on the reasons for seed deterioration. One of the earliest theories attributed the loss of viability to the exhaustion of food reserves. This theory, on examination, is untenable because seeds lose viability even though ample reserves are available. In 1915 Crocker and Groves (9), and in 1917 Groves (11) were exponents of the theory that loss of viability was due to the precipitation of proteins in the embryo. Although it has been demonstrated that there are changes in the nitrogenous fractions as seed age, it is difficult to link these changes with seed deterioration per se.

The following speculative theory was presented by Ewart in 1908 (10): "Longevity depends not on the food materials or seed coats, but upon how long the proteid molecules into which the living protoplasm disintegrates, when drying, retain their molecular grouping which permits of their recombination to the active protoplasmic molecule when the seed is moistened and supplied with oxygen." There has been no experimental evidence to support this theory. In fact, seed deterioration is more rapid with high moisture contents which would be adverse to the disintegration through drying.

In more recent years the theory that chromosomal aberrations are the principal cause of deterioration has gained considerable support. Various workers have shown that aberrations increase with age. These were first noted in *Crepis tectorum* (17), and later in *Datura* (1, 2, 6-8). Aberrations associated with the age of seed have been found also in onions (18, 19), lettuce (14), sugar beets (16), oats, barley, wheat, rye, corn, and peas (12, 13, 21). Several factors support this theory: (*a*) the similarity of the effects of aging and the reaction of seeds to x rays; (*b*) the inhibiting effects on fresh seeds of extracts from aged seed; (*c*) the gradual increase in mutations with age, and a rapid increase corresponding to a rapid decline in germinative capacity. Mutations observed in the above-mentioned plants were mostly visible ones, but there is also a possibility that massive aberrations prevent the normal mitotic behavior of cells and results in a failure of the first mitotic division. Were this the case, seed which appear viable would not germinate at all. In the final analysis aberrations associated with aging may be only a dependent cause, the first being the accumulation of respiratory end products with mutagenic properties. Although there is much evidence supporting the chromosomal aberration theory, further work is required for its confirmation, including the extent to which mutations occur under cold storage. The fact that longevity can be prolonged when seeds are stored under low temperatures and humidities leads us to assume that the development of mutagens would be eliminated or at least greatly reduced.

The preceding discussion relating to seed storage and deterioration merely lends a background for the establishment of a national seed repository. The need for a facility of this type was first proposed by the National Research Council about 1947 or 1948. The idea was presented to a meeting of the National Coordinating Committee for New Crops in 1949 and action was taken to investigate the feasibility of a national storage. A standing subcommittee was appointed in 1950, and through its efforts support of the various agricultural societies and agencies was obtained. A brochure in support of a National Seed Storage Laboratory was presented to Congress and the Budget Bureau in 1955. Action by Congress was delayed until 1956, when funds were appropriated for the construction of the laboratory. Construction of the National Seed Storage Laboratory was begun in 1957 and was essentially complete in September 1958.

Fig. 1. Exterior view of National Seed Storage Laboratory.

An exterior view of the Laboratory building is shown in Fig. 1. One of the laboratories is shown in Fig. 2. There are nine storage rooms with a capacity of 250,000 pint cans. These rooms are to be maintained at 35% R.H. with a temperature range of 20° to 40°F. In addition, there are also a 0-30°F room and a room for seed stratification. Adequate laboratory space has been provided for germination tests and research work.

The Agricultural Research Service requested a six-member advisory group to make recommendations on broad policies for the Laboratory as a national facility. The members of this group are: D. W. Robertson (Colorado) and W. M. Meyers (Minnesota) representing State Experiment Stations; F. L. Winter (Association of Seed Growers, Inc.) representing the National Council of Commercial Plant Breeders; E. M. Page (Corneli Seed Co.) representing the American Seed Trade Association; H. A. Rodenhiser and C. O. Erlanson, representing the Agricultural Research Service. The statements and recommendations made by this group

Fig. 2.   Germination Laboratory and equipment.

are listed below and have been accepted as general policy by the Agricultural Research Service.

1. The Laboratory is a federal facility and all seed accepted for storage becomes federal property.

2. Only seed will be accepted for storage.

3. Valuable seed stocks will be accepted from feredal, state, and private institutions and individuals. The basic criterion of acceptability will be its value as germ plasm for future use and comparison. Documentation as to value will be required, along with other information as to source and developmental history.

In a number of discussions the question has arisen as to the definition of valuable seed stocks. I believe clarification of this question can be effected best by listing the types of seed which are encompassed by this term. They are as follows: (*a*) world collections, including domestic, which have potentials for future breeding programs (documentation of these may be limited); (b) old standard varieties which have become obsolete; (c) foundation stocks of new varieties; and (d) genetic stocks, provided that a year-to-year maintenance program is not involved.

4. Any bona fide research worker of the United States, its territories, or possessions may receive seed from collections stored at the Laboratory. However, seed will not be issued if readily available elsewhere.

If requests for seed are received by the Laboratory they will be referred to the person who placed the seed in storage. The Laboratory will supply seed if the working stocks of the supplier are exhausted.

5. The Laboratory will have no responsibility in relation to commitments with foreign countries. All requests from foreign sources will be channeled to headquarters of the New Crops Research Branch at Beltsville, Maryland, where decisions in relation to foreign countries will be made.

6. A series of crop-group informal committees will be established by the Agricultural Research Service to advise the Laboratory Director as to valuable stocks to be held, sources when known, proper documentation, and to expedite the movement of these stocks to the Laboratory. These committees will work directly with the Laboratory. The responsibility for acceptance of seed lies with the Laboratory Director or his superiors and the committees will not be expected to screen stocks for the Laboratory.

Crop-group committees have been appointed for cereals, forages, oilseeds, vegetables, fibers and sugar crops, trees, fruits, and miscellaneous crops. The recommendations of these committees are used to determine the acceptability of seed for storage.

7. No seed will be held by the Laboratory for the exclusive use of one or more agencies, organizations, or individuals. Once accepted by the Laboratory, the seed will be available to any research worker subject to such limitations as are here laid down.

8. The Laboratory will not be a procurement agency for seed. The Laboratory will furnish seed only from stocks it is holding.

9. The Laboratory is not a warehouse or seed distributing center. The Laboratory will not hold bulk supplies or seasonal

stocks. Rather, it is a germ plasm bank for valuable stocks to be held over the years for the use of research workers when needed.

In some cases where seed are very small less than one ounce is sufficient for our purposes. On the other hand, we may require several pounds when seed are as large as lima beans or castor beans.

10. The Laboratory will issue periodic inventories of the stocks held in storage to inform research workers of material available.

11. The Laboratory will be responsible for the rejuvenation or replenishment of seed stocks held.

Periodic germination tests will be used to follow the decline in viability. We have tentatively set 60% germination as the point where we may expect a rapid increase in the rate of deterioration. When this point is reached, regeneration of stocks will be effected through contract arrangements with the original supplier or some other seed-producing agency.

12. No charge will be made by the Laboratory for the service of furnishing seed. The Laboratory will use every care in keeping good records, but is not responsible for errors which may occur in documentation.

13. Fresh clean seed is one criterion of acceptability by the Laboratory.

14. The principal objective of the Laboratory is long-time holding of valuable seed. Research projects will be carried on at the Laboratory related to their objective, i.e., physiological problems in seed viability and longevity.

REFERENCES

1. Avery, A. G., and A. F. Blakeslee. Visible mutations from aged seeds. *Am. Naturalist, 70*, 36-37 (1936).

2. Avery, A. G., and A. F. Blakeslee. Mutation rate in *Datura* seed which had been buried 39 years. *Genetics, 28*, 69-70 (1943).

3. Barton, L. V. Effective of storage on the vitality of delphinium seeds. *Contribs. Boyce Thompson Inst., 4*, 141-153 (1932).

4. Barton, L. V. Storage of some coniferous seeds. *Contribs. Boyce Thompson Inst., 7*, 397-404 (1935).

5. Barton, L. V. Storage of the seeds of the Regal Lily. *American Lily Yearbook 1948*, pp. 51-53. (Professional Paper Vol. 2, No. 26, Boyce Thompson Inst., 1948.)

6. Blakeslee, A. F. The aging of seeds and mutation rates. *Ann. N. Y. Acad. Sci.*, *57*, 488-490 (1954).

7. Blakeslee, A. F., and A. H. Avery. Visible genes from aged seeds. *Am. Naturalist*, *68*, 466 (Abs.) (1934).

8. Carteledge, J. L., and A. F. Blakeslee. Mutation rate increased by aging seeds as shown by pollen abortion. *Proc. Natl. Acad. Sci. U. S.*, *20*, 103-110 (1934).

9. Crocker, W., and J. F. Groves. A method of prophecying the life duration of seeds. *Proc. Natl. Acad. Sci. U. S.*, *1*, 152-155 (1915).

10. Ewart, A. J. On the longevity of seeds. *Proc. Roy. Soc. Victoria*, *21*, 2-203 (1908).

11. Groves, J. F. Temperature and life duration of seeds. *Botan. Gaz.*, *63*, 169-189 (1917).

12. Gunthardt, Helga, L. Smith, Mary E. Haferkamp, and R. A. Nilan. Studies on aged seed. II. Relation of seed to cytogenetic effects. *Agron. J.*, *45*, 438-441 (1953).

13. Haferkamp, Mary E. Germination and other tests on super-annuated cereal seeds. *Proc. Assoc. Offic. Seed Analysts*, *39*, 111-114 (1949).

14. Harrison, B. J., and J. McLeish. Abnormalities of stored seeds. *Nature*, *173*, 593 (1954).

15. Issac, L. A. Cold storage prolongs the life of noble fir seed and apparently increases germinative power. *Ecology*, *15*, 216-217 (1934).

16. Lynes, F. F. Polyploidy in sugar beets induced by storage of treated seed. *J. Am. Soc. Agron.*, *37*, 402-404 (1945).

17. Navasin, M. Origin of spontaneous mutations. *Nature*, *131*, 436 (1933).

18. Nichols, C. Spontaneous chromosome aberrations in *Allium*. *Genetics*, *26*, 89-100 (1941).

19. Nichols, C. The effects of age and irradiation on chromosome aberrations in *Allium* seed. *Am. J. Botany*, *29*, 755-759 (1942).

20. Pack, D. A., and F. V. Owen. Viability of sugar beet seed held in cold storage for 22 years. *Proc. Am. Soc. Sugar Beet Technol.*, pp. 127-129, 1950.

21. Peto, F. H. The effects of aging and heat on chromosomal mutation rate in maize and barley. *Can. J. Research*, *9*, 261-264 (1933).

22. White, Jean. The ferments and latent life of resting seeds. *Proc. Roy. Soc. (London)*, *B81*, 417-442 (1909).

Perpetuation and Protection of
Germ Plasm as Vegetative Stock[*]

R. E. Larson

Pennsylvania State University, University Park, Pennsylvania

In discussing the need for and utilization of additional sources of germ plasm of horticultural crops, Dr. Cullinan (p. 91) defined certain examples that illustrated the importance of previous collections of germ plasm to our present fruit, vegetable, and ornamentals production and indicated where certain needs still exist. It would therefore be redundant for me to present individual examples showing why it is important to protect the germ plasm of certain vegetatively propagated plant materials presently widely scattered throughout the United States.

I have served on a subcommittee of the National Coordinating Committee of the New Crops Program for several years. This subcommittee was requested to study the need for national repositories for valuable germ plasm of species normally vegetatively propagated. The committee members, representing the several regional projects, included Quentin Zielinski and H. P. Olmo of W-6; I. C. Johnson and S. A. McCrory of NC-7; J. C. Miller of S-9; the late Fred Krantz of IR-1; W. E. Whitehouse of the United States Department of Agriculture, and myself representing NE-9 and serving as chairman. The material for my address is taken primarily from the report prepared for the National Coordinating Committee (4).

It has been ably stated by Hodge and Erlanson (2):

Agriculture in the United States is based on the best plants and crops that can be grown under its conditions. Most of the basic stock came from elsewhere, and from this foreign material we have evolved strains and varieties by selection and breeding to fit the needs of our environment—it is imperative that the agriculture of every state in the Union

---

[*] Authorized for publication on January 6, 1961, as paper No. 2518 in the journal series of the Pennsylvania Agricultural Experiment Station.

be constantly supplied through plant introductions with new materials for trial, and that reservoirs of basic plant materials be maintained to supply the needs of the plant breeder.

The federal government has expended many hundreds of thousands of dollars to find and to introduce potentially important germ plasm from foreign countries to the United States. Many of these collections were made at a time when certain countries of the world were more freely accessible to our plant explorers. Expanding populations and improvements in agricultural technology have tended to remove previously good sources of native plant materials. It is highly probable that this situation will continue and that diverse types of plants resulting from natural selection at and around their points of evolutionary origin will be lost. Conceivably then, it may be impossible to replace germ plasm even though we received full international cooperation. This may be likened to the situation with maize where the adoption of improved hybrids in the United States and the Central American countries was resulting in rapid loss of native races and open-pollinated strains. Fortunately this situation was recognized by scientists of the Plant Introduction service and by corn breeders who received support of various foundations and associations to collect and maintain valuable maize lines.

The basic problem of germ plasm preservation has been recognized and acknowledged by others as may be noted in several reports of the Agriculture and Biology Division of the National Research Council—National Academy of Sciences, and by a report of the Western Agricultural Experiment Station Directors (4) from whom I wish to quote.

There is great need in the agricultural research program of the United States for repositories of basic material which would be available to the various state experiment stations as well as the various federal agencies to use in connection with their agricultural research programs. Such repositories would include such things as authentic strains of the various disease organisms of livestock, plant genetic material of one kind or another, virus and disease-free plant material, etc. Examples of this type of repository are the seed storage facility at Colorado and the animal disease center at Ames, Iowa. It is believed that the establishment and maintenance of such repositories are logically the responsibility of the Agricultural Research Service (USDA) because of the position of the Agricultural Research Service as a nation-wide agency.

The experiment station directors of the western states have a responsibility to aid the Agricultural Research Service in obtaining federal financing to develop and maintain repositories which the western directors believe to be needed.

It is evident that many plant scientists, scientific societies, and administrative personnel are aware of and concerned with the problem of conservation of biologic resources.

The task of plant introduction and distribution has long been handled by the Plant Introduction Section of the United States Department of Agriculture. It has been the responsibility of the research agencies receiving the introduced stock to preserve the materials for future uses. These agencies consist largely of state experiment stations. Within the Agricultural Research Service (ARS) the responsibility for maintenance and inventory of breeding stock of importance to agricultural research lies with the Crops Research Division through its New Crops Research Branch. Such an arrangement was satisfactory as long as these research agencies were responsible for only a limited number of materials, but has become impractical with an increasing volume of introductions and a limited budget. Few plant breeders and fewer experiment station directors wish to have their limited time and funds consumed in a maintenance program. The pressure of other research problems has caused concern, particularly on the part of state agencies, as to whether they can afford to maintain these plant materials, as a service function, in lieu of much needed research in other areas. Because of this, valuable germ plasm has been lost and other stocks are in danger of being lost unless positive action for preservation is taken.

Conversely, the better known varieties, cultivars, and breeding lines are being maintained at a large number of experimental stations throughout the United States, each planting of which requires certain funds for support. Many of these plantings could be reduced and the funds diverted to other meaningful research if a central source of valuable germ plasm were convenient and available to all qualified personnel. This is of lesser importance in the over-all preservation problem but nevertheless should be considered.

The problem of valuable plant germ plasm preservation has received partial recognition by the Congress of the United States when that body authorized the establishment of a National Seed Storage Facility at Fort Collins, Colorado, to preserve valuable germ plasm of plant materials that can be maintained through sexual reproduction.

Unfortunately a large number of valuable species, strains, varieties, and cultivars cannot be perpetuated adequately through seed propagation but rather must be maintained clonally. The USDA Plant Introduction Gardens at Chico, California, Glenn Dale, Maryland, Savannah, Georgia, and Coconut Grove, Florida, constitute important reservoirs for plant germ plasm. As introduction gardens, however, their main objectives are to propagate and distribute foreign introductions to plant scientists, and to encourage cultivation of new plant materials from all parts of the world. Certain state experiment stations including New York, New Jersey, South Dakota, California, and others have assumed a major responsibility but, for reasons indicated, many are now faced with the necessity of reducing or eliminating this service function to the nation as a whole.

An example of the type of situation with which we are confronted is taken from the joint publication of the South Dakota Agricultural Experiment Station and North Central Region (3). This report presents an evaluation of many of the apples, pears, and apricots collected by the late Dr. N. E. Hansen from plant explorations made in 1897, 1906, 1913, 1924, and 1934 to southern Russia, Siberia, Manchuria, North Korea, Finland, and the Scandinavian countries. Many of these materials are known to have exceptional winterhardiness, disease resistance, and other valuable characteristics. A rather crucial statement is made in this bulletin which I quote, "It is hoped that the information presented may suggest uses for the material. Those for which no use can be found must be eliminated."

One has only to consider the significance of such foreign plant introductions to the United States as the Washington Navel Orange, tung trees, Chinese chestnuts, avocado, and lines of peaches, lemons, white potatoes, sweet potatoes, and apples to appreciate what Hodge and Erlanson (1) have written, namely, "how indispensable is sustained plant introduction work to the agricultural economy of our nation." To this might be added sustained plant introduction and preservation.

During the course of the study made by the subcommittee, suggestions and recommendations were requested of the regional technical committees of the New Crops Projects, from state and federal experiment station plant breeders, and from directors of arboreta and botanic gardens throughout the United States. It was virtually unanimously agreed by those contacted that valuable germ plasm of asexually propagated species should be preserved, and it was generally agreed that a nationally supported and coordinated program for germ plasm maintenance should be concerned with food, fiber, oil, drug, and other crops for industrial use, and should exclude ornamental species for the present. This opinion was also held by directors and representatives of arboreta and botanic gardens, who suggested that their respective institutions were able and willing to serve this function with respect to ornamental plants. Practically all departments, associations, and individuals contacted feel that there is an urgent need to establish either (a) national repositories specifically for the purpose of preservation or (b) a contract procedure for preservation of valuable germ plasm and rootstocks. Many have suggested that this may be handled best by establishing national repositories under a grant from the Congress and under the supervision of the Agricultural Research Service, USDA. The procedure recommended by the S-9 Regional Technical Committee and supported by certain other plant scientists is, however, to seek additional federal support for maintenance of clonally propagated materials at the several state stations or federal field stations interested in so doing. In my own opinion, which I am certain is shared by others, repositories should be developed for the basic purpose of germ plasm preservation and not as a secondary function of an existing experiment station. Changing personnel and interests in the various stations would fail to give continuity and might therefore inadvertently incur losses of valuable materials.

Most replies suggested that major attention should be given to tree fruits (temperate and subtropical), with the inference that small fruits, sweet potatoes, forages, etc., be added as early as feasible. Valuable germ plasm of white potato is presently preserved through Inter-Regional Project No. 1.

A complete list of valuable germ plasm of materials normally propagated through clonal division is not available. In the Northeast and Western regions, however, sufficient information has been collected to indicate the magnitude of the problem. A partial listing of several major economic species includes 1100 lines of apple, 102 crabapple, 242 apple rootstocks, 987 pears, 206 citrus, 692 grape, 128 tree nuts, 1452 Prunus species (peach, cherry, plum, and nectarine), 17 sweet potato, 100 olive, 1100 forage, and 1300 other lines of small fruits, vegetables, and drug plants. There are, I am certain, many duplications in this preliminary list. But to this inventory must be added the many valuable citrus, sweet potato, and forages from the Southern Region; the large pear and apple collection and other fruit and forage materials in the North Central Region, the important collections, mentioned earlier, as made by the late Dr. N. E. Hansen, from explorations in Russia, Siberia, and North China, which are now maintained by Dr. S. A. McCrory of South Dakota, and the extensive collections presently maintained at several USDA Plant Introduction Gardens and Horticultural Field Stations.

It is proposed that national repositories for asexually propagated plant materials should be concerned with maintenance of stocks that are believed to be of value because (a) they are known to contain superior germ plasm, (b) they represent primitive species which may contain superior germ plasm for certain characters, and (c) they contain factors of interest to research workers in plant genetics. It was the consensus among research personnel contacted that committees of specialists should be appointed for the various crop plants to advise as to the inclusion of the various items. After the repositories have become established these committees of specialists should periodically review accessions being preserved in the repositories and consider inclusion of additional items.

Minimum requirements would probably include at least four separate repositories, two for temperate zone, one for subtropical zone, and one for tropical zone crops or species. The locations should be determined by suitable ecological situations rather than on regional, geographic, or economic considerations. Selection of the sites would be determined by the Crops Research Division, ARS, USDA in conjunction with the National Coordinating Committee.

The physical facilities required at each location would include laboratory and office space, greenhouse, screen house, cold storage, adequate land, and field machinery. Staff requirements for each location would include one professional horticulturist, one professional phytopathologist, two technicians, one clerk, and a service force for field and greenhouse work.

Propagating stock (bud and scion wood and root divisions) as well as pollen would be available in limited quantities to all qualified research personnel. In certain instances it is probable that the research worker may be interested in increasing propagating stock for wider distribution. The national repositories would consist primarily as a source for limited supply of materials, however, rather than a source for wide distribution. May I repeat, the repositories would be basically for the preservation of valuable germ plasm of clonally propagated plants.

Specifically the subcommittee recommended that:

1. Repositories be established which will be concerned with food, fiber, drug, oil, and other industrial plants, and should exclude ornamentals which are presently maintained by existing botanical gardens and arboreta.

2. The administrators of the Agricultural Research Service provide leadership in compiling an inventory of valuable germ plasm of clones presently being maintained throughout the nation.

3. Existing facilities should be investigated to determine if they might be usable as National Repositories, particularly the Federal Plant Introduction Gardens and Horticultural Field Stations.

4. Special financing be obtained to enlarge existing or establishing new facilities.

5. The administration of national repositories should be under the ARS of the USDA and annual allocations should be obtained to insure adequate staffing and maintenance.

6. Two repositories should be planned for the temperate

zone, one for a tropical and one for a subtropical zone. The selection of sites should be based on ecological situations and economical maintenance.

7. Only those materials having potentially valuable germ plasm or whose potential is suspected but unknown and those of genetic interest shall be maintained and preserved.

8. Specialist committees representing the various crop plants or groups of crop plants shall be requested to recommend lists of stocks to be preserved or to be eliminated and to counsel on specific problems involved in preservation.

9. Plant materials in the national repositories shall become national property and limited supplies shall be made available to qualified investigators only when supplies are not otherwise available.

10. The national repositories shall be responsible for preservation of viable materials, for the acquisition of descriptive data, and cataloging of all materials under their jurisdiction.

11. All reasonable precautions should be taken to ensure freedom from serious diseases.

12. A file giving origin and pertinent descriptive matter should be maintained for each accession.

13. The repositories shall be a functional reserve of breeding material and not a museum.

14. Only the minimum number of specimens necessary to retain the clones shall be maintained.

15. Foreign requests should be coordinated through the Plant Introduction Section-ARS-USDA.

Finally, the subcommittee requested and the National Coordinating Committee approved, that these recommendations be activated as early as feasible by:

1. Requesting the Agricultural Research Service to provide leadership in compiling a national inventory of valuable germ plasm of asexually propagated food, fiber, drug, oil, and other industrial plant materials.

2. Appointment of crop specialist committees by the chairman of the National Coordinating Committee to evaluate inventories

of materials for possible inclusion in proposed repositories. These committees to include: (*a*) deciduous fruits and nuts, (*b*) subtropical and tropical species, (*c*) small fruits, (*d*) vegetables, and (*e*) forage and turf.

I am pleased to advise that Dr. T. C. Byerly, Deputy Administrator, Agricultural Research Service, United States Department of Agriculture, has approved and encouraged the New Crops Research Branch to do everything it can to expedite inventories of asexually propagated germ plasm within the funds made available for such purposes. Dr. C. O. Erlanson, Chief New Crops Research Branch ARS, USDA, and Dr. W. E. Whitehouse have taken the leadership. The program is being initiated within an inventory of tree and small fruits. Forms have been developed and have been submitted to state and federal experiment station personnel. These will be returned to Beltsville for amalgamation and processing by the fruit group. The inventories thus developed will be made available to the committee or committees appointed by the National Coordinating Committee chairman who is Dr. E. F. Frolik, Associate Director of the Nebraska Agricultural Experiment Station.

Once the fruit inventory is underway other categories of materials will be given attention.

The success of the program is dependent upon cooperation of each experiment station. An adequate inventory is a necessary prelude to further action. It would seem essential that we use every means to ensure adequate materials for solving agricultural problems and agricultural needs of the future. As a concluding remark, I would ask that each of you assist in the project by encouraging personnel at your respective locations to submit the data requested and to do so within a reasonable period after receipt of the forms.

REFERENCES

1. Hodge, W. H., and C. O. Erlanson. Plant introduction as a federal service to agriculture. *Advances in Agron.*, 7, 189-211 (1955).

2. Hodge, W. H., and C. O. Erlanson. Federal plant introduction: A review. *Econ. Botany*, 10 (4), 299-334 (1956).

3. McCrory, S. A. Preliminary evaluation and descriptions of domestic and introduced fruit plants. *South Dakota Agr. Expt. Sta. Bull. 471* and *North Central Regional Publ. No. 90*, 1958.

4. Minutes of the National Coordinating Committee Meeting, April 9-10, 1959 (New Crops Program).

Preservation of Animal Breeding Stocks through Storage of Germ Plasm

N. L. VanDemark

Department of Dairy Science, University of Illinois, Urbana, Illinois

For years animal breeders and geneticists were faced with the problem of maximum utilization of animals capable of transmitting superior productive ability. In addition to the limited number of animals that could be mated naturally to the superior individual, the germ plasm of the selected animal was often lost by incapacitation to breeding or by death. Even with the good fortune of long, healthy lives for the selected animals, the generation interval of some classes of farm animals limited effective planned breeding programs to breeders who could devote a lifetime to such a project. Even then progress was slow.

Although artificial insemination of farm animals was known to be possible even before the turn of the century, widespread use of the practice in utilizing tested and proved sires has come largely in the last thirty years. The growth of artificial insemination has been phenomenal and largely due to the numbers of females that can be bred to a single male and to the length of time that sperm cells can be preserved without the loss of fertility. These changes have brought the geneticist a potent tool for the improvement of large populations of livestock, and they may make possible the planning of experimental matings for as much as several generations ahead.

Still another tool is the superovulation and transfer of ova from one female to another. Perhaps an even more important prospect is that of the passage of superior ovarian tissue from one to many individuals by destroying the recipient's ovarian tissue and supplying surgically new tissue from a donor.

Whether the approach be from the male or female standpoint, preservation of selected animal genetic materials has to come either through the more widespread utilization of selected sires and dams or through the preservation of their genes over a period of time so that planned and experimental matings can be made. In essence the genetic materials must either be stored *in vivo* by having many offspring preserve and pass along the genetic materials of a selected animal or the germ plasm must be stored *in vitro*. With either of these techniques the effectiveness hinges first of all upon obtaining a large number of germ cells from the selected animal. The novelty and glamour of artificial insemination and ovum transfer has tended to overshadow this important aspect. Next, the success depends upon the preservation of these cells without detrimental effects that will (*a*) render the germ cell physiologically incapable of meeting and uniting with the germ cell of the opposite sex or (*b*) damage the genetic components of the cell so that the united cells cannot produce a normal individual.

It is the purpose of this paper to review some of the developments in germ cell production and storage that have led to much greater utilization of superior animal breeding stocks.

DEVELOPMENTS IN SEMEN PRODUCTION AND STORAGE

The developments in semen production and storage have been along three principal lines, namely (*a*) increasing the number of sperm produced by the males, (*b*) extending semen to breed more and more females from a single ejaculate, and (*c*) prolonging the storage time through which fertile germ plasm can be kept without harm to the genetic components of the cells. These developments have come largely in the last twenty to thirty years and principally in the area of artificial insemination of cattle. Thus much of the following discussion is limited to a chronological survey of these developments.

The first attempts at *in vitro* handling of semen were aimed at the breeding of more than one female from a single ejaculate by dividing the ejaculate into four or five equal portions (67). No particular attempt was made to prolong the life of the sperm. The Russians seem to have been the first to begin adding various salt and sugar solutions to the semen at a low ratio of diluent to semen, thus prolonging life and more than doubling the number of females that could be inseminated (32). Although these Russian diluents supplied nutrients and buffers, they gave little protection against cold shock. Also these diluting media did not support sperm life for more than a few days at room temperatures.

Short-Term Storage of Semen

As the demand for artificial insemination spread, especially into the parts of the world where individual farms are widely dispersed as they are in the United States, the need arose for preserving semen during a period of transport. This need brought the development of nutrient diluents which started with Phillips' (42) discovery of the beneficial effects of a buffered nutrient solution consisting of one part fresh egg yolk and one part of a phosphate buffer. Soon after this, Salisbury and his associates (53) published on the yolk-citrate diluent. The egg yolk protected the sperm against the harmful effects of cooling known as cold shock. Thus semen could be cooled to slow the metabolism of the sperm cells and promote longer life.

Soon the egg yolk-buffered diluents were widely used at rates of one, two, or even four parts of diluent to one part of bovine semen. Then the Cornell workers showed that no loss in fertility occurred with semen diluted 1:50, 1:100, or even more (47, 49, 51). The breaking point in fertility came when the number of sperm inseminated into the cow was reduced below about 5 million. Today most progressive cattle artificial insemination units make dilutions of the semen on the basis of sperm numbers. Approximately 5 to 10 million motile sperm are usually placed into the 1 milliliter of diluent that is commonly used in breeding the cow.

Use of Subnormal Temperatures for Storage. The egg yolk diluent permitted semen to be cooled below the temperature of the body to temperatures near freezing (12, 73). The cooling reduced the metabolic activity of the sperm and at about 7°C sperm motility ceased. The successful use of subnormal storage temperatures was dependent on slow and careful cooling. Too rapid cooling caused cold shock, and fewer sperm recovered motility and fertility upon rewarming.

A number of storage temperatures between body temperature

and freezing were investigated for their suitability in storing bovine semen (73). The most practical was the temperature of most normally operating refrigerators. Diluted semen could be safely cooled to this temperature from body temperature in about 90 minutes. Lower storage temperatures above freezing required even slower cooling from 5°C on down.

Diluted bovine semen properly cooled and stored at 5°C drops in fertility about 5 percentage units with each day of storage for the first three or four days (20, 55). Then the drop is frequently more rapid. Thus routine use of bovine semen stored at 5°C is usually limited to three or four days.

Several diluents have been developed for the storage of bovine semen at a temperature near 5°C. The early egg yolk diluents have served as the basis for many diluents to which additions and modifications have been made. One main addition has been that of antibacterial agents. The Cornell workers pioneered this phase with the addition of sulfanilamide (54). Sulfanilamide also exerts a beneficial inhibitory effect on sperm metabolism. Later penicillin and streptomycin were added to help control bacterial growth (4). In some instances the fertility of low-fertility bulls was improved by the addition of antibacterial agents (2). Other additions to the yolk diluents have included glycerol, glycine, sugars, and milk. Modifications have been made by changing the buffers, by reducing the proportion of egg yolk used, and by using the whole egg. These modifications were recently reviewed by Salisbury (48). For the most part each of these changes and additions has brought a slight increase in the efficiency of the diluent or in some cases a reduction in the cost of preparation.

Since 1950 milk has become a widely used diluent for the storage of bovine semen at 5°C (48). Whole milk, skim milk, buttermilk, cream, and reconstituted dried milk have all been used with varying degrees of success. Glycerol has become a favorite additive to milk for the storage of bovine semen. Also mixtures of milk and the egg yolk diluents are being used. For the most part fertility levels obtained with semen in the milk and egg yolk diluents appear to be comparable, although individual breeding units usually favor one or the other because of the ease of preparation or some swaying experience they have had.

Use of Chemical Inhibition. To date the preservation of spermatozoa has been accomplished largely by means of temperature control. However, scientists long have known that sperm stay alive for as long as sixty days and fertile for thirty days in the isolated epididymis. Such isolated sperm are being maintained at a temperature only a few degrees below that of the body through the chemical controls supplied in the epididymis. Attempts to duplicate the conditions of the epididymis were started at the University of Illinois in 1954 by the author and his students. A flow dialysis system was arranged so that spermatozoa in a cellulose sac would have sugars supplied and waste products removed by a continuous flow of fresh solution past the membrane. With this arrangement it was found that neat semen would live for as long as a week at room temperature compared to 24 hours survival for controls in test tubes at the same temperature. Studies of the effects of nutrients and gases on sperm in the flow dialysis system led to the discovery that carbon dioxide reversibly inhibited the motility and the metabolism of spermatozoa (64, 66). Prior to this, CO_2 had been considered toxic to sperm if the sperm were kept under high CO_2 tensions for long after they became immotile (58).

Out of the Illinois investigation was developed a carbon dioxide saturated diluent which gave exceptional sperm survival at room temperature if the diluted semen was sealed in glass ampules to prevent the escape of the CO_2. This diluent was called the Illini Variable Temperature diluent (IVT) for in it sperm could withstand wide fluctuations in temperature. Early fertility trials showed that fertility was maintained with little or no loss over six to seven days storage at room temperature (66). In large-scale trials in the field, the results were less promising (62, 63).

An exceptionally promising report on the storage of boar semen by the use of the CO_2 saturated IVT diluent has come out of France (15). In general, swine artificial insemination has been hindered by the fact that boar semen does not store well. In most reports fertility has dropped off rapidly and embryonic death has increased rapidly after the first day of use. The French reported that by using the IVT diluent to store boar sperm, a fertility level of 66% was obtained with semen stored for three days at ambient temperature (17-22°C) and 50% (45-day non-returns to service) for semen stored six days at 15°C. Litter size was normal in both groups of sows.

Although extensive reports have not appeared on their widespread use, diluents similar to IVT to which glycine and glutathione have been added seem to be preserving sperm in excellent condition for use over periods up to five to seven days (18, 24).

Carbon dioxide saturated diluents would appear to be only one of several possible means of chemical control of sperm activity. The full use of chemical means of preserving sperm can likely come no faster than the development of our knowledge concerning the metabolic behavior of spermatozoa. In time it may well become the preferred method of semen preservation for limited periods of time.

Long-Term Storage of Semen

Even though the combined use of chemical control and above freezing temperatures have kept semen fertile for two weeks, this is still short-term storage compared to the development and use of frozen semen. This procedure has undergone phenomenal developments in the last ten years.

Preservation by Freezing. Early attempts at freezing semen date back more than sixty years (13). More attempts were made in the late thirties and early forties (26, 27, 35). These early investigators found that some of the sperm of human semen without any pretreatment would survive exposure to the temperatures of liquid gases. The sperm of other species would not survive the plunge to these very low temperatures. It was not until 1949 when the British found that glycerol would protect spermatozoa against the damages wrought by very low temperatures that the bottleneck was broken in using freezing as a method of routine semen preservation (44). The original discovery of the beneficial effects of glycerol was made with fowl sperm. It was soon learned that glycerol permitted a higher proportion of human sperm to survive freezing. Sperm of the bull, boar, goat, guinea pig, rabbit, ram, and stallion will not withstand freezing without pretreatment with glycerol and slow cooling, but by using glycerol and slow cooling a large portion of the sperm of all these animals survives freezing.

The techniques of adding glycerol, the optimal rates of cooling, and other procedures in the preparation for freezing and in the freezing process differ with the sperm of different species (43). The most extensive investigations of freezing procedures have been with bull semen and widespread usage is now made of frozen semen in routine artificial insemination. Many large cattle breeding operations in the United States and abroad are now run completely with frozen semen.

The fertility of semen stored frozen has not been widely tested except in cattle. In this species, even though there is a gradual decline in the number of sperm that live through storage in the frozen state, samples have been stored and were highly fertile for more than four years (45).

There is little question but that the successful freezing of semen so that it can be stored for long periods at $-79°C$, the temperature of solid carbon dioxide, or -190 or $-196°C$, the temperatures of liquid air and liquid nitrogen, has placed in the hands of the geneticist a new tool for carrying germ plasm to future generations in a more effective way than ever before was possible. In addition to making possible the establishment of breeding programs in the field in which any sire can be used any day of the week, in many instances the semen of superior sires can be utilized more fully, for the wastage that frequently occurs due to the aging and loss of fertility of semen stored at higher temperatures can be eliminated. Also the possibilities of breeding to a sire during a period of incapacitation or after death can be realized.

Still another advantage of long-term storage of semen by freezing includes the collection and storage of semen in a slack breeding season for use during a heavy breeding season. In certain cases it may be worthwhile to collect and build a bank of semen from young unproved sires for later use. However, this aspect has yet to prove desirable because of the high cost of maintaining large semen banks if large portions of the semen are later to be discarded. In addition our methods of selecting sires are not yet perfected to the point where it would seem advisable to breed 100 to 200 thousand cows to a single bull in a year. This potential number of breedings may be realized with many bulls even without building large semen banks.

Freeze-Drying of Semen. The freezing of tissue to temperatures low enough to cause crystallization of all the water and then removing the crystals by sublimation of the water under vacuum is known as lyophilization or freeze-drying. The principle has been applied to microorganisms and has permitted their return to room temperature after they are dried if sealed in ampules (19). Since the cells are dry, they remain inactivated until the water is restored to them. Some microorganisms can be stored in this condition for years, and they remain capable of growth and normal functioning when they are reconstituted. This means of preserving spermatozoa has been the dream of researchers for years. Many attempts at freeze-drying sperm have been reported (1, 6, 28, 56). Most have given negative or only very poor results. However, a Russian report contains an account of the successful freeze-drying of rabbit and ram sperm and the production of twelve litters of normal rabbits from freeze-dried semen stored for forty days at room temperature before being reconstituted and used for inseminating does (28). At least one unsuccessful attempt to duplicate these results in the United States is known (57). A recent report indicates that Meryman and Kafig of the Naval Medical Research Institute at Bethesda have obtained at least one pregnancy with lyophilized bovine sperm (31).

In spite of the progress that has been made in storing sperm cells in a fertile condition, little has been learned concerning the effects of storage on the genetic components of these cells. The effects apparently are not too severe for too great alterations most certainly would result in fertilization failure or embryonic death. However an increase in the apparent embryonic death rate occurs with the routine storage of bovine semen at 5°C (52). Recent evidence indicates there is a disappearance of Feulgen positive material, presumably deoxyribonucleic acid, during storage of bovine semen at 5°C (50). Whether damage is caused to the gene carrying components by oxidative changes, by hydrogen peroxide formation, or other conditions in storage is unknown.

Such conditions have been shown to cause mutations in certain strains of bacteria (74), and the possibilities of similar damage to spermatozoa in storage was pointed out several years ago (65).

Increased Semen Production

The years since 1950 have brought some changes in the practices of semen collection from bulls that have increased the number of potential breedings to a bull several-fold. In the early days of cattle artificial insemination in the United States, bulls were used only once every ten to fourteen days, and then once a week at the most. Careful studies of the effects of collection frequencies and the potential sperm reserves of the bull indicate a much greater potential than is used. Collection frequencies of two and three times per week similar to those being used in Europe were found to have no detrimental effect on a bull's semen-producing ability, but the number of sperm produced per week was greatly increased (61). It has now been shown that many bulls can be maintained on a collection frequency of one ejaculate per day. Bulls in New York and Pennsylvania investigations have been on such a schedule for as long as fourteen months with no loss in fertility (3, 23). Although the number of sperm per ejaculate is reduced by frequent collection, the total output per week is increased twofold to fourfold. The possibilities of 100 to 200 thousand offspring from a single bull in a year are not remote.

DEVELOPMENTS IN OVUM PRODUCTION AND STORAGE

The number of ova produced by the mammalian female is infinitely small compared to the sperm produced by the mammalian male. Nevertheless, some developments of the past few years suggest the possibilities of increasing the available germ plasm from female animal breeding stocks and perhaps even storing it for future use.

Superovulation and Ovum Transfer

The first demonstration that fertilized ova could be transferred from one female to another with the successful development and production of young was made with rabbits in England in 1890

(25). Since then numerous attempts at ovum transfer have been made and successful transfers have been reported for rats (33, 34), mice (17), rabbits (9, 14, 25), pigs (29), sheep and goats (7, 68), and cattle (70, 71). Along with the recent renewed interest in ovum transfer has come a renewed interest in superovulation in order to obtain numbers of ova from species that normally only shed one ovum. Superovulation is usually accomplished by subcutaneous injections of follicle-stimulating hormone followed by an intravenous injection of luteinizing hormone (69). Such a procedure in the cow may result in ten, twenty, or more ova being shed. Insemination is performed on the donor so that the ova are fertilized before they are collected.

In the larger animals collection of the fertilized ova has required surgery. The ova remain in the oviducts for about four days after ovulation so they cannot be flushed out without resorting to surgery during this time. Although to date the recovery of the ova after they have reached the uterus has been partially successful, placing them in the uterus of the recipient at that stage tends to cause infection (46, 72). Since the estrous cycles of the donor and recipient have to be synchronized, no way around these difficulties has yet been found. Until ovum transfer can be made without surgery (on both the donor and the recipient), the procedure will likely be restricted to laboratory use.

Storage of Ova

Successful ovum transfer is dependent on the fertilized ova being for a period (short or long) in an environment *in vitro* that could be detrimental. Studies of storage are more limited than are those concerning semen storage, and the studies of ova have been largely with laboratory animals. The fertile life of the ovum in the female is limited after ovulation to a period ranging from 6 to 20 hrs (11, 21, 30). Thus storage of ova probably will be dependent on supplying conditions that will slow metabolism or furnish more ideal conditions than the female tract.

Most attempts at storing ova have been made by using homologous blood serum (8). Other mixtures including saline and egg white have been used. As with sperm, rapid cooling to 0 or 5°C and holding the ova at that temperature have been shown to be harmful. Slow cooling was less harmful, and at 10°C Chang (10) found that 80% of the fertilized rabbit eggs stored for 24 hours cleaved when they were returned to 37°C. Normal development occurred more regularly in ova stored after fertilization than occurred in ova stored before fertilization.

In many attempts at storing ova by freezing, it has been found that by a slow buildup of glycerol and slow cooling and freezing to −79°C little visible harm is produced. However, to date few eggs have divided normally in culture upon thawing and removing of the glycerol (59).

Storage of ova has not advanced to the point of semen storage. Yet in time, we shall probably see phenomenal advances in this area too.

STORAGE OF GONADAL TISSUE

Although the attempts to freeze and store ova have been only partially successful, the British have found that glycerol treated ovarian tissue from the rat will withstand freezing (38). Slow freezing is essential, and the use of a homologous serum-glycerol medium permits more tissue "takes" after freezing than other media (37). The endocrine tissues of the ovary seem to be less susceptible to damage during freezing and low-temperature storage than are the ova. After storage at −79°C for fourteen and twenty-six weeks, mouse ovarian tissue has produced active autografts. The British workers are fairly confident that it will be possible to maintain ovarian tissue in the frozen state for long periods of time and still have it produce endocrinologically active grafts. The recovery of the oocyte-producing ability appears to be more of a problem. Yet one litter of mice has been produced from ovarian tissue after freezing and grafting (37).

Parrott and Parkes (40) have introduced a technique of inactivating the recipient's ovaries by x irradiation. Such a procedure simplifies the transplantation of ovarian tissue to a simple surgical routine free of the damage and adhesions caused by surgical removal of the recipient's ovaries. In using this technique these investigators obtained a succession of nine litters out of fourteen attempts with grafted ovaries in mice (41). Such a technique in itself suggests a method for wider use of ovarian tissues of selected females, but many difficulties of recipient incompatibility will have to be solved first by immunologists.

These same investigators from the National Institute of Medical Research in England have shown that testicular tissue can be transplanted after freezing and storage at −79°C or lower (36, 39). Testicular tissue was taken from young male rats and soaked in 15% glycerol-saline. Then the tissue was frozen to −79°C or −190°C by slow cooling. Upon rapid thawing and transplantation, active grafts were established. The endocrine activity of the grafts was established by the growth of the male accessory glands. The success of the restoration of the spermatogenic function of this tissue has still not been determined.

Summary

In recent years developments in the storage of germ plasm have greatly increased the possibilities of planned breeding programs for the animal breeder and geneticist. These developments have occurred in the potential *in vitro* storage time of both germ cells and gonadal tissue. Some of the advances are still in the trial stages and may be several years in reaching a practical utilization basis. Other developments have passed rapidly into widespread usage.

The utilization and storage of semen of superior sires of some species have progressed well beyond the simple dividing of an ejaculate to breed more females by artificial insemination. In other species this stage still prevails. In cattle especially, many more sperm are collected from the male than formerly thought possible, and these can be diluted so there are several hundred potential breedings in a single collection. Electrical ejaculation ensures the collection of large numbers of sperm even if injury occurs or sex drive is impaired. Semen can be stored at 5°C for a few days with satisfactory fertility maintained in several diluents with egg yolk or milk to protect the sperm and antibacterial agents to control bacterial growth. Chemical control of sperm metabolism and motility, as with CO_2, may well become the procedure for short-term sperm storage in the future. By slow cooling and the protective action of glycerol, sperm of several species can be frozen and stored at the temperature of dry ice ($-79°C$), liquid air or liquid nitrogen (-190 and $-196°C$). Frozen bovine semen has remained fertile for over four years. Lyophilized (freeze-dried) sperm of the rabbit stored at room temperature have been reconstituted and successfully used in producing litters. Lyophilized bovine sperm have produced a pregnancy.

The production of large numbers of ova from superior females is possible by superovulation. However, the transfer of fertilized ova from these females is still hampered because surgical techniques are required. The use of a technique of sterilizing a recipient by x irradiation and then supplying ovarian tissue of a superior donor may well have greater potential than ovum transfer. This seems possible since to date ova have not survived freezing or storage well, but frozen ovarian tissue has been used to restore the fertility of x-ray sterilized mice. Frozen testicular tissue recovers its endocrine functions also, and at least some of its spermatogenic activity is restored. The completeness of the latter is not yet established.

TABLE I. Some highlights in the development of methods
of storing animal germ plasm

Date	Contribution	Investigator—Country[a]
1785	First recorded artificial insemination (dogs)	Spallanzani, Italy (60)
1785	Sperm and eggs subjected to cold survive	Spallanzani, Italy (60)
1890	Use of artificial insemination on farm livestock	Ivanov, Russia (67)
1890	First transfer of fertilized ova (rabbits)	Heape, England (25)
1897	Human sperm revived after freezing	Davenport, U. S. (13)
1914	First artificial vagina (dog)	Amantea, Italy (5)
1927	First demonstration of superovulation (mice)	Engle, U. S. (16)
1936	Electro-ejaculation used on farm animals	Gunn, Australia (22)
1939	Buffered egg yolk diluent for sperm	Phillips, U. S. (42)
1946	Extensive dilution of bovine semen possible	Salisbury et al., U. S. (49, 51)
1947	Antibacterial agents added to semen diluents	Salisbury and Knodt, U. S. (54)
1949	Semen freezing made possible by use of glycerol	Polge et al., England (44)
1953	Fertilized ova withstand freezing	Smith, England (59)
1953	Ovarian tissue active in transplants after freezing	Parkes and Smith, England (38)
1957	CO_2 used to preserve sperm at room temperature	VanDemark et al., U. S. (64, 66)
1957	Restoration of fertility by ovarian transplants after x-ray sterilization	Parrott and Parkes, England (41)
1957	Litters from transplanted ovarian tissue after freezing	Parkes, England (37)
1958	Litters produced from frozen-dried rabbit sperm	Juscenko, Russia (28)
1959	Lyophilized bovine sperm produced a pregnancy	Meryman and Kafig, U. S. (31)

[a] Numbers in parentheses are references.

By the use of frozen semen (which has been shown to remain fertile over long periods) or lyophilized semen and the storage and transplantation of frozen ovarian tissue (which is still in the developmental stages), the animal geneticist may soon be able to plan for matings several years in advance.

References

1. Albright, J. L., R. E. Erb, and M. H. Ehlers. Freeze-drying bovine spermatozoa. *J. Dairy Sci.*, *41*, 206 (1958).

2. Almquist, J. O. A comparison of penicillin, streptomycin and sulfanilamide for improving the fertility of semen from relatively infertile bulls. *J. Dairy Sci.*, *32* (8), 722 (1949).

3. Almquist, J. O., E. B. Hale, and R. P. Amann. Sperm production and fertility of dairy bulls at high-collection frequencies with varying degrees of sexual preparation. *J. Dairy Sci.*, *41*, 733 (1958).

4. Almquist, J. O., W. T. S. Thorp, and P. J. Glantz. The influence of streptomycin upon the livability and bacterial content of bull semen. 42nd Ann. Meeting American Dairy Science Association (Abs.), *J. Dairy Sci.*, *30* (8), 542-543 (1947).

5. Amantea, G. Investigations on the spermatic secretions (trans. title). *Arch. ital. biol.*, *62*, 35-46 (1914).

6. Bialy, G., and V. R. Smith. Freeze-drying of bovine spermatozoa. *J. Dairy Sci.*, *40*, 739-745 (1957).

7. Casida, L. E., E. J. Warwick, and R. K. Meyer. Survival of multiple pregnancies induced in the ewe following treatment with pituitary gonadotrophins. *J. Animal Sci.*, *3*, 22-28 (1944).

8. Chang, M. C. Normal development of fertilized rabbit ova stored at low temperature for several days. *Nature, 159*, 602-603 (1947).

9. Chang, M. C. Probability of normal development after transplantation of fertilized rabbit ova stored at different temperatures. *Proc. Soc. Exptl. Biol. Med.*, *68*, 680-683 (1948).

10. Chang, M. C. Fertilizability of rabbit ova and the effects of temperature *in vitro* on their subsequent fertilization and activation *in vivo*. *J. Exptl. Zool.*, *121*, 351-382 (1952).

11. Chang, M. C., and G. Pincus. Physiology of fertilization in mammals. *Physiol. Revs.*, *31*, 1-26 (1951).

12. Chang, M. C., and A. Walton. The effects of low temperature and acclimatization on the respiratory activity and survival of ram spermatozoa. *Proc. Roy. Soc. (London)*, *B129*, 517-527 (1940).

13. Davenport, C. B. *Experimental Morphology*, Part I. The Macmillan Company, New York, N. Y., 1897.

14. Dowling, D. F. Problems of transplantation of fertilized ova. *J. Agr. Sci.*, *39*, 374-395 (1949).

15. Du Mesnil Du Buisson, F., and L. Dauzier. Maintien du pouvoir fécondant du sperme de Verrat en présence de gaz carbonique. *Compt. rend.*, *247*, 2472-2475 (1958).

16. Engel, E. T. Pregnancy following superovulation in the mouse. *Proc. Soc. Exptl. Biol. Med.*, *25*, 84-85 (1927).

17. Fekete, Elizabeth. Differences in the effect of uterine environment upon development in the DBA and C57 Black Strains of mice. *Anat. Record*, *98*, 409-415 (1947).

18. Foote, R. H., D. C. Young, and H. O. Dunn. Fertility of bull semen stored for one and two days at 5°C. in 20% yolk-citrate-glycine-glucose extenders. *J. Dairy Sci.*, *41*, 732 (1958).

19. Fry, R. M. The Preservation of Bacteria. In *Biological Applications of Freezing and Drying*, pp. 215-252. Academic Press, New York, N. Y., 1954.

20. Fryer, H. C., G. B. Marion, and E. L. Farmer. Nonreturn rate of artificially inseminated dairy cows as affected by age of semen, breed of bull, and season. *J. Dairy Sci.*, *41*, 987-993 (1958).

21. Green, W. W., and L. M. Winters. Studies on the physiology of reproduction in the sheep. III. The time of ovulation and rate of sperm travel. *Anat. Record*, *61*, 457-470 (1935).

22. Gunn, R. M. C. Fertility in sheep, artificial production of seminal ejaculation and the characters of the spermatozoa contained therein. *Bull. Australian Council Sci. Ind. Research No. 94*, 1936.

23. Hafs, H. D., R. S. Hoyt, and R. W. Bratton. Libido, sperm characteristics, sperm output, and fertility of mature dairy bulls ejaculated daily or weekly for thirty-two weeks. *J. Dairy Sci.*, *42*, 626-636 (1959).

24. Hayden, J. S., and O. T. Stallcup. Storing bovine semen at room temperature. *Arkansas Agr. Expt. Farm Research*, 7, 6 (1958).

25. Heape, W. Preliminary note on the transplantation and growth of mammalian ova within a uterine foster mother. *Proc. Roy. Soc. (London)*, *48*, 457-458 (1890).

26. Hoagland, H., and G. Pincus. Revival of mammalian sperm after immersion in liquid nitrogen. *J. Gen. Physiol.*, *25*, 337-344 (1942).

27. Jahnel, E. Über die Widerstandsfahigkeit von menschlichen Spermatozoen gegenüber starker Kälte. *Klin. Wochschr.*, *17*, 1273. (1938).

28. Juscenko, N. P. Proof of the possibility of preserving mammalian spermatozoa dry (trans. title). *Doklady Akad. Seljskohoz. Nauk Lenin.*, *22* (6), 37-40 (1957); Abs. in *Animal Breeding Abstracts*, 26 (1), 17 (1958).

29. Kvasnickiv, A. V. Interbreed Ova Transplantation (trans. title). *Sovet. Zootekh.*, *1*, 36-42 (1951); Abs. in *Animal Breeding Abstracts*, *19*, 224 (1951).

30. Lewis, L. L. The vitality of reproductive cells. *Oklahoma Agr. Expt. Sta. Bull.*, *96*, 1911.

31. Meryman, H. T., and E. Kafig. Survival of spermatozoa following drying. *Nature, 184,* 470-471 (1959).

32. Milovanov, V. K., and O. H. Selivanova. Dilutors for sperm of livestock (trans. title). *Problomy Zhivotnovodstva, 2,* 75-86 (1932); Abs. in *Animal Breeding Abstracts, 1,* 153 (1933).

33. Nicholas, J. S. Development of transplanted rat eggs. *Proc. Soc. Exptl. Biol. Med., 30,* 1111 (1933).

34. Noyes, R. W. Fertilization of follicular ova. *Fertility and Sterility, 3,* 1-12 (1952).

35. Parkes, A. S. Preservation of human spermatozoa at low temperatures. *Brit. Med. J.,* 2, 212-213 (1945).

36. Parkes, A. S. Transplantation of testis after storage at very low temperatures. *J. Endocrinol., 10,* 7 (1954).

37. Parkes, A. S. Viability of ovarian tissue after freezing. *Proc. Roy. Soc. (London), B147,* 520-528 (1957).

38. Parkes, A. B., and A. U. Smith. Regeneration of rat ovarian tissue grafted after exposure to low temperatures. *Proc. Roy. Soc. (London), B140,* 455-470 (1953).

39. Parkes, A. S., and A. U. Smith. Storage of testicular tissue at very low temperatures. *Brit. Med. J., 1,* 315 (1954).

40. Parrott, D. M. V., and A. S. Parkes. Orthotopic ovarian grafting after sterilization by x-rays. *Brit. Vet. J., 112,* 550-554 (1956).

41. Parrott, D. M. V., and A. S. Parkes. Restoration of fertility in the x-irradiated mouse by orthotopic grafting of ovarian tissue. *J. Endocrinol., 14,* 36 (1957).

42. Phillips, P. H. Preservation of bull semen. *J. Biol. Chem., 130,* 415 (1939).

43. Polge, C. Low-temperature storage of mammalian spermatozoa. *Proc. Roy. Soc. (London), B147,* 498-508 (1957).

44. Polge, C., A. U. Smith, and A. S. Parkes. Revival of spermatozoa after vitrification and dehydration at low temperatures. *Nature, 164,* 666 (1949).

45. Rowson, L. E. The low temperature preservation of germinal cells. *III Intern. Congr. Animal Reproduction, Plenary Papers,* p. 75, 1956.

46. Rowson, L. E., G. E. Lamming, and R. M. Fry. The relationship between ovarian hormones and uterine infection. *Vet. Record, 65,* 335-340 (1953).

47. Salisbury, G. W. Fertility of bull semen diluted at 1:100. *J. Dairy Sci., 29,* 695-697 (1946).

48. Salisbury, G. W. Recent developments with bull semen diluents. *Animal Breeding Abstracts, 25,* 111-123 (1957).

49. Salisbury, G. W., G. H. Beck, P. T. Cupps, and I. Elliott. The

effect of dilution rate on the livability and the fertility of bull spermatozoa used for artificial insemination. 38th Ann. American Dairy
Science Meetings (Abs.). *J. Dairy Sci., 26* (8), 1057-1069 (1943).

50. Salisbury, G. W., L. de la Torre, W. J. Birge, and J. R. Lodge.
Effect of 5°C storage in yolk-citrate on Feulgen-positive material
(DNA) of sperm heads. *J. Dairy Sci., 43,* (6), 882 (1960).

51. Salisbury, G. W., and R. W. Bratton. Fertility level of bull
semen diluted at 1:400 with and without sulfanilamide. *J. Dairy Sci.,
31,* 817-822 (1948).

52. Salisbury, G. W., R. W. Bratton, and R. H. Foote. The effects
of time and other factors on the non-return to service estimate of fertility level in artificial insemination of cattle. *J. Dairy Sci., 35* (3), 256-
260 (1952).

53. Salisbury, G. W., H. K. Fuller, and E. L. Willett. Preservation
of bovine spermatozoa in yolk-citrate diluent and field results from its
use. *J. Dairy Sci., 24,* 905-910 (1941).

54. Salisbury, G. W., and C. B. Knodt. The effect of sulfanilamide in
the diluent upon fertility of bull semen. *J. Dairy Sci., 30* (6), 361-369
(1947).

55. Schultze, A. B., H. P. Davis, C. T. Blunn, and M. M. Oloufa.
The influence of length of storage of bovine semen on conception rate
under field conditions. *Univ. Nebraska Agr. Expt. Sta. Bull., 154,* pp.
3-18, 1948.

56. Sherman, J. K. Freezing and freeze-drying of bull spermatozoa.
Am. J. Physiol., 190, 281-286 (1957).

57. Sherman, J. K. Personal communication, 1959.

58. Shettles, L. B. Carbon dioxide tension and its relation to the
quiescence of spermatozoa. *Proc. Soc. Exptl. Biol. Med., 45* (1), 318-
322 (1940).

59. Smith, A. U. Behavior of fertilized rabbit eggs exposed to glycerol and to low temperatures. *Nature, 170,* 374 (1952).

60. Spallanzani, M. *Experiments to Serve in the History of the Generation of Animals and Plants.* Barthelemi Chirol, Geneva, 1785.

61. VanDemark, N. L. Quantitative aspects of semen production in
bulls. *III Intern. Congr. Animal Reproduction,* pp. 80-89, 1956.

62. VanDemark, N. L. Progress in storing bovine semen at room
temperatures. *Proc. 10th Conv. Natl. Assoc. Artificial Breeders,* pp.
107-113, 1957.

63. VanDemark, N. L., and F. D. Bartlett, Jr. Prolonged survival of
bovine sperm in the Illini variable temperature diluent. *J. Dairy Sci., 41,*
732 (1958).

64. VanDemark, N. L., and L. R. Couturier. Flow dialysis as a means
of preserving bovine semen at room temperature. *J. Dairy Sci., 41* (4),
530-536 (1958).

65. VanDemark, N. L., G. W. Salisbury, and R. W. Bratton. Oxygen

damage to bull spermatozoa and its prevention by catalase. *J. Dairy Sci., 32*, 353-360 (1949).

66. VanDemark, N. L., and U. D. Sharma. Preliminary fertility results from the preservation of bovine semen at room temperatures. *J. Dairy Sci., 40* (4), 438-439 (1957).

67. Walton, A. *The Technique of Artificial Insemination.* Imperial Bureau Animal Breeding and Genetics, Oliver & Boyd, Edinburgh, 1933.

68. Warwick, B. L., and R. O. Berry. Inter-generic and intra-specific embryo transfers in sheep and goats. *J. Heredity, 40*, 297-303 (1949).

69. Willett, E. L. Egg transfer and superovulation in farm animals. *Iowa State Coll. J. Sci., 28*, 83-100 (1953).

70. Willett, E. L., W. G. Black, L. E. Casida, W. H. Stone, and P. J. Buckner. Successful transplantation of a fertilized bovine ovum. *Science, 113*, 247 (1951).

71. Willett, E. L., P. J. Buckner, and G. L. Larson. Three successful transplantations of fertilized bovine eggs. *J. Dairy Sci., 36*, 520-523 (1953).

72. Willett, E. L., W. H. McShan, and R. K. Meyer. Relation of source of hormone dosage, and stage of cycle to superovulation in heifers. *J. Animal Sci.*, 7, 545-546 (1948).

73. Willett, E. L., and G. W. Salisbury. The effect of various diluters, cooling rate, temperature of storage, and some other factors on the livability of spermatozoa in stored samples of bull semen. *Cornell Univ. Agr. Expt. Sta. Memoir 249*, 1942.

74. Wyss, O., J. B. Clark, F. Haas, and W. S. Stone. The role of peroxide in the biological effects of irradiated broth. *J. Bacteriol., 56*, 51-57 (1948).

Identification and Elimination of Defects in Animals

F. B. HUTT

*Department of Poultry Husbandry, New York State College of
Agriculture, Cornell University, Ithaca, New York*

The relegation of this topic to its penultimate position in this
symposium might suggest that the elimination of genetic defects in
domestic animals is considered of relatively minor importance in the
development and protection of germ plasm resources in agricul-
cure. Any inference can easily be counteracted by extending one's
definition of a defect somewhat beyond the familiar bulldog calves
and rumpless roosters that the term implies to some people, and
thus ensuring a larger field in which to manoeuvre.

DEFECTS

Accordingly, for purposes of this discussion, a defect is any
condition that reduces the animal's viability or its capacity to
compete with others of its kind in the physical, biological, and
economic environments for which that animal is produced.

The scope of this definition can be illustrated with a few examples from my favorite species. As I write, some of our chickens
are dying of lymphomatosis, others from heat prostration, and
some from operation of a sex-linked lethal gene effective at a few
weeks of age. All are victims of genetic defects. So are the hens
discarded last week for low egg production and some of those
that went out in April because of their inability to reproduce.
When the egg dealers of Los Angeles announced two years ago
that they would buy no more brown-shelled or tinted eggs, their
action rendered defective for that economic environment the
biologically superior Austra-white hens, long-time favorites in
that area and particularly well adapted to it because of their
comparatively good resistance to respiratory diseases.

In 1934 (29 years after Cuenot's report of what later proved to be the first lethal character recognized in animals, the yellow mouse), a review (11) described 23 lethal traits then known in cattle, horses, sheep, and swine. Stormont (28) now lists 64 lethals or semilethals in these same species, with 34 in cattle, 6 in the horse, 13 in swine and 11 in sheep. There were only 5 lethal genes known for the fowl in 1934, but now there are at least 27. Evidently we are gradually learning more about lethal genes in domestic animals, and it is certain that there are many yet to be recognized.

In addition to genes that are fully lethal to homozygotes, and the semilethals (killing at least half those having the defective genotype), there are numerous genetic defects which impair viability [the "subvital" genes of Hadorn (10)], or make the animals otherwise undesirable. Stormont lists 15 such defects for cattle and 13 for swine, and the numbers grow each year.

Statistical geneticists, who breed bulls in scores or hundreds, are inclined to belittle the importance of monogenic lethals and defects. It is true that any one abnormality showing up only once in a thousand calves or more may be unimportant so far as a breed or an industry is concerned, but that same genetic defect can be a tragedy for the herd that has it. This applies particularly to those in which successive use of bulls carrying the same deleterious gene has raised its frequency to undesirable levels. Gregory et al. (8) found a herd of Jerseys in which three successive herd sires were heterozygous for lethal spasms. We should remember that when one carrier is mated with the daughters of another, only about one calf in eight shows the defect, but 57% of the normal calves carry the causative gene.

Gotink et al. (7) described 9 lethals and 31 other defects that had been recognized in cattle in Holland. A similar list for Swedish cattle (19), includes 6 of those same lethals, plus 4 more and 10 other defects. It is probable that similar assorted "genetic junk" is to be found in cattle anywhere.

There is neither need nor time to present here any review of lethal genes and other hereditary defects in domestic animals. Most of them are given in the useful annotated lists compiled by

Stormont (28) and Bogart (2) and have been described in detail by Koch *et al.* (17).

Lest anyone consider simple genetic defects unimportant because comparatively few have been identified thus far in domestic animals, the fact should be emphasized that the true numbers must be far greater than the data cited earlier would suggest. Bad genes are brought to light by inbreeding, but that practice is taboo for most animal breeders. In species that have been deliberately inbred to reveal their genetic defects, the frequency of deleterious genes is found to be very high. Thus, in *Drosophila pseudo-obscura* Dobzhansky (4) found that, even among wild flies subject to natural selection, 85% carried a chromosome that would be lethal in double dose, and over half had at least one chromosome that would cause the homozygote to be sterile. We have no proof that the chromosomes of our cows and chickens are similarly studded with bad genes, but, recalling that animals vary more under domestication than in the wild, and that much effort is expended to salvage and to protect the less fit, it seems probable that, in comparison with our domestic animals, Dobzhansky's flies were relatively immaculate.

DISSEMINATION OF DEFECTS

Even before the days of artificial insemination, genetic defects managed to migrate not only from herd to herd but also from one country to another. A favorite device on their part was to hide in some high-priced animal, whose pedigree, burnished with the glamour of importation from abroad, ensured wide distribution of his genes, both good and bad. Classical examples include the Percheron stallion, Superb, sent from Ohio to Japan in the 1880's and found (too late) to carry a gene for lethal *atresia coli*. Some forty years later 26% of the stallions of heavy breeds in Hokkaido were descended from Superb (32).

Similarly, blood of the bull, Prins Adolph, imported to Sweden from Germany in 1902, was widespread in Swedish Holsteins by the time, twenty-six years later, when Mohr and Wriedt (22) showed that he had carried a gene for lethal hairlessness. Migrations of bad genes still continue. In 1957, about 25% of American Red Danish cattle were estimated by Thompson *et al.* (29) to carry the lethal paralysis of the hind legs which ten years earlier was almost equally prevalent in Red Danes in Denmark (25).

The possibilities for dissemination of such genetic defects by centers for artificial insemination of cattle are interesting to contemplate. We are told by Foote *et al.* (6) that it is now possible for one bull to have 25,000 to 50,000 offspring per year. Their assurance that there is no evidence that artificial insemination has increased the frequency of undesirable genes is less assuring when we recall that in six dairy bulls selected at random Mead *et al.* (21) found (by breeding test) two lethal genes, four for subvital defects, and two causing female sterility. If no case has yet been reported of widespread dissemination of bad genes through an A.I. center, that happy situation might be attributed to good luck, to the fact that it takes many years for the full record to unfold, or even to understandable astuteness—and muteness—on the part of those operating the center.

IDENTIFICATION OF DEFECTS

My topic calls for some comment on the identification of defects. There is little difficulty in identifying legless pigs, short-spined dogs, and most other genetic defects in form, but genetic weaknesses in function are more difficult to recognize, especially if they show up only under conditions of stress.

The big problem is to identify animals that are *heterozygous* for recessive defects. It has been generally assumed that these could be detected only by breeding test. Warwick (31), Kidwell (16), and Johansson and Robertson (15) have computed the number of offspring necessary in matings of various kinds to reduce to 0.05 or less the probability that a sire is heterozygous for an undesirable lethal gene. Only three such tests are likely to be used with uniparous mammals like cattle.

To determine whether or not a Holstein-Friesian bull carries the unwanted gene for red, he may be mated (*a*) with red cows, (*b*) with black ones known to be heterozygous, or (*c*) to his daughters. To reduce to 5% the probability that he is carrying the gene, the numbers of normal offspring needed are 5, 11, and 23, respectively, in the three kinds of matings. When a lethal gene is involved, the sire cannot be mated to homozygotes, so must be tested with known carriers, or with his daughters. The practicability of such tests and the need for them will vary in different circumstances. Foote *et al.* (6) consider that if the frequency of a lethal gene is 1%, any bull siring about 1000 calves in a year is likely to have been mated to about 20 cows that are carriers, which should be ample to show up the recessive lethal. They point out that this sort of test has the advantage of yielding a verdict within a year, but they do not mention that, in that year, any such bull carrying a bad gene will have passed it to 500 apparently normal offspring.

With uniparous species, progeny tests of females for recessive defects are impracticable, although heterozygotes of both sexes can sometimes be identified by tracing lines of descent from ancestors proven to transmit the gene. Poultry breeders can test females easily once a heterozygous male has been identified, and to some extent this applies also to swine and dogs.

At best, progeny tests for recessive defects in large animals are costly and time-consuming except when numbers of known heterozygotes are available for that purpose. It is to be hoped that in many cases such tests will be made unnecessary by the discovery of other means of identifying the carriers. This field of study has long been neglected by geneticists concerned with domestic animals, and we are indebted to the dwarf calves in beef cattle for forcing it upon us.

Special credit is due to Dr. P. W. Gregory, of the University of California, who, to the best of my knowledge, was the first geneticist to attempt to identify, by some means other than a breeding test, domestic animals heterozygous for a specific deleterious gene. His profilometer was developed to reveal small differences in the shape of the head between young bulls heterozygous for dwarfism and those free of that gene. It was an attempt to measure quantitatively some of the incomplete recessivity which caused the heterozygotes to be preferred by judges and breeders.

Gregory *et al.* (9) found it highly effective for that purpose. Another method, based on detection in x-ray photographs of abnormalities in the thoracolumbar vertebrae of calves a week old, or less (Fig. 1), is being tested by Emmerson and Hazel (5), who state that it gives promise of being more accurate than the profilometer. Identification of genotypes at early ages is particularly desirable.

All this is good, but it is only a beginning, with only one genetic defect, and in only one species. Some years ago, Neel (24) listed thirty-three genetic defects in man which show in the heterozygous carrier some detectable trace of the defect fully expressed by the homozygote. Others, like the phenylalanine test for carriers of phenylketonuria, have since been discovered. When a similar list is available for domestic animals, the elimination of defects will be greatly facilitated.

Apart from the dwarf calves, there are other examples of the occasional preference of breeders for some undesirable gene in the heterozygous state. A lethal gene is the distinguishing feature of the breed in Creeper fowls, Dexter cattle, Grey Karacul (Shiraz) sheep, Silver Sable minks, and in Platinum foxes.

In the last three of these, a distinctive color serves as an indicator of biologically defective germ plasm. So does the Stewart dilution in minks, which, though highly valued by the fur trade, causes sterility in homozygotes. Similarly, Shorthorn breeders can expect up to 40% of their white heifers to be sterile. At the other end of the color scale, about 5% of the chick embryos that try to develop black down are unable to do so on ordinary levels of riboflavin. Most of these die in the attempt, and those that do hatch have bare backs to show for their struggle. This trouble cost one Connecticut hatchery over $178,000 in a decade (12).

Genetic defects causing sterility or reduced fertility range from underdevelopment of the reproductive tract and hypoplasia of the gonads, through nymphomania and impotency, to spermatozoa with defective acrosomes. A recent review by Rollinson (27) of those already known in cattle lists enough of such abnormalities—some of them transmitted as simple recessive traits—to suggest that further studies of genetic aspects of infertility are highly desirable.

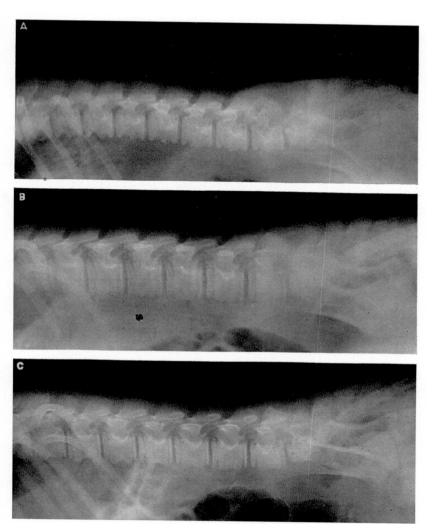

Fig. 1. Radiographs of thoracolumbar vertebrae of young calves, showing differences in the ventral profiles of the centra. A, a dwarf; B, a calf later proven heterozygous for dwarfism; C, a calf believed not to carry the gene for dwarfism. (From M. A. Emmerson and L. N. Hazel, *J. Am. Vet. Med. Assoc.*, pp. 381-390, 1956; courtesy of L. N. Hazel.)

ELIMINATION OF DEFECTS

Natural selection helps to eliminate bad genes, but grinds slowly, and is counteracted by recurrent mutation. Detection of carriers by progeny tests, from pedigrees, or by other criteria, will accelerate matters. When even a simple recessive defect becomes common enough to alarm the breeders, special precautions may be forced upon them. In Denmark, where descendants of Tjalfe Kristoffer produced enough Red Danish calves with paralyzed hind legs to alarm the breeders, it is now the custom at cooperative breeding centers to pay only half the agreed price when a new bull is bought. The remainder is held in escrow and paid only if the bull is proved not to carry the gene causing paralysis. Quick tests are feasible in this case because there are plenty of cows known to be carriers. This system is now being extended to cover other lethal traits as well. American breeders of Red Danish and of beef cattle might well consider the merits of the Danish scheme.

The Holstein-Friesian Association of America distributes to its members a leaflet describing 10 genetic defects, 8 of them lethals, and urges that the Association be given the names of the sire and dam when any of these abnormalities appear. The Association maintains a record of animals found to be carriers. This is a desirable educational program. If the breeders cooperate, it should help to keep at a minimum not only the 10 defects now listed but also others that will undoubtedly be added later.

The general objective of eliminating bad genes will also be facilitated as more veterinarians learn to recognize genetic defects and to appreciate their significance. It would be helpful if the American Veterinary Medical Association would ask its members to stop repairing umbilical hernia, cryptorchidism, and other congenital and hereditary defects except in animals that are to be marketed. Until De Groot and Numans (3) showed that a certain type of impotency in bulls is transmitted as a sex-limited recessive character, it was the practice of veterinarians in Holland to overcome the difficulty by myectomy of the *retractor penis* muscle. Obviously, informed veterinarians can play an important role in the elimination of genetic defects.

Adaptation to Environment

It is important to recognize that genotypes satisfactory in one environment can be fatal in others. The lamb genetically unable to excrete phylloerythrin, a derivative of chlorophyll, can safely go in the sun so long as it does not eat grass, or it can eat grass if it keeps out of the sun; but if it has both grass and regular exposure to sun, it eventually dies.

Although a few of the conditions rendering animals unsuitable for certain environments are monogenic traits like that just cited and porphyria, most of them are influenced by quantitative genes and many show up only under various degrees of stress.

The turkey with a genetic weakness that causes a pendulous crop has no trouble in coping with the environment where temperatures are low enough, as at Tomales, California, to make excessive drinking of water unnecessary, but reveals its defect when subjected to the somewhat more critical test afforded by the summer climate at Davis (1).

Other examples are provided by the European cattle that are less able than the Zebus to thrive in the tropics, by the turkeys that develop arthritis when raised on slats but not if kept on the floor, and by any animals less able than their fellows to cope with that usually inevitable part of environment, the organisms that cause disease.

Complexities of adaptation to the economic environment are illustrated by a pair of alleles (W and w) in the fowl which cause white skin and yellow skin, respectively. Nature does not discriminate between the two phenotypes, but man does. White-skinned birds are discounted by American dealers, but are preferred in the markets of Britain and Holland, where yellow-skinned fowls are at a disadvantage.

Genetic Resistance to Disease

While animal breeders must envy the comparative ease with which plant breeders produce varieties resistant to disease, the possibilities of doing the same with animals are not so hopeless as the unfortunate lack of research in the field might suggest. The available evidence of genetic resistance of domestic animals to various diseases was summarized in 1958 (13) and needs no hurried review here.

Some ubiquitous pathogens cannot be eradicated by any known means and others can be banished only temporarily. It is evident to any observer that some animals can resist such organisms more easily than others, and, when the disease cannot be effectively controlled by other means, it would seem only logical to multiply the kind of animals that can withstand it.

With respect to one such disease, leucosis of fowls, the feasibility has been demonstrated of breeding strains of White Leghorns so resistant that in exposed birds mortality from that disease up to 500 days of age runs about 1% or less, whereas in birds of a susceptible strain intermingled with the others mortality from leucosis is now 40% or more in different years (14).

Selection was also made against other diseases in these same strains, and, over a period of 22 years (i.e., 22 generations), mortality from all causes was reduced by some 80% below that in 1935 (Fig. 2). Some of that improvement can be attributed to better management, but, since mortality remained consistently high in the susceptible strain, most of the reduction in the resistant lines can be credited to the selection exercised.

Samples of this resistant stock sent for three consecutive years to a random-sample laying test and there compared with twenty-four concurrent entries of the country's best stocks were found to have the least leucosis, the lowest mortality from all causes, and to excel all the others, except one, in profit per chick started (13). Clearly it is feasible to combine genetic resistance to disease with economically desirable productivity.

Admittedly, to breed disease-resistant stock is simpler with fowls than with larger domestic animals, but, in cases where other methods of control are inadequate, surely the genetic approach should be attempted. Mastitis in cattle will serve as an example. In spite of all attempts to control this condition by orthodox sanitation and the omnipresent antibiotics, a committee of the American Dairy Science Association concluded in 1956 that "mastitis is the most costly disease of dairy cattle *not under satisfactory control*." The incontrovertible evidence of Ward

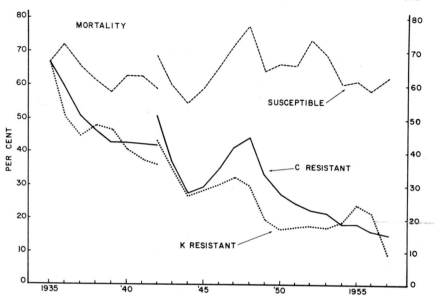

Fig. 2.   Mortality from all causes (from 42 to 500 days of age) in annual flocks of two strains of White Leghorns bred for resistance to leucosis and other diseases, and in a third strain bred for susceptibility. Fluctuations from year to year have been smoothed out somewhat by the use of three-year moving averages except for the terminal points. (Data of F. B. Hutt and R. K. Cole.)

(30), Murphy *et al.* (23), Legates and Grinnells (20), and Reid (26), that resistance to mastitis is genetically determined was recently summarized elsewhere (13). Some of it (Table I) suggests that a single generation of simple mass selection—and that on the dam's side only—is more effective in reducing mastitis than all the sanitary procedures combined, and Reid (26) has shown that most of these are greatly overrated.

Although it ill becomes a mere chicken expert to instruct his betters on what they should do, a little speculation may, perhaps, be forgiven. If, through the wonders of reincarnation, I should ever again become a young animal geneticist in some brave new world, I should hope to do a little work on mastitis. Undoubtedly it would be there.

The procedure would be relatively simple. I should collect

TABLE I.   Mastitis in dams and daughters

Investigator and Place	Herds, Number	Susceptible Dams		Resistant Dams		Effective Reduc- tion,[a]%
		Number	Daugh- ters sus- ceptible, %	Number	Daugh- ters sus- ceptible, %	
Ward (30) Canter- bury, N. Z.	20	86	89.5	109	56.0	38
Ward (30) Mana- watu, N. Z.	15	128	81.3	171	54.4	33
Legates and Grin- nells (20) North Carolina	11	144	53.0	82	35.0	34

[a] From equivalent of one generation of mass selection among females only.

some fifty pairs each of monozygotic and dizygotic twin heifer calves of dairy breeds, being careful to have their apparent zygosity verified by tests of their blood antigens. By applying to these heifers the methods of experimental infection with *Streptococcus agalactiae* proven feasible by Lancaster and Stuart (18) and by Murphy and Stuart (23), their susceptibility to infection of the udder could easily be measured. That susceptibility is not an all-or-none reaction—it increases with age. However, the degree of susceptibility can be measured fairly accurately, as both pairs of workers have shown, by clearing up any one infection with penicillin and repeating the test. All one then needs to do is to measure the concordance in the identical twins and compare it with that for the dizygotic ones.

Kallmann and his associates have shown that the twin-study method is the most useful technique available for distinguishing in man between the influences of heredity and environment on resistance to tuberculosis, on schizophrenia, and on the duration of life. It should be similarly useful with mastitis in cattle, and I should expect results of the experiment outlined above to convince cattle breeders and would-be controllers of mastitis that breeding for resistance to that disease is worth trying. The bare figures from such studies of concordance and discordance in twins of both types should make the facts crystal clear to anyone with even a high school knowledge of biology, but, to ensure that desirable end, the meat on the platter should be garnished with only an indispensable minimum of the apparently inevitable statistical parsley.

For further demonstration, it is not desirable to attempt to breed a strain of cattle completely resistant to mastitis but, rather, to determine the feasibility of reducing that disease by selective breeding without sacrificing yield of milk and fat. In that field lies a great opportunity for owners of large herds, for experiment stations, and for centers of artificial breeding.

Finally, it seems important to recognize (*a*) that domestic animals carry many deleterious genes, (*b*) that effects of some of these become evident only under the stress of adverse environmental conditions (including disease), and (*c*) that breeders may sometimes have to impose those conditions to find the genotypes desired.

References

1. Asmundson, V. S., and W. R. Hinshaw. On the inheritance of pendulous crop in turkeys (*Meleagris gallopavo*). *Poultry Sci.*, *17*, 276-285 (1938).

2. Bogart, R. *Improvement of Livestock*. The Macmillan Company, New York, N. Y., 1959.

3. De Groot, T., and S. R. Numans. Over de erfelijkheid der impotentia coeundi bij stieren. *Tijdschr. Diergeneesk.*, *71*, 372-379 (1946).

4. Dobzhansky, T. Genetic loads in natural populations. *Science*, *126*, 191-194 (1957).

5. Emmerson, M. A., and L. N. Hazel. Radiographic demonstration of dwarf gene-carrier beef animals. *J. Am. Vet. Med. Assoc.*, *128*, 381-390 (1956).

6. Foote, R. H., C. R. Henderson, and R. W. Bratton. Testing bulls in artificial insemination centres for lethals, type and production. *Proc. III Intern. Congr. Animal Reproduction*, pp. 49-53, 1956.

7. Gotink, W. M., T. De Groot, and T. Stegenga. Erfelijke gebreken in de rundveefokkerij. *Tijdschr. Diergeneesk.*, *80* (Extra Aflev.), 1-48 (1955).

8. Gregory, P. W., S. W. Mead, and W. M. Regan. Hereditary congenital lethal spasms in Jersey cattle. *J. Heredity*, *35*, 195-200 (1944).

9. Gregory, P. W., C. B. Roubicek, F. D. Carroll, P. O. Stratton,

and N. W Hilston. Inheritance of bovine dwarfism and the detection of heterozygotes. *Hilgardia, 22,* 407-450 (1953).

10. Hadorn, E. Letalfaktoren in ihrer Bedeutung für Erbpathologie und Genphysiologie der Entwicklung. Georg Thieme, Stuttgart, Germany, 1955.

11. Hutt, F. B. Inherited lethal characters in domestic animals. *Cornell Vet., 24,* 1-25 (1934).

12. Hutt, F. B. Lethal action of the gene for extension of black pigment in the fowl. *Genetics, 36,* 213-234 (1951).

13. Hutt, F. B. *Genetic Resistance to Disease in Domestic Animals.* Cornell University Press, Ithaca, New York; Constable & Co. Ltd., London, 1958.

14. Hutt, F. B., and R. K. Cole. Control of leukosis in fowl. *J. Am. Vet. Med Assoc., 131,* 491-495 (1957).

15. Johansson, I., and A. Robertson. Progeny testing in the breeding of farm animals. *Proc. Brit. Soc. Animal Production,* 79-105, 1952.

16. Kidwell, J. F. The number of progeny required to test a male for heterozygosity. *J. Heredity, 42,* 215-216 (1951).

17. Koch, P., H. Fischer, and H. Schumann. *Erbpathologie der landwirtschaftlichen Haustiere.* Paul Parey, Berlin and Hamburg, Germany, 1957.

18. Lancaster, J. E., and P. Stuart. Further experimental infections of the bovine udder with *Streptococcus agalactiae. Vet. Record, 63,* 141-145 (1951).

19. Larsson, E. L. *Arftliga fel hos Svenska nötkreatur.* LTs Förlag, Stockholm, Sweden, 1952.

20. Legates, J. E., and C. D. Grinnells. Genetic relationships in resistance to mastitis in dairy cattle. *J. Dairy Sci., 35,* 829-833 (1952).

21. Mead, S. W., P. W. Gregory, and W. M. Regan. Deleterious recessive genes in dairy bulls selected at random. *Genetics, 31,* 574-588 (1946).

22. Mohr, O. L., and C. Wriedt. Hairless, a new recessive lethal in cattle. *J. Genet., 19,* 315-336 (1928).

23. Murphy, J. M., and O. M. Stuart. The individual cow as a factor in *Streptococcus agalactiae* infection artificially induced by means of the Hadley-Wisconsin swab technique. *Cornell Vet., 44,* 268-275 (1954).

24. Neel, J. V. The detection of the genetic carriers of inherited disease. In *Clinical Genetics,* A. Sorsby, Editor, Chap. 3. Butterworth & Co., London, 1953.

25. Nielsen, J. Arvelig lamhed hos kalve. Andelsbogtrykkeriet i Odense og det Danske Forlag, Copenhagen, Denmark, 1950.

26. Reid, J. J. Bovine mastitis II. A study of underlying causes of mastitis and evaluation of various measures that may be taken to effect control. *Penn. Agr. Expt. Sta. Bull. 581,* 1954.

27. Rollinson, D. H. L. Hereditary factors affecting reproductive efficiency in cattle. *Animal Breeding Abstracts, 23,* 215-249 (1955).

28. Stormont, C. Genetics and disease. *Advances in Vet. Sci., 4,* 137-162 (1958).

29. Thompson, N. R., L. J. Cranek, Sr., and N. P. Ralston. Genetic and environmental factors in the development of the American Red Danish cattle. *J. Dairy Sci., 40,* 56-66 (1957).

30. Ward, A. H. Inheritance of susceptibility to mastitis. *New Zealand Dairy Board, 21st Ann. Rept.,* pp. 59-61, 1945.

31. Warwick, B. L. Probability tables for Mendelian ratios with small numbers. *Texas Agr. Expt. Sta. Bull. 463,* 1932.

32. Yamane, J. Über die "Atresia coli" eine letale erbliche Darmmissbildung beim Pferde, und ihre Kombination mit Gehirngliomen. *Z. Induktive Abstammungs.- u. Vererbungslehre, 46,* 188-207 (1927).

Discussion of Perpetuation and Protection of Breeding Stocks

T. C. Byerly

Agricultural Research Service, United States Department of Agriculture, Washington, D. C.

Hutt's usual delightful and thought-provoking mixture of genetic sophistication and enthusiasm for the potential usefulness of genetics in reducing disease losses in livestock serves as an appropriate climax for this excellent symposium on germ plasm resources in agriculture. He chided all of us for neglected opportunities to select that which we preserve. For while seed storage, semen banks, gardens of primitive species, varieties, clones and cultivars are needed to assure resource material, most of the genes will be present in our domestic stocks, which would surely be more useful if freed from lethal, deleterious and nonproductive germ plasm. I assume Dr. Hutt would not object to a herd or flock carrying all of these abhorrent genes. Indeed, this notion has always intrigued me. Dr. C. W. Knox once assembled a poultry flock at Beltsville which carried some 22 recessive genes. For chromosome mapping we need such research flocks. In my opinion, geneticists will again find classical studies of cytogenetics, of linkage and chromosomal aberration fruitful. We go to a lot of bother to find genes for blood antigens to use as markers—oh yes, the whole blood antigen area is intriguing as a basic research area per se—but why not use obvious markers, too?

Semen banks, seed banks, clones, cultivars—what limits will we set? What standards for selection of the germ plasm which should be selected? I would settle for inclusion of every identified gene, but not necessarily the stock in which it occurred nor even the known gene complement, though I suppose we shall have to save a lot of duplicate genetic trash because of uncertain identification.

The maize project of the National Academy of Science–

National Research Council reported to the International Cooperation Administration in July 1959 that over 11,000 collections of
corn had been made in Latin America and that these would probably be allocated to about 400 different races. How many different
races must be preserved? The collection and screening task alone
is very large.

Our present inventory of germ plasm is very extensive, very
diffuse and, of course, incomplete and often inaccessible because
of lack of information as to who has what, where. We have, for
example, no inventory of breeders of the multitudinous varieties
of chickens, bantams, and pigeons. Only through letters of inquiry,
advertisements, show lists, personal acquaintance, and card files
can such stocks be located. Many plant and animal breeders have
preserved for a few years the stocks which have resulted from
their research. Plant and animal pathologists have similarly maintained and exchanged cultures of bacteria, viruses, cells, and fungi.
These stocks have been wont to disappear with transfer, retire-
ment, or shift of interest of the developer, as pointed out by Dr.
Larson.

There are, however, numerous extensive and valuable stocks in
many areas, readily accessible. Dr. Larson has noted the continuing though limited activity of the United States Department
of Agriculture Plant Introduction Group. Both Dr. Larson and,
in more specific terms, Dr. James have referred to the loss of introduced stocks. There has been a recent encouraging renewal of
exchanges of plant materials with scientific institutions in the
USSR. A horticulture exchange group from the USSR brought
with them to the United States during 1959 300 lots of vegetable seeds. Through the good offices of C. O. Erlanson, Chief of
the New Crops Research Branch of the United States Department of Agriculture Crops Research Division, about 600 other
different lots of material have been received from the USSR, and
a similar number of different lots have been sent to the USSR
in exchange. We are presently exchanging world cereal collections
beginning with oats. Both the United States and USSR are increasingly concerned with obtaining wild relatives of cultivated
crops. Whereas Russia is emphasizing wild relatives of vegetables

and fruits, we are more concerned with wild relatives of forage plants.

I think a partial inventory of germ plasm we are presently perpetuating will be of interest. This inventory *is* partial. First, the United States Department of Agriculture cooperates with the four experiment station regions in maintenance of collections. The collections named are only examples of the materials at each regional center.

The Pullman, Washington, collections in the western experiment station region include stocks of safflower and beans; those for the north central region at Ames, Iowa, include sunflower and tomatoes; those in the northeastern region at Geneva, New York, include forage stocks; those in the southern region at Experiment, Georgia, include vegetable stocks. Other collections include cotton stocks maintained cooperatively by the Crops Research Division and state agricultural experiment stations at Stoneville, Mississippi; College Station, Texas; Raleigh, North Carolina; Tempe, Arizona; and Iguala, Mexico. The cotton collections include about 1200 stocks of upland cotton, 200 stocks of extra long staple (Barbadense) types, 22 wild species, and a number of interspecific hybrids.

Cereal stocks, many of which will be stored at the Seed Laboratory at Fort Collins with its 300,000 quart-size sample capacity, include: wheat, 15,000 stocks; rye, 200 stocks; oats, 6000 stocks; and barley, 7500 stocks.

About 4000 rice stocks are presently at Beltsville, Maryland, and Crowley, Louisiana; 300 grain sorghum stocks at Chillicothe, Texas; and 120 buckwheat stocks at University Park, Pennsylvania. A collection of about 4500 seed accessions of sweet sorghum, including wild forms of 12 species, is located at Beltsville, where 1500 clones of 6 species of sugarcane are also maintained. The Davis onion collection is also maintained at Beltsville, and about 1000 stocks of 60 Nicotiana species are kept at Beltsville and Raleigh, North Carolina. Among stocks of forage species are about 40 alfalfa species at St. Paul, Minnesota, 100 introduced bluestems at Stillwater, Oklahoma, and 100 stocks of Bermudagrass at Tifton, Georgia. The potato collection maintained cooperatively at Sturgeon Bay, Wisconsin, includes about 1000 potato stocks.

Materials maintained at the USDA Plant Introduction Station include 800 apple clones and 900 Dioscorea stocks at Glenn Dale, Maryland; 600 cherry stocks at Chico, California; a substantial collection of bamboo at Savannah, Georgia, and a USDA-ICA collection of coffee, cacao, and rubber at Miami, Florida.

Dr. Larson has presented an inventory of vegetatively propagated plant materials in the northeast and western experiment stations. There may be some duplication, especially with his "other species" category in the list I have given.

In addition to the plant materials maintained, there is a cooperative wheat stem rust collection at St. Paul, Minnesota; a wheat leaf rust collection at Manhattan, Kansas; a cereal bunt collection at Pullman, Washington; and a cereal virus collection at Beltsville.

I fully agree with the importance of perpetuating and protecting vegetatively propagated plant materials stressed by Dr. Larson.

The American Type Culture Collection receives, obtains, propagates, and distributes bacterial, mold, and viral cultures. Several thousand cultures are currently maintained. It is probable that it will eventually include cell cultures.

The Department of Health, Education and Welfare maintains substantial numbers of virus and bacterial cultures. Their Salmonella Typing Center at Chamblee, Georgia, is widely useful to animal pathologists.

There are various other collections of microbiological material, including types of foot-and-mouth disease viruses at the USDA Plum Island Animal Disease Laboratory, where they are maintained for research and diagnostic purposes at that installation. A collection of Newcastle disease viruses is maintained for research and reference use at the University of Wisconsin. The United States Department of Agriculture's capacity and program for maintaining research stocks of pathogens will be increased upon completion in 1961 of the National Animal Disease Laboratory at Ames, Iowa.

The location and availability of many laboratory animal genetic stocks maintained by individuals and institutions is assured by the informational activities of the Institute of Laboratory Animal Resources of the National Academy of Sciences–National Research Council.

Our most difficult problem in preservation of germ plasm resources is in the livestock field. Our zoos contain some of the wild relatives of our domestic species but the necessity for protecting our domestic livestock against exotic diseases makes access to wild and domestic stocks in other countries difficult. Presently, we lack any method which will positively assure us that a bovine bred in a country where foot-and-mouth disease exists is itself free of the infective agent. Until research provides such a method, we must exclude animals of foot-and-mouth susceptible species originating in countries where the disease exists from importation into the United States. This is equally true of semen importation from foot-and-mouth infested countries, for there is no known method of assuring that the semen is free of virus. Freezing preservation of semen equally assures preservation of virus it may contain.

With domestic livestock species we may view the future optimistically from the standpoint of bull semen storage, with some optimism for frozen storage of semen of other species. Dr. Van-Demark's interesting summaries of chemical inhibition as a tool in semen storage, of experiments on ova storage and gonadal tissue storage give promise of productive research in these areas.

Dr. James has presented an excellent review of information and problems limiting seed viability. While storage conditions for seeds are better known, and perhaps simpler, than those limiting storage of vegetatively propagated materials, my curiosity is roused as to whether we need research on storage of such materials. Since we can store bull semen and viruses in the deep freeze, what possibilities does this method offer for pollen, bud, scion, rootstock, and other propagating materials? If CO_2 storage is hopeful as a means of preserving seeds and semen, why not for vegetative materials?

Artificial insemination is, as VanDemark pointed out, an excellent method for assuring the storage of selected animal genetic materials *in vivo*. The process itself gives no assurance that the genetic material so stored is in any wise superior. Dr. Hutt's warning that widespread use of selected sires has in the past assured, and in the future probably will continue to assure, the preservation of genetic defects is timely.

Perpetuation and protection of germ plasm has two related purposes: first, the establishment of a resource which will be continuously and directly useful in breeding improvement; second, the provision of a necessary bank of material for genetic research to establish genetic principles and genetic composition and capacity and the effects of genes and their interactions. The first purpose cannot be fully achieved without diligent and effective pursuit of the second.

Each of the contributors to the session on perpetuation and protection of breeding stocks—Dr. James, Dr. Larson, Dr. Van-Demark, and Dr. Hutt—has contributed to the definition of problems related to the topic of Part V and has assembled and evaluated the information relevant to them. They have proposed research and action to meet those problems. Solution will require men, money, and time. How much can be done by individual effort? How much with existing facilities? What part must be done through group action? What part will require new facilities?

The United States Department of Agriculture has always had an important role in the perpetuation and protection of genetic stocks. It will continue to have such a role. Questions raised which require research will find their response from research workers in USDA, state experiment stations, and other public and private institutions. Some actions, those involving international movement of stocks, will continue to be subject to regulations of the United States Department of Agriculture and may be modified as research results and their application in this and other countries make such modification safe. Assumption by USDA of an expanded role in the perpetuation and protection of genetic stocks largely depends upon the availability of funds, facilities, and personnel. Research workers in the United States Department of Agriculture, like those in other institutions, must often give priority to new research in the allocation of time, facilities, and funds.

Index